This book is dedicated to those
who have dared to taste the elixir of flight,
and to those who have dared greatly.

Cover: Mooney 231 by Roger Rozelle

THE PROFICIENT PILOT

by Barry Schiff

Aircraft Owners and Pilots Association
Washington, D.C.

Foreword

Aviation is an activity which requires proficiency as much from the novice as from the professional. Flying is aesthetic and exciting, safe and practical. It can also be unforgiving. Proficiency in the art and science of flight is critical. One's life, and the lives of many others, often depend on a pilot's ability to perform.

Designers and engineers can develop durable, relatively safe machines. Airframe manufacturers can construct them to exacting specifications and tolerances. The wizardry of space-age electronics can provide navigational data with high accuracy.

Nevertheless, the final responsibility for the management of aircraft and systems rests with the pilot. It doesn't matter whether he is the captain of the single-engine, VFR trainer or a wide-body jetliner during a letdown in a blizzard. The responsibility owed to others in the air and on the ground is enormous.

Every pilot must recognize that maintaining proficiency is a continual learning process, one that is not assured by, for instance, earning a new certificate. Pilot certificates and ratings must be regarded as licenses to learn. After a few thousand hours of flying throughout the West to report and photograph news events for my nightly television broadcast, I can attest to the need of any pilot to constantly strive to maintain his proficiency.

Barry Schiff's book is destined to become a classic, because it presents needed expertise and advice rarely found between two covers. Having received considerable instrument and commercial pilot instruction from the author, I am delighted that many other pilots, who may have missed the information in its original form, can now obtain it in this book.

Hal Fishman
Anchorman
KTLA-TV News
Hollywood, California
AOPA Number 258762

Table of Contents

Chapter One — Dynamics of Flight

Chapter Two — Proficiency and Technique

Chapter Three — The Art of Navigation

Chapter Four — The World of IFR

Chapter Five — Emergency

Chapter Six — Flightworthy Considerations

About the Author

Barry Schiff has achieved international recognition for his general aviation expertise. An award-winning aviation writer, Schiff is rated as a captain in 707 and 727 aircraft and flies for TWA. He began flying at fourteen (against parental protestation) and has accumulated almost every FAA category and class rating available. These include single- and multi-engine airplane (land and sea), helicopter, gyroplane, glider and lighter-than-air (free balloon). He also is certificated to instruct in all of these aircraft and is one of very few pilots with all seven flight instructor ratings.

He is an FAA-designated flight examiner and an experienced light aircraft test pilot with more than 15,000 hours in 200 types of aircraft.

Schiff also has an aviation teaching credential from the California Department of Education and a ground instructor certificate with all ratings. He has established or broken eight official world speed and altitude records in piston and jet-powered airplanes.

Dedicated to aviation safety, Schiff has written a dozen books and almost 400 articles for publications all over the world. His first novel, "The Vatican Target," was published in June, 1979.

Schiff's various contributions to aviation have earned him numerous awards including the Louis Blériot Air Medal (France, 1969) and a congressional commendation.

Currently, he is an editor-at-large for the AOPA PILOT.

CHAPTER ONE
DYNAMICS OF FLIGHT

THE MIRACLE OF LIFT

*How and why the airflow over a wing produces
enough force to sustain an airplane in flight*

*"In the beginning, God created the heaven and the earth, but it is doubtful if
He had intended for man to travel between the two, otherwise man would have
been born with wings."*
(Author unknown)

This antiquated piece of philosophy is, of course, fallacious. Otherwise, so the rebuttal goes, if God had intended for man to drive upon the earth, man would have been provided with little wheels on his feet.

When man observed that birds had wings, he was jealous. But as centuries passed, jealousy evolved into curiosity and eventually into challenge.

It was natural for man to emulate the birds and he contrived all manner of flapping-wing devices in a valiant effort to mimic his feathered friends. These contrivances were called ornithopters; none were successful.

Ornithopter proponents argued vehemently that "Nature must know best" and that experiments with flapping wings should continue. But these arguments were illogical, otherwise the great sailing vessels would have spanned the seven seas by wiggling their rudders like fish and stagecoaches would have had legs instead of wheels.

Nature's suggested method of flight was eventually and fortunately discarded in favor of the nonflappable wing.

The modern fixed wing truly is the heart and soul of the airplane. Without it, flight as we know it would be impossible. It is ingeniously designed to produce awesome quantities of lift, yet has no moving parts.

The shapely, sculptured lines of a wing perform miraculous feats, but only a handful of pilots can properly explain how lift is created. There are all manner of half-truths and concocted explanations to be heard, many of which unfortunately originate in some otherwise highly respected training manuals. Accuracy is sacrificed for simplicity.

There is, for example, this amusing fable: "Air flowing above the wing has a greater distance to travel (because of camber) than air flowing beneath the wing. Therefore, air above the wing must travel faster so as to arrive at the wing's trailing edge at the same time as air flowing underneath."

This is pure nonsense. How could the air molecules flowing above and below the wing gain the anthropomorphic intelligence to determine that they must arrive simultaneously at the trailing edge? The truth is that, because of viscosity, once the airflow divides at the wing's leading edge, the separated air particles never again meet (unless by coincidence in some typhoon over the South China Sea).

There are those who contend that a pilot doesn't need to know how a wing creates lift. They say that this knowledge is as useless to a pilot as a study of the laws of buoyancy is to a swimmer. But I disagree.

Pilots are a generally curious, intelligent breed who desire to learn as much as possible about the science of flight. This separates them from most automobile drivers who don't know and couldn't care less about the difference between a distributor and a differential.

Pilots use lift; their lives depend on it. They read and talk about it, are quizzed about it and even try explaining this miracle of flight to their lay friends. The problem is that most pilots really don't know how lift is created; they only think they do.

Early pioneers did learn something from the birds—with the help of Sir Isaac Newton and his third law of motion: *"To every action there is an equal and opposite reaction."* Experimenters realized quite early in their studies that birds created lift (a reaction) by beating down air (the action). The principle is very much like what happens when a rifle is fired. The bullet is pushed out of the barrel (an action) causing kickback (or recoil), an equal and opposite reaction.

Ornithopter devotees were on the right track. They tried every possible way to design a pair of wings that could flap sufficiently to force down enough air to lift a man and his machine.

The modern wing, working silently and much more efficiently than any ornithopter ever did, does much the same thing. It is designed to force down great quantities of air, which in turn causes the reaction called lift.

To learn how this is accomplished requires traveling a somewhat circuitous route. Our aerodynamic journey begins at a familiar location: the Venturi Tube. It terminates in the Land of Crystal Clarity, an aeronautical Shangri-la where everything is easily understood.

Almost every pilot is familiar with a venturi tube, that hollow chamber with the narrow throat (Figure 1-1a).

Aha!" you say, "I know all about that thing—airspeed increases in the center of the tube causing a reduction in atmospheric pressure against the inside of the tube."

"And aha! to you," I say. "But do you know *why* the pressure against the inside of the tube decreases?" Be careful, you might take the wrong fork and wind up in Confusion Canyon instead of Crystal Clarity.

The mysterious workings of the venturi tube can be explained partially, using a flow of water as an example. It's easy to see that whatever amount of water enters the inlet (A) certainly must come out the other end (C). If this were not true, the water would have to bunch up in the throat (B) and become compressed. But since water is virtually incompressible, this simply cannot happen.

The same amount of water, therefore, must pass point B as passes points A and C. Since there is less room in the throat, the water is compelled, therefore, to accelerate and travel more rapidly.

A more graphic example is what happens when you partially block the outlet of a garden hose with your thumb or add a nozzle to the hose. In either case, a venturi-type constriction (or throat) is created and the water escapes much faster than it normally would.

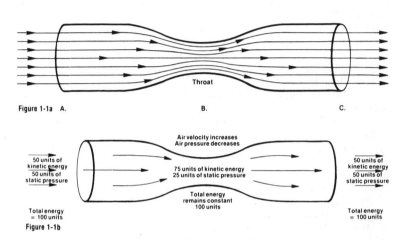

Figure 1-1a A.   B.   C.

Figure 1-1b

What many do not fully appreciate is that air and water behave similarly; both are fluids. And since free-flowing subsonic air also is considered incompressible, the same happens to it when flowing through a constriction; it accelerates.

Up to this point, everything should seem quite plausible, nothing really new or exciting. But now the stinger, the question rarely answered except in sophisticated textbooks. Why does an increase in airspeed produce a decrease in pressure inside the venturi tube? The answer, to be fully appreciated, requires a slight detour.

There are many different forms of energy, the most familiar being light, heat, sound and electricity. There are two other forms of energy that are not quite so well known.

One is *kinetic energy*. This is a form of energy contained by an object in motion. An automobile speeding along the highway possesses kinetic energy; the faster it moves, the more kinetic energy it has. When the brakes are applied, this kinetic energy (of motion) does not simply disappear. Instead, it is converted to another form of energy, heat, which can be felt on the brake linings. Also, some of the kinetic energy is converted to heating the tires (and sometimes to melting the rubber).

The process of energy conversion works in reverse, too. A car at rest has no kinetic energy because it is not in motion. But when the driver depresses the accelerator pedal, fuel is burned and some of its chemical energy is converted to kinetic energy. The car is again in motion.

The point to remember is that *energy can neither be created nor destroyed;* it simply changes form. Another example of energy conversion is the light bulb, which changes electrical energy to light and heat.

Air in motion (like any other object) possesses kinetic energy. Air also possesses a second form of energy, *static pressure.* An inflated toy balloon is an excellent example of static pressure (energy) being stored. If the air inside is allowed to escape, the static pressure (one form of energy) changes to kinetic energy (another form of energy). The air pressure inside decreases (causing the balloon to deflate) and the airspeed increases while escaping through the balloon's "nozzle."

Two very important pieces of the lift puzzle, therefore, state that: (1) energy can neither be created nor destroyed, and (2) air entering a venturi tube consists of two significant forms of energy: kinetic energy (of motion) and static (atmospheric) pressure.

The air entering the venturi tube (Figure 1-1b) has a given amount of total energy, equal to the sum of its kinetic energy and its static pressure.

As the airflow approaches the venturi constriction, its velocity increases. This represents an increase in kinetic energy. Yet it has been stated earlier that energy cannot be created. It would seem as though the law regarding the conservation of energy has failed. But, as you may have guessed, it has not.

What happens is that some of the air's pressure energy is sacrificed (or converted) into kinetic energy. In this manner, the total energy content of the air remains unchanged. This process of energy conversion is identical to what happens when air escapes from a balloon: air velocity increases and air pressure decreases. Within the venturi tube, *static air pressure is sacrificed to accelerate the airflow* resulting in reduced pressure against the inside of the venturi tube.

It should now be easier to understand why airspeed and air pressure are so closely related and why an increase (or decrease) of one results in a decrease (or increase) of the other. This relationship between airspeed and pressure originally was expressed by Daniel Bernoulli, an eighteenth-century Swiss physicist, and has come to be known as Bernoulli's Principle.

Figure 1-2 shows the "circulation" or airflow pattern about a wing. Notice that the wing's cambered (curved) upper surface is shaped much like the bottom half of a venturi tube. The upper half of this imaginary tube is simply the undisturbed airflow at some distance above the wing.

Notice also what happens to the air flowing over the wing's upper surface. As it enters the constriction formed by the wing's camber, the air accelerates just the way it does when passing through a conventional venturi tube. The result is a corresponding decrease in pressure along the upper surface of the wing.

This reduced air pressure is frequently and erroneously called suction. Actually the pressure decrease is quite small. The amount of "pressure reduction" is much less than that created by an infant suckling a breast. A fully loaded Cessna 177 Cardinal, for example, has a gross weight of 2,500 pounds; its wing area is 172.4 square feet. Dividing the gross weight (2,500) by the wing area (172.4) results in the Cardinal's wing loading of 14.5 pounds per square foot. In other words, each square foot of wing is responsible for lifting 14.5 pounds of weight. Since there are 144 square inches in a square foot, it is easily determined that each square inch of wing creates only one-tenth of a pound, or less than two ounces, of lift.

It seems logical that the relatively high pressure air beneath the wing would attempt to flow to the area of reduced pressure above the wing. After all, this is what happens in the free atmosphere; air always moves from a high to a low. But in the case of an airplane, a wing separates the regions of high and low pressure and is forced to rise into the low pressure region above it. (Some of the relatively high pressure air actually does "curl" around the wingtip in an attempt to "fill the low" created above the wing. This curling of air about the wingtip breeds that hazard known as the wingtip vortex and also is responsible for induced drag.)

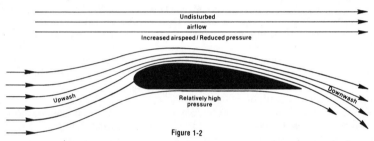

Figure 1-2

The explanation of lift often ends at this point, but this still leaves the serious student far short of his destination.

Notice how the airflow in Figure 1-2 completes its journey across the wing. It flows not only rearward, but downward as well. This action is called downwash. Remember the lessons of Sir Isaac Newton and, more specifically, of the birds? When air (or anything else for that matter) is deflected downwards, there must be an equal and opposite reaction. The reaction to downwash is, in fact, that misunderstood force called lift. If it were possible to determine and add together the vertical component of force with which each particle of air is deflected downwards, the total would exactly equal the lift being created by the entire wing. Welcome to the Land of Crystal Clarity.

Once this is accepted, it should be obvious that additional lift can be created only by increasing the downwash of air behind the wing. Aerodynamicists are well aware of this fact of flight and try to get as much air above the wing as possible because all of it is ultimately directed downward from the wings's trailing edge. This is accomplished by an ingenious application of the rules already discussed.

The low (or reduced) pressure area above the wing is required because this influences the air approaching the wing's leading edge.

5

This air is attracted to the area of reduced pressure and flows not only from in front of the wing, but also from *below* the wing. This increases the "mass airflow" above the wing, and, therefore, the downwash behind it.

There is a stagnation point on the wing's leading edge where the air seemingly can't make up its mind as to whether it should flow over or under the wing.

When the wing is flown at a large angle of attack, a more highly constricted "venturi tube" is created. The effects of increased airspeed and reduced pressure over the wing are increased. Larger quantities of air are attracted over the wing's leading edge and, as a result, considerably more downwash is created. Lift is increased. (The reaction produced by downwash is particularly significant when you consider that each cubic yard of sea level air weighs two pounds.)

When air strikes the bottom of the wing (during flight at a large angle of attack) it, too, is deflected downwards, and creates even more reaction and contributes to total wing lift.

This deflection of air from the bottom of the wing is particularly significant at large angles of attack and explains the flight of a kite or the planing of water skis. Air (or water) is deflected downwards, causing an upward reaction. This is why it can be said truthfully that, given enough power, anything can be made to fly . . . including the proverbial barn door.

Anyone who doesn't believe in the tremendous forces created by hurling air downward in large quantities has only to stand beneath a hovering helicopter. This downward blast of air is precisely what occurs during fixed-wing flight.

The rotors of a helicopter create lift identically to the manner in which a fixed-wing creates lift. The only significant difference is that helicopter wings rotate and create relative wind without any movement of the helicopter. Fixed-wings encounter relative wind only when the airplane is in motion.

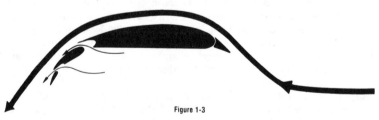

Figure 1-3

At slow airspeeds, the wing needs help. Aircraft designers come to the rescue by adding trailing edge and sometimes, leading edge flaps. These devices add both area and camber to the wing, increasing the ability to generate lift at slow speeds.

Man has learned much from the birds, but he still watches them with envy. We have more, much more, to learn.

STALL TALK

What really happens during a stall

A Golden Rule of Flight is: "Maintain thy airspeed lest the earth shall arise and smite thee."

This platitude has survived for a century of manned flight and, although it is certainly well intended, it can be grossly misleading. This is because airspeed is related only indirectly to the stall. Most pilots know that an airplane can be made to stall at *any airspeed* while being flown in *any attitude*.

A stall, we have been taught, results only from an excessive angle of attack. To relate a stall to airspeed can be as erroneous as the advice given by Daedalus to his impetuous son, "Don't fly too high, Icarus, lest the heat of the sun shall melt your waxen wings and thee shall plummet from the skies."

Figure 1-4a shows air flowing smoothly about a wing, caressing it fondly to produce lift. In the second case, the air (relative wind) strikes the wing at such a large angle of attack that it cannot negotiate a change in direction quickly enough to hug the wing's upper surface. Instead, the air separates from above the wing and burbles; lift is destroyed.

Air, like every other mass, has inertia and resists making sharp turns.

Consider an athlete sprinting around a race track at maximum speed. As long as the track consists of straight-aways and gentle curves, he has no difficulty following the oval course. But ask the runner to make a sharp, ninety degree turn without slowing down and we ask the impossible. There is no way it can be done without either overshooting the corner or toppling in the attempt. Airflow about a wing behaves similarly; it can make only gradual changes in direction.

The elevator controls angle of attack. With it, a pilot determines the angle at which he would like the air to meet the wings. When the control wheel (or stick) is brought aft, the angle of attack increases. With sufficient back pressure on the wheel, the angle of attack reaches a critical value, an angle at which the air can no longer "make the turn." The air is asked to perform the impossible. The result is a rebellious stall and occurs irrespective of airspeed and attitude. (In an

7

effort to make some aircraft "stall-proof," their designers simply limited up-elevator travel.)

The purpose here is not to belabor the significance of angle of attack. This drum is beaten loudly by every flight instructor and in every

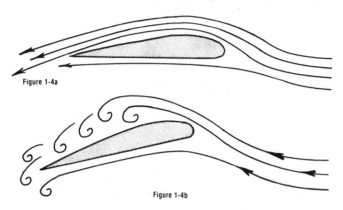

Figure 1-4a

Figure 1-4b

training manual. Unfortunately, these sources often drop the ball as soon as the pilot gets interested. The subject is presented like a strip-tease act; rarely do we get to see the whole picture.

A major problem arises when a stall is illustrated as in Figure 1-4b. The pilot is given the impression that when a specific angle of attack is reached, the entire wing stalls. This is *seemingly* verified in flight when, during a practice stall, all lift *seems* to disappear suddenly. But this is not the way it works.

The figure is misleading because it shows only an airfoil, a narrow, cross-sectional slice of wing. It represents what occurs at a specific point along the wing, but not what happens along the entire span. In other words, the pilot sees only one small, albeit important, piece of the puzzle. He is not shown the big picture.

One of the best ways to learn the stall characteristics of an entire wing is to actually observe airflow behavior. Since this is difficult without a wind tunnel, settle for second best: a tufted wing. By attaching small strands of yarn to a wing's upper surface, the development or erosion of lift can be seen at various angles of attack.

A low-wing airplane works best. Similar tests can be conducted with a high-winger, but without mirrors the pilot would have difficulty observing the tuft patterns above the wing.

Although tufting a wing is not difficult, it is simplified with the help of a volunteer. My partner during one series of stall investigation tests was NASA's Cal Pitts, who was particularly interested in observing the stall characteristics of the subject airplane, a Cherokee 180.

Armed with two skeins of black yarn, a large roll of masking tape and a pair of scissors, we began the tufting process. After two hours of wrapping, taping and snipping, Cal and I stood back to admire the Cherokee's quaintly attired left wing. We couldn't help but wonder what it would be like to work for Boeing's flight test department. Can you imagine tufting the wing of a 747?

During the subsequent takeoff roll, neither of us paid much attention to the mechanics of flying; we were preoccupied watching the tufts line up with the relative wind, watching the fruits of our effort come to life.

Prior to takeoff, Pitts also attached a 10 foot strand of yarn to the right wingtip. During climbout, it whipped about like a small cyclone, describing a long cone in revolution. There it was, for all to see: a wing-tip vortex. It makes a believer of you. It is one thing to read about vortices, but it is quite another to see one in action.

We began a stall series high above the smog oozing from the nearby Los Angeles basin. Throttle retarded and wings level, Pitts slowly raised the nose. With the wing flying at a relatively small angle of attack, we noticed a stall developing at the wingroot near the trailing edge. The tufts there were no longer lying flush with the wing. Instead, they had flipped forward, wriggling and writhing, reacting to the burbling, turbulent eddies of air. The airflow had separated from this area of the wing. We were witnessing the strangulation of lift.

Raising the nose farther, we could *see* the stall spread or *propagate* forward and spanwise, stealing larger and larger chunks of it.

The stall warning came alive and the familiar buffet was felt. With the control wheel full aft, the Cherokee bucked lightly and the nose pitched downward.

When the wing had been flown at the maximum angle of attack, we noted that only the inboard half of the wing had stalled. During this and subsequent stalls, it was apparent that at no time did the entire wing stall.

Such a demonstration raises this question, "If a stall develops progressively and the wing is always developing some lift, what causes the sudden 'break' or 'nose-drop' associated with a stall?"

The answer is only incidental to the loss of lift. In normal flight, downwash from the wing (Figure 1-5) strikes the upper surface of the horizontal tailplane. This action helps the elevator-stabilizer combination to produce a downward force that keeps the nose up in straight-and-level flight. Without "tailfeathers," a conventional aircraft would dive uncontrollably.

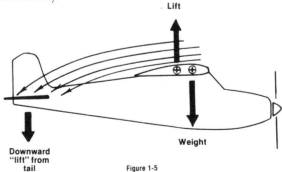

Figure 1-5

As a stall is approached, turbulent air from above the stalled portion of wing strikes the tail (and sometimes the aft fuselage). This is usually the cause of the familiar stall buffet. The wing doesn't buffet, the tail does. When enough of the wing stalls, insufficient downwash remains to keep the tail down. In a sense, the horizontal stabilizer stalls, too. This, in addition to the air striking the bottom of the stabilizer (at large angle of attack), combines to raise the tail.

As a result, the nose drops, a form of longitudinal stability that automatically assists stall recovery.

The stall pattern demonstrated by the Cherokee 180 wing is typical of a rectangular wing. Other wing shapes (Figure 1-6) exhibit different stall patterns. The stall of a swept wing, for example, begins at the trailing edge tip and propagates inboard and forward.

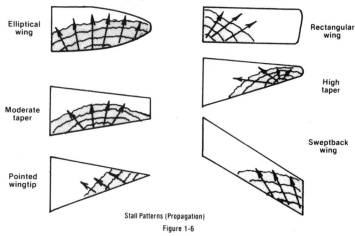

Stall Patterns (Propagation)
Figure 1-6

The rectangular wing has the most ideal stall pattern (i.e., an inboard, root stall). Such a stall provides a tail buffet to warn of an impending stall and allows the wingtips to remain flying as long as possible. This is, of course, where the ailerons are and it is important for these controls to remain as effective as possible.

A tip stall, on the other hand, is bad news. The tailplanes are not behind the stalled portion of the wings and therefore may not provide the warning buffet. The ailerons become ineffective early in the stall and may not be counted upon to provide roll control during flight at minimum airspeed. Also, the stabilizing effect of a nose-down pitching moment may not occur during a tip stall. A tip stall on a swept wing can be particularly hazardous because loss of aft lift on the wing could produce a nose-up pitching moment and drive the airplane into a deeper stall.

For obvious reasons, aircraft designers go to great lengths to make certain that their aircraft exhibit optimum, root stall patterns. Four methods are commonly used to achieve this.

• *Wing twist.* The wings of high-wing Cessnas are twisted slightly so that the angle of attack of an inboard wing section is always larger than that of the outboard wing section. This is also called "washing out" a wing. For example, the wing twist of a Cessna 172 is 3°. In other words, when the inboard section of a 172 wing is at an angle of attack of 14°, the outer wing section has an angle of attack of only 11°. Such a scheme forces the root to stall before the tip.

• *A stall strip* is a narrow length of metal usually having a triangular cross section that is mounted spanwise on the leading edge of a wing. At large angles of attack, the strip interferes with airflow at the leading edge and induces a stall to form behind. In this manner, the initial stall pattern of a wing can be placed almost anywhere along the wing. A similar, but more expensive technique, is to sharpen the leading edge near the wingroot.

• *Variable airfoil wings* behave much like twisted wings. Such a wing incorporates two or more airfoils, an airfoil being a wing's cross-sectional shape at some given point. The airfoils are selected in such a way that those used near the wingroots have smaller stalling angles of attack than the airfoil(s) used near the tip. The result: a root stall. This sophisticated technique has been used in the design of many aircraft including the Navion and most jet transports.

• *Wingtip slots* are expensive, which explains why they are uncommon. The Swift, for example, has a moderately tapered wing and might have an unsatisfactory stall pattern where it not for the built-in wing slot on the outboard section of each wing. The slots tend to delay airflow separation behind them. Such slots delay stalling of the outboard wing sections and, as a fringe benefit, increase aileron effectiveness at slow airspeeds.

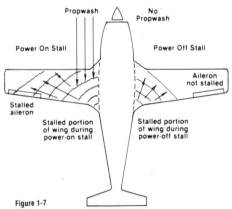

Figure 1-7

With the help of a tufted wing, it is possible also to observe the main difference between power-on and power-off stalls (Figure 1-7).

During an approach to a power-on stall, propwash flowing over the inboard wing section preserves lift in that area. Additionally, propwash helps to keep the tail flying longer.

Consequently, the airplane can be forced into a deeper stall that involves considerably more wing area.

At the moment of truth, so much of the wing is stalled that it is unable to provide much in the way of lateral stability. As a result, the aircraft often exhibits surprisingly strong rolling moments toward the wing most deeply involved in the stall, a problem that is compounded when flaps are extended.

A pilot's reaction to such an abrupt rolling moment is to counter with opposite aileron. But since these controls may be located in the stalled portion of the wing, their deflection can have an adverse effect and actually contribute to *increasing* the roll rate.

Without experience in a particular aircraft, it is difficult to predict which wing will drop during a full-power stall. This is because the factors causing one wing to stall before the other often consist of minute flaws on a leading edge such as a dent, a flat spot or even a landing light.

Engine and propeller forces often cause the left wing to drop during a power-on stall, but only if both wings are identical, *exactly* identical—a condition rarely found on production-line airplanes.

Since the elevator usually is in the propwash, it is considerably more effective during an approach to a power-on stall. This, combined with the vertical component of thrust from the engine, results in the ability to force the aircraft into a more complete stall.

When the power-on stall pays off, the combined pitching and rolling moments are considerably more abrupt than during a power-off stall. The pilot must be prepared to use skillful recovery techniques and be particularly attentive to proper control usage.

Two other factors are noteworthy. During a *climbing* turn, the outside wing is at a slightly larger angle of attack than the inside wing. If the aircraft is stalled under these conditions, the outside (or high) wing usually stalls first, resulting in an abrupt reversal in the direction of bank. Such a maneuver is called an "over-the-top" stall. Failure to execute a timely recovery (without using ailerons) can lead to a full roll followed by a conventional spin.

During a descending turn, the converse occurs. The inside wing has the larger angle of attack. If the aircraft stalls while turning and *descending,* the inside wing tends to stall first, resulting in an increased bank angle. An attempt to recover using ailerons can aggravate the "under-the-bottom" stall and result in an increased bank angle and possible spin.

The difference between power-on and power-off stalls explains why stalling a twin with an engine out can be so vicious. One wing is protected from an early stall by propwash from the operative engine; the wing with the inoperative engine has no such protection. When the angle of attack is increased under these conditions, only one wing stalls and it can force the aircraft into something similar to a snap roll followed by a spin.

Quite obviously, airspeed—or the lack of it—is not the primary cause of a stall. This has been a rather involved discussion without mentioning knots or miles per hour. This is because any airplane can be made to stall at any airspeed (as long as excessive load factors don't break the machine first).

A stall occurs for only one reason: the pilot has tried to fly the wing at too large an angle of attack. Recovery is just as simple: reduce the angle of attack.

UNDERSTANDING
THE POWER CURVE

*Getting caught behind one may lead
to unpleasant results*

The unsuspecting hero of this tale was on final to a critically short mountain strip. Since this pilot had had recent experience with power-on, drag-'em-in, short-field landings, he wasn't particularly concerned about the successful outcome of this one.

The airspeed was a steady 65 knots, comfortably above the 51 knot stall speed. A half mile from the approach end of the runway, the pilot sensed he was a mite low and raised the nose gingerly, but alas! the sink rate increased and the airspeed slipped to 60. Power was added. More back pressure, but the sink rate increased and the airspeed fell farther. More power. 56 knots! Desperately, the pilot shoved the throttle to the firewall, but not in time.

The aircraft thudded to earth just short of the runway, resulting in a damaged left main landing gear assembly and a blown right tire. A perplexed pilot stumbled out of his crippled craft wondering what mystical force had pulled him from the sky.

The insidious culprit responsible for this not-so-unusual type of accident is not well understood by most general aviation pilots, as I learned while teaching at a flight instructor revalidation clinic. More often than not, when a pilot "falls" from flight on the back side of the power curve, he attributes the experience to a nonexistent downdraft or an inadvertent stall entry, neither of which is responsible.

Before the "back side of the power curve" can be easily understood, the two types of aerodynamic drag should be reviewed. The first, parasite drag, is familiar to all pilots and is simply the air resistance created by an object as it moves through the air. Parasite drag is the force that tries to break your arm when it is extended through the open window of a speeding automobile. The faster the speed, the more forceful the drag. Actually, parasite drag increases in proportion to the square of airspeed—i.e., if airspeed doubles, parasite drage quadruples.

Figure 1-8 shows the relationship of parasite drag and airspeed. At relatively low speeds parasite drag is nominal; at faster speeds, it becomes increasingly influential. To maintain a constant airspeed in

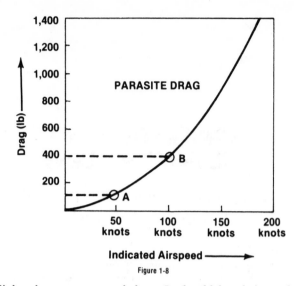

Figure 1-8

level flight, thrust must equal drag. It should be obvious, therefore, that doubling aircraft speed quadruples parasite drag and requires not twice as much thrust but, rather, about four times the thrust required at the lower cruising speed.

Parasite drag, however, is a relatively unimportant character in this story. The plot thickens when induced drag sneaks into the act. Unfortunately, induced drag is either ignored or scantily explained in most basic textbooks, yet it plays a leading role in slow flight.

Figure 1-9 shows a wing flying (mushing) at a large angle of attack and relatively slow airspeed. As the free air stream approaches from in front of the wing, it deflects downward somewhat. Consequently, the average relative wind "felt" by the wing results in a smaller angle of attack than might otherwise be imagined. Since lift always acts 90° to the *average* relative wind and not the remote free air stream, it is easily seen that the total lift generated by the wing acts slightly rearward. The vertical or effective component of lift supports aircraft weight. The horizontal component of lift acts rearward and retards forward progress. This rearward force is induced drag, an unavoidable by-product of lift.

Induced drag is most influential at large angles of attack and low airspeeds; it is minimal in high speed flight. Figure 1-10 illustrates how induced drag varies with airspeed at a constant altitude. Notice that induced drag is at a maximum when parasite drag is at a minimum, and vice versa.

Induced drag varies inversely with the square of airspeed—i.e., when airspeed is halved, induced drag quadruples; when airspeed doubles, all but one-fourth of induced drag disappears. This behavior is opposite to that of parasite drag. It is worth remembering that induced drag predominates in slow flight and parasite drag predominates in cruise.

It is the combination of parasite and induced drag which determines

14

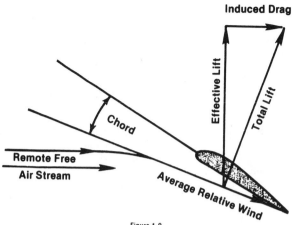

Figure 1-9

the total drag acting on an airplane at any given indicated airspeed and the amount of thrust required to overcome it.

The heavily curved line of Figure 1-11 represents the combined effect of induced and parasite drag for a fictitious general aviation aircraft at a given gross weight. This "total drag" curve is obtained by geometrically adding the parasite and induced drag curves.

Notice that considerable drag exists during slow flight. This is the effect of induced drag. At high speeds, parasite drag predominates. In Figure 1-11, the bottom of the curve (point A) is the speed (80 knots) at which total drag is at a minimum. It is interesting to note that minimum drag occurs at the speed where induced and parasite drag are equal. The total drag at this speed is 500 pounds. Since thrust must equal drag in level flight, the required thrust at 80 knots is also 500 pounds. At slower speeds, additional thrust is required to offset the increased induced drag. Extra effort must be spent to keep the aircraft airborne during slow flight. Above 80 knots, thrust requirements again increase because additional effort is required to overcome the rapidly increasing effect of parasite drag.

The minimum drag speed is of more than esoteric interest. It is at this indicated airspeed that an airplane flies most efficiently; this is the speed—the only speed—at which the lift/drag ratio of the airplane is at a maximum. Gliding at this speed, for example, results in the flattest or most efficient glide. At this airspeed, an airplane glides the farthest for every foot of altitude lost. To glide at any other airspeed—faster or slower—results in a steeper descent profile. Cruising at the minimum drag speed may be a time-consuming affair, but this is the way to achieve maximum range and get the most mileage from every gallon of fuel. In other words, a pilot running low on fuel can increase the likelihood of reaching an airport by cruising at an indicated airspeed that is very nearly the same as the optimum gliding speed, a rather nifty rule-of-thumb to keep handy.

Technically, the minimum drag speed varies slightly with gross weight, but for most light aircraft this variation can be ignored.

A drag curve offers other vital information too. The speed at which induced drag is three times as great as parasite drag is the speed to use when a pilot is not anxious to get anywhere and simply desires to remain aloft as long as possible.

Referring again to Figure 1-11, for example, it can be seen that at point B (60 knots), induced drag is three times as great as parasite drag (75 percent of the total drag). This point usually occurs at a speed equal to 75 percent of the minimum drag speed. By cruising at this relatively slow indicated airspeed, a pilot will remain airborne for the longest period of time. This is called "endurance flying" and should be performed at as low an altitude as is practicable. This is the optimum speed to use when a pilot is assigned to the rigors of a holding pattern, or whenever he wishes to remain aloft over a given area and is not concerned about getting anywhere. Hourly fuel consumption is at a minimum.

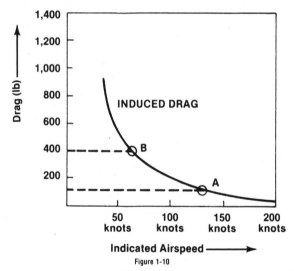

Figure 1-10

This same speed—power-off—results in a minimum sink glide (i.e., the rate of descent is at a minimum), a maneuver used when a pilot needs to descend as slowly as possible and is not concerned about "stretching" his glide.

If a pilot knows only the optimum gliding speed for an airplane, then he also knows a good deal more. An aircraft with a 90 knot gliding speed, for example, should be flown at this same indicated airspeed to achieve maximum range. For maximum endurance or minimum sink, the aircraft should be flown at 68 knots indicated (75% of 90 knots = 68 knots).

A drag curve can be called a thrust curve because drag and thrust are equal while a constant airspeed and altitude are maintained.

Once the drag curve is understood, it becomes easier to comprehend the significance of a power curve. Although drag (thrust) and power curves seem identical, they are not. A fallacy arises when thrust and

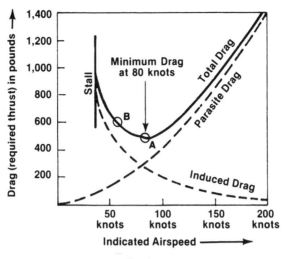

Figure 1-11

power are equated; they are not the same. Thrust is simply a *force* created by the propeller and is used to overcome drag. On the other hand, power is a measure of work performed by an engine. Simply stated, an engine *works* by turning a propeller, which in turn exerts a *force* by accelerating air rearward.

The power curve in Figure 1-12 shows the amount of power (not thrust) needed to maintain any indicated airspeed at a constant altitude. Notice that for flying on the front side of the power curve (in the "region of normal command"), increased speed requires increased power. Nothing unusual about that. But notice what happens on the back side of the power curve (in the "region of reversed command"). Increased power is required to maintain altitude at progressively slower speeds. At first blush, it seems illogical to suggest that it takes increased power to fly more slowly, but it does. Such is the effect of induced drag, and this explains why super-STOL aircraft need so much power—to fly slowly.

Additionally, notice that as much power is required to fly at 30 knots (point C) as to maintain 115 knots (point D). For each speed on the back side of the power curve, there is a corresponding speed on the front side that requires just as much power.

Points B (speed for maximum endurance and minimum sink glide) and A (speed for optimum glide and maximum range) correspond to points B and A on the drag curve in Figure 1-11. Point B is always the low point on a power curve and represents the speed at which power and hourly fuel consumption are at a minimum. Point A is located by drawing a line from the origin (zero-zero point on the chart) so that it is tangent to (barely touches) the power curve. Notice that flying at 80 knots requires slightly more power than flying at 60 knots, but the speed increase (20 knots) is considerable when compared with the slight additional power required. This explains why point A represents the

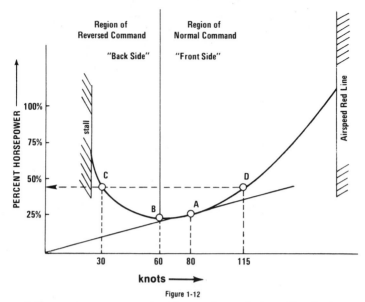

Figure 1-12

speed for maximum range. At this speed, an airplane flies farther per gallon than at any other speed (indicated).

It is important to recognize the differences in aircraft behavior when flying on one side of the power curve and the other. Only a proper understanding of these differences can help to prevent the anxiety and the resulting accident described at the beginning of this story.

Figure 1-13 is a typical power curve. Assume the airplane is flying at constant altitude and is trimmed to maintain 120 knots (point M). The engine is turning at 2,200 rpm. The pilot momentarily applies slight forward pressure on the wheel and the airspeed increases temporarily to 130 knots (point N). To maintain this higher airspeed without sacrificing altitude, power must be increased. Otherwise, the aircraft will decelerate—on its own—to 120 knots, the original trimmed airspeed.

Conversely, if the pilot raises the nose while at the trimmed airspeed, the aircraft will decelerate to 110 knots (point P). This lower speed requires less power, but since the throttle hasn't been touched, the aircraft will accelerate—on its own—to the original 120 knots.

When flying on the front side of the power curve, an aircraft has "speed stability." When airspeed fluctuates, an airplane tends to return to its original trimmed airspeed as long as the power setting is not changed.

But aircraft behavior changes somewhat when the plane flies into the region of reversed command.

Assume the aircraft is mushing on the back side of the power curve at 70 knots (point X in Figure 1-13). The throttle is set to the required setting (2,100 rpm) and the aircraft is trimmed for hands-off flight.

Now assume the nose dips temporarily, and the airspeed increases

18

to 80 knots (point Y). To maintain this higher airspeed, less power is required. Unless the throttle is retarded, the airplane will be flown with a slight excess of power. The result of excess power is a climb.

It may seem confusing that lowering the nose causes an airplane to climb, but that's the way things work on the back side of the power curve. There's nothing serious about this. No one objects to a bit of extra altitude. But suppose the opposite were to occur.

A pilot is on a flat approach to a short field. The airplane is hanging on the prop with an airspeed of 70 knots (point X), requiring 2,100 rpm. During the approach, the pilot senses he is a bit low on altitude and raises the nose slightly to arrest the sink rate. The airspeed slips to 60 knots (point Z).

Because of additional induced drag at this lower airspeed, additional power is required. Otherwise, at 60 knots, the airplane is flying with a power deficiency. Instead of decreasing the sink rate, the hapless pilot has unwittingly increased the sink rate by raising the nose. Further back pressure only aggravates the problem and causes a steeper descent. The only solution is to add power and, if necessary, lower the nose to increase airspeed and reduce the sink rate.

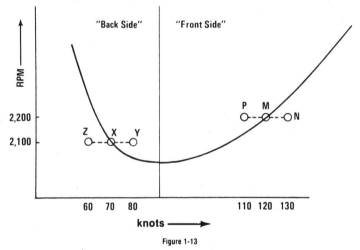

Figure 1-13

It seems paradoxical that raising the nose causes a descent and lowering the nose produces a climb, but such is aircraft behavior when flying behind the power curve. At faster speeds, altitude can be controlled by varying pitch, but not at slow speeds. This points out and reemphasizes the importance of controlling altitude with power and airspeed with pitch, especially during a landing approach.

To fully appreciate the idiosyncrasies of flying in the region of reversed command, the interested pilot should fly there in his own airplane at a reasonably safe altitude. If he desires, he can also construct a power curve for his aircraft and determine the significant airspeeds discussed earlier.

While in cruise flight at constant altitude, jot down the observed airspeed and power setting. Then reduce airspeed in increments of 10 knots and record the power setting required to maintain each lower speed.

Finally a point is reached where increases of power are required to maintain altitude at progressively slower airspeeds. The speed at which minimum power is required is the entrance to the region of reversed command. At slower speeds, notice how power requirements increase.

After the data has been recorded, choose a speed halfway between stall and minimum power. While maintaining altitude, trim the ship to establish and hold this speed. Give the wheel a gentle backwards nudge and let go. As the airspeed begins to fall, watch the sink rate develop. (A nose-up gust can produce the same results.) Next, nudge the nose down and observe the sink rate flatten. Repeat this procedure, varying power to prevent climbs and descents. This exercise provides excellent insight into aircraft behavior when flying behind the power curve.

Next, lower gear and flaps and plot another power chart while maintaining a constant altitude. This chart is useful in determining "back side" characteristics in the approach configuration.

Familiarity with the region of reversed command and a review of basic flying techniques can help to prevent a pilot from landing on his back side—of the power curve. And that can be a real drag.

GROUND EFFECT

How it can work for—or against—you

High above the Pacific, the Boeing 377 Stratocruiser droned along the great-circle route from Honolulu to San Francisco. Thus far, the flight had been routine. Not much to report other than a minor hydraulic leak.

The clouds below drifted by with metronomic regularity and Aircraft Commander Tyson was becoming weary. He glanced casually at the matrix of instruments before him, yawned compulsively, and took mental note of how difficult it was to stay awake. But Tyson didn't have time to consider how delicious such boredom could be.

Without warning, the four-bladed propeller separated from the number two, 28-cylinder engine and spun away toward infinity—but not before smashing into its companion engine on the same side. With "two churning and two burning," the heavily laden Stratocruiser began to descend. Tyson applied METO (maximum except takeoff) power to the two remaining engines on the right wing and eased back on the control yoke. But this wasn't sufficient to arrest the alarming sink rate. The calm waters of the Pacific were rising steadily.

Everyone aboard struggled into their Mae Wests and prepared nervously for the mid-Pacific ditching. But Tyson soon noticed a strange turn of events. When the crippled Boeing was within striking range of a healthy shark, the sink rate began to decrease. Seconds later, the aircraft began to hold its own and Tyson found he was able to at least postpone what had appeared to be an inevitable swim.

Struggling against powerful, unbalancing forces, Tyson managed to avoid the continuously threatening stall. After hundreds of miles just mere feet above the water, sufficient fuel had been consumed to lighten the airplane and allow the flight to continue at not so precarious an altitude.

The dramatic discovery Tyson made about the performance characteristics of an aircraft at extremely low altitude was so profound that the phenomenon was named after him: T-effect. But now that the subject has been fully investigated and accurately explained, it is referred to as "ground effect."

The average pilot may not have or cherish the opportunity to experiment with ground effect during an oceanic crossing, but he does encounter it at least twice during every flight—when taking off and landing. The "ground cushion," as it is sometimes called can be significantly influential during these operations.

Many pilots believe ground effect is the result of air being compressed between the wing and the ground. Presumably, this increased air density creates a cushion beneath the wing and improves performance. This seems plausible, but is incorrect. Unfortunately, the FAA perpetuated this myth in its VFR Exam-O-Gram No. 47. So let's set the record straight. Air is not compressed between wing and ground.

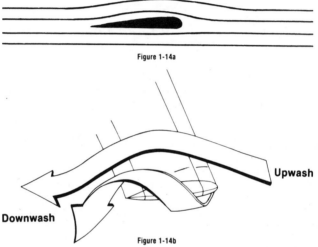

Figure 1-14a

Upwash

Downwash

Figure 1-14b

Figure 1-14a shows the airflow about a wing. The streamlines separate at the leading edge and follow the upper and lower wing surfaces. This model is used almost universally to teach how a wing develops lift. But the diagram is too simplistic. It shows only an "airfoil section," a cross-sectional sliver of a wing. To appreciate the reality of lift, the airflow about the entire wing must be investigated.

From the view shown in Figure 1-14b, it can be seen that high-pressure air from beneath the wing attempts to curl over the tip toward the low pressure region above the wing. This curling combines with the relative wind to produce a tornado of air—the wingtip vortex (wake turbulence).

During slow flight when the angle of attack is larger, the difference in pressure between the lower and upper wing surfaces is obviously greater and results in a stronger vortex. (This explains why wake turbulence is more intense behind a slow aircraft than a fast one.)

The effect of the vortices is to induce considerable "upwash" to air approaching the wing and "downwash" to the air flowing aft.

Figure 1-15 shows a wing in slow flight at a relatively large angle of attack while maintaining a constant altitude. The angle between the chord of the wing and the free airstream is 16°. This is referred to as the wing's angle of attack. But because of the upwash coming from ahead of the wing, the *average* or *local* relative wind doesn't come from the same direction as the free airstream. The wing "feels" a relative wind induced by the immediately surrounding airflow which, at slow speeds, results in a smaller angle of attack than might be otherwise expected.

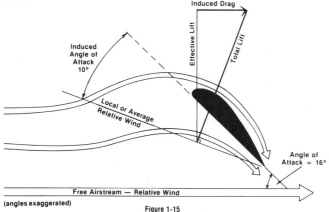

(angles exaggerated)

Figure 1-15

In this case, the "induced" angle of attack felt by the wing is only 10°. Since lift acts perpendicular to the induced relative wind (not the free airstream), it can be seen that wing lift acts slightly rearward. The horizontal component of this rearward-acting lift is a retarding force called induced drag, an unavoidable by-product of lift. Induced drag has the same detrimental effects as the more familiar parasite drag (skin friction, form drag, and interference drag). An increase in either induced or parasite drag requires additional power to maintain a constant airspeed. But while parasite drag increases with airspeed, induced drag lessens.

Conversely, induced drag increases rapidly as airspeed decreases. At just above stalling speed, for example, induced drag may account for more than 80% of the total drag acting upon an airplane. The remaining 20% (or less) is parasitic drag (air resistance).

Parasite drag can be reduced somewhat by cleaning the wings, substituting flush-mounted antennas for those that protrude, and making other minor aerodynamic improvements. With the exception of redesigning the aircraft, there's little else a pilot can do.

Absolutely nothing can be done about induced drag. It is the constant companion to lift (something most pilots are unwilling to sacrifice). But if induced drag *could* be reduced substantially, aircraft performance at large angles of attack would improve dramatically.

One way to reduce induced drag would be to decrease the amount of upwash ahead of the wing. And the only way to accomplish this would be to fly the wing very close to the ground. The degree of upwash would decrease because air preceding the wing wouldn't have enough room to develop any significant vertical motion. Also, the wing

23

would produce less downwash. Air flowing from the trailing edge would be forced more parallel to the ground. Figure 1-16 shows the airflow about a wing being flown in and out of ground effect, the term used to describe the reduction of induced drag resulting from a wing being flown in close proximity to the ground.

Those are the basics. Ground effect is caused by a reduction of induced drag, not a compression of air beneath the wings.

Wingtip vortices also are reduced when the wing is flown near the ground. This is because the ground interferes with vortex formation. Reducing the diameter of a vortex also reduces induced drag, creating the same effect as increasing the aspect ratio of the wing.

Ground effect doesn't have any measurable influence unless the wing is flown at an altitude no greater than its span—which is very close to the surface. A Cessna Cardinal, for example, has a wing span of 36

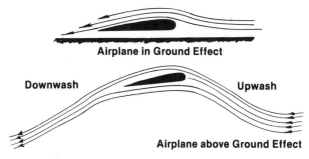

Airplane in Ground Effect

Downwash **Upwash**

Airplane above Ground Effect

Figure 1-16

feet. To benefit from ground effect, the wing must be flown at or below 36 feet above the ground. At 36 feet, 2% of the induced drag disappears. At 18 feet above the ground (half the wing span), 8% of the drag is eliminated, When flying at only nine feet (25% of the wing span), induced drag is reduced by 24%. If the wing could get to within three feet of the runway (which would require smashing the landing gear), more than half the induced drag would be eliminated.

It's evident, therefore, that low-wing aircraft usually are more influenced by ground effect than high-wing aircraft simply because a low wing can be flown closer to the ground. Nevertheless, high-wings are influenced by ground effect *almost* as noticeably. The reduction of induced drag enhances aircraft performance considerably. At times, embarrassingly so.

Consider the takeoff. As the hapless pilot urges his heavily laden aircraft along the runway, he notes the minimum "unstick" speed on the IAS gauge and abruptly rotates the nose skyward, Since he desires to impress his passengers with a maximum angle climb, he maintains the airspeed barely above stall. But as the aircraft leaves the influence of ground effect, induced drag increases dramatically and the pilot finds that his machine suddenly has a will of its own. It doesn't want to go anywhere.

The speed that enabled the airplane to climb at four feet isn't enough at forty. The pilot gets that uneasy feeling in the pit of his stomach as the ship begins to settle. But by now the runway has been left behind. Plane and pilot are about to land . . . in the sagebrush.

The pilot's mistake was simple. He tried to fly out of ground effect without sufficient airspeed and power to cope successfully with an inevitable 100% increase in induced drag.

This type of accident occurs most frequently at high density altitude airports. Simply because an airplane has enough airspeed to get off the ground doesn't mean it can climb above the influence of ground effect. A few feet of altitude can make the difference.

The point to remember is that additional power is required to compensate for increases in drag which occur as an airplane leaves ground effect. But during a takeoff climb, the engine is already developing maximum available power. If a pilot is climbing at the ragged edge without a cushion of airspeed, he may be unable to cope with a substantial increase in drag.

Those who fly retractable gear aircraft should be particularly careful. Numerous accidents are caused annually by pilots who prematurely raise the landing gear. Settling back to the runway with the wheels in the wells is embarrassing, expensive, and dangerous. When takeoff and initial climb performance is marginal, delay raising the gear until safely above the influence of ground effect.

Although ground effect can lead the unsuspecting pilot astray, it also can be used to advantage. Since slow speed performance is improved while in ground effect, why be in a hurry to leave it? The knowledgeable pilot will takeoff, lower the nose slightly, and maintain altitude just a few feet above the runway. This is because an airplane accelerates more rapidly in ground effect than above it.

A skillful pilot literally aims the aircraft at the obstacle over which he wishes to climb, seemingly in sheer defiance. Once a safe climb speed has been attained he raises the nose gingerly and soars over the trees with the maximum possible safety margin. This technique is considerably more efficient than *forcing* an aircraft into a premature climb.

After a heavily loaded takeoff from a critically short runway at high density altitude, an airplane *may* climb satisfactorily to the upper limits of ground effect at minimum speed, but as induced drag steadily increases, the airplane may reach a point where it will climb no more. FAA files bulge with accident reports describing how pilots have mushed headlong into obstacles when acceleration in ground effect might have provided the performance necessary to climb safely.

Ground effect is noticeably influential also during landings. As an aircraft descends into ground effect at a constant attitude, induced drag decays rapidly and is made noticeable by a floating sensation. As a result, the aircraft often won't land until well beyond the original touchdown target. If the runway is too short, abort the landing and try again. More than one pilot has just sat there occupying space while waiting for the wheels to touch only to discover that the runway had receded behind him.

If a pilot is approaching the runway with excessive airspeed, he might consider reducing airspeed while *above* the influence of ground effect. This is where induced drag is most powerful and causes maximum deceleration. Or, if a pilot is caught short with his airspeed down, he might lower the nose and descend into ground effect where he can expect a drag reduction and a slightly prolonged glide. This is recommended only as an emergency measure and when the terrain preceding the runway is flat and unobstructed.

But if the touchdown target is halfway down a long runway, such as during a spot-landing contest where a premature landing doesn't smart so badly, then this playing with ground effect can impress the judges. Knowing precisely what ground effect can and cannot do for a particular aircraft, however, takes practice, lots of it.

After landing, some pilots prefer to keep the nose high and use aerodynamic braking to slow the aircraft. This is most effective when the wing is partially stalled. But because of the large reduction of induced drag caused by the wing being so close to the ground, aerodynamic braking is not as effective as using conventional brakes to decelerate (for most aircraft).

Another point to consider about ground effect is its influence on longitudinal or pitch stability. Remember the downwash of air that flows from the trailing edge of a wing? Normally, this descending air strikes the top of the horizontal stabilizer and helps to keep the tail down.

As an aircraft enters ground effect, downwash is reduced and the tail wants to rise. Unless the fuselage bends in the process, this causes the nose to drop slightly. This explains why an aircraft becomes slightly more nose-heavy immediately prior to touchdown. Experienced pilots expect this or simply react subconsciously; students learn the hard way and wonder why they tend to land nosewheel first. This is also why it is difficult to make a "hands-off" landing. As an airplane gets to within five or ten feet of the runway, it tends to pitch nose down.

Conversely, as a pilot climbs out of ground effect and downwash from the wing is restored, the tail becomes heavier and the nose wants to pitch up. This is of no help to a pilot climbing on the verge of a stall and emphasizes the foolishness of minimum speed climbs.

This nose-up tendency is especially critical when flying an aircraft loaded at or beyond the rearward center of gravity limit. The aircraft might behave quite normally as the wheels leave the tarmac, but the pilot may be in for quite a surprise when the aircraft leaves the influence of ground effect and he has difficulty holding the nose down.

Ground effect also causes local increases in static pressure which cause the airspeed indicator and altimeter to indicate slightly less than they should. For the same reason, the rate of climb indicator usually indicates a descent during the takeoff roll.

Whether or not pilots are aware of it, ground effect plays a key role during every takeoff and landing. The knowledgeable pilot, however, is aware of how to use this phenomenon to his advantage.

TURN DYNAMICS

*Knowing the why of what can happen
is the best stall/spin preventative*

It has been said the 180° turn is one of aviation's most difficult maneuvers. This is because a course reversal usually is contrary to plan and forces a pilot to admit defeat in the face of adversity.

But these are psychological reasons. The maneuver itself is relatively simple. Or is it? An astonishing number of fatal accidents occur annually because many pilots apparently do *not* appreciate the dynamics of a turning airplane.

Table 1-A reviews two variables associated with turning flight that every student discovered while learning to fly. Unfortunately, however, many seem to have forgotten these early lessons. So it might be appropriate to review them before discussing advanced concepts.

As the angle of bank is increased during a coordinated turn, the load factor also increases, something easily detected by the gluteus maximus. But a larger G-load causes more than temporary discomfort of the pilot's posterior. It also burdens the wings with additional "weight." At two G's, for example, the wings must provide twice the lift required during level flight. This, in turn, requires a larger angle of attack, which increases drag, which reduces airspeed (unless additional power is applied).

It is interesting to note that an increased load factor results in the same airspeed loss (or requires the same amount of additional power) as if the airplane were loaded with the equivalent excess payload while in level flight.

For example, an airplane in a 40° banked turn encounters 1.31 G's. The resultant airspeed loss in such a turn is the same as if the airplane were 31% heavier while in level flight. Similarly, the airplane's climb capability is reduced. In other words, as bank angle steepens, the airplane becomes increasingly "heavier" and its performance suffers accordingly.

The lesson here is obvious. When maximum performance is required, don't turn.

Table 1-A

Bank angle in coordinated turn	0°	10°	20°	30°	40°	50°	60°	70°	80°	90°
Load factor	1.0 G	1.02 G's	1.06 G's	1.15 G's	1.31 G's	1.56 G's	2.0 G's	2.92 G's	5.76 G's	infinite
Stall speed increase	0%	1%	3%	7%	14%	25%	41%	71%	140%	infinite

NOTE: Load factor = 1 ÷ cosine of bank angle,
and stall speed increase = square root of load factor

Since aircraft weight effectively increases during a turn, it is logical to assume stall speeds also would rise—which, of course, they do.

Table 1-B illustrates the effects of varying bank angle and airspeed. Not surprisingly, rate of turn at any given airspeed increases as the bank angle steepens. But often not considered is that rate of turn decreases as true airspeed increases (for any given bank angle).

The effect of airspeed on turn rate is particularly distressing to pilots of the SR-71, which is probably the world's fastest airplane. When this remarkable machine is rolled into a 30° bank while cruising nonchalantly at 2,000 knots, the rate of turn is only .3° per second. A 360° turn would take 19 minutes and the circle would have a diameter that stretches from Dayton, Ohio, across Indiana to Chicago. Now that's what is meant by having to plan ahead.

Although an extreme example, this indicates the need to initiate turns from base leg to final approach a little earlier when using unusually fast approach speeds and when checking out in high performance aircraft. Failure to plan ahead can result in either overshooting final approach or having to roll into an excessively steep turn at a dangerously low altitude, one of many causes for the infamous stall/spin accident.

Most pilots realize that a standard-rate turn is 3° per second. But this is only for relatively slow airplanes. Such a turn at 500 knots, for example, would require a 54° (1.7 G) bank angle. That's why a standard-

Table 1-B

True Airspeed \ Bank Angle	10°	20°	30°	40°	50°	60°	70°	80°
50 knots	3.8°/s 1,259 ft	7.9°/s 610 ft	12.6°/s 385 ft	18.3°/s 265 ft	26.0°/s 186 ft	37.8°/s 128 ft	60.0°/s 81 ft	124°/s 39 ft
100 knots	1.9°/s 5,037 ft	4.0°/s 2,440 ft	6.3°/s 1,538 ft	9.2°/s 1,058 ft	13.0°/s 745 ft	18.9°/s 513 ft	30.0°/s 323 ft	61.9°/s 157 ft
150 knots	1.3°/s 1.9 nm	2.6°/s 5,490 ft	4.2°/s 3,461 ft	6.1°/s 2,381 ft	8.7°/s 1,677 ft	12.6°/s 1,154 ft	20.0°/s 727 ft	41.2°/s 352 ft
200 knots	1.0°/s 3.3 nm	2.0°/s 1.6 nm	3.1°/s 1.0 nm	4.6°/s 4,234 ft	6.5°/s 2,981 ft	9.4°/s 2,051 ft	15.0°/s 1,293 ft	30.9°/s 626 ft
250 knots	.8°/s 5.2 nm	1.6°/s 2.5 nm	2.6°/s 1.6 nm	3.7°/s 1.1 nm	5.2°/s 4,658 ft	7.6°/s 3,205 ft	12.0°/s 2,020 ft	24.8°/s 979 ft

Effect of True Airspeed and Bank Angle on Rate of Turn and Turn Radius

(Numbers in shaded boxes are rates of turn, numbers in boxes not shaded represent turn radius.)

$$\text{Rate of turn (degrees/second)} = \frac{(1,091)\ (\text{tangent of bank angle})}{(\text{true airspeed in knots})}$$

$$\text{Turn radius} = \frac{(\text{true airspeed in knots})^2}{(11.26)\ (\text{tangent of bank angle})}$$

rate turn in subsonic, jet-powered airplanes is only 1.5° per second.

The variables of turning flight give rise to an interesting problem. Assume that a pilot were flying through a very narrow canyon and had to make a minimum radius, 180° turn without gaining or losing altitude. What technique should he use?

He knows that, for a given bank angle, the greatest rate of turn occurs at the slowest airspeed. He knows also that, for a given airspeed, turn radius decreases as the bank angle steepens. This suggests, therefore, the canyon turn should be performed with a steep bank angle and minimum airspeed. But could this intrepid aviator complete the turn before stalling? Probably not.

In theory, the minimum radius, or *maximum performance,* turn is achieved by maintaining the airplane's maneuvering speed (Va) and using the maximum possible bank angle without inducing either a stall or an excessive load factor. For aircraft certificated for 3.8 G's (which is *most* light planes), this is about a 75° bank angle. The resultant maneuver is a balance between structural and aerodynamic limits. When turning with a 75° bank angle, the load factor would be 3.8 G's (maximum allowable). Also, with any less airspeed or with additional bank angle, the airplane would stall. Quite obviously, this is a tricky, delicate maneuver.

Most light aircraft, however, are incapable of performing such a turn. At 3.8 G's, the airplane effectively weighs almost four times as much as when in level flight. To maintain altitude in such a configuration requires tremendous power, something lacking in many airplanes especially when operating at high density altitudes. To attempt such a maximum performance maneuver when near the ground, therefore, is to flirt with disaster.

When flying an *underpowered* airplane, such a turn can be performed only when a pilot is willing to sacrifice altitude. (Curiously, turn radius is *slightly* less when climbing or descending compared to an identical turn while maintaining altitude.)

Parenthetically, when flying through a narrow valley, it is usually best to fly along the downwind side. If a turn has to be made, it will be into the wind, which *decreases* turn radius. Conversely, a turn away from the wind *increases* turn radius and requires considerably more elbow room. Also, flying along the downwind side of a valley often places an airplane in orographically rising air which can improve cruise performance.

Many airplanes lacking sufficient power for maximum performance turns also are similarly underpowered during moderately steep turns at reduced airspeed. This is because of the increased induced drag which occurs as angle of attack is enlarged.

Consider an airplane climbing over an obstacle at full power and reduced airspeed. If the pilot enters a 45° banked turn, induced drag may double; in a 60° banked turn, induced drag can more than triple. As a result, considerable power is required not only to climb, but simply to maintain altitude. Lacking sufficient power, the airplane simply may descend with the throttle wide open. This helpless sensation may not be as dramatic as a stall, but can be just as lethal. Raising the nose farther to arrest the sink rate worsens the dilemma and leads to a stall.

The solution? Roll out of the turn.

Accident statistics reveal that such a stall accident most frequently occurs while departing high elevation airports when airplane and engine performance may be marginal.

An approach accident of this type may occur when a pilot on base leg fails to recognize that the normal indicated approach airspeed converts to a much faster true airspeed when flying into a high elevation airport. As a result, he peripherally senses an abnormally fast approach speed through the side window and subconciously reduces airspeed. Then, because he may still have a faster than normal groundspeed (because of the faster true airspeed), he may overshoot final approach and tighten the turn to line up with the runway. *Voila!* He has just met the admission requirements to join that elite society of flagging fliers. A missed approach isn't good for the ego, but it is much preferred to steep turns near the ground.

Stalls resulting from climbing and descending turns often create a unique brand of havoc: initially uncontrollable rolling moments that can lead to inverted flight and possible spinning. During a climbing, turning stall, the angle of attack of the outside wing is larger than that of the inside wing. As a result, the outside, or high wing stalls first and causes a rapid roll *opposite* to the direction of turn. Such an involuntary maneuver is called an "over-the-top" spin entry, which if unchecked results in a complete roll followed by a spin.

During a descending, turning stall, the angle of attack of the inside wing is larger than that of the outside wing. Consequently, the inside, or low wing stalls first and simply drops lower. Less dramatic than flipping on your back, but equally as dangerous, this is known as an entry to an "under-the-bottom" spin.

It must be noted that any attempt to correct either of these situations by applying "opposite" aileron control usually aggravates the crisis.

It is not easy to visualize why the outside wing in a climbing turn and the inside wing in a descending turn have larger angles of attack than their opposite wings. To understand this important concept, it is necessary to analyze the motion of an airplane about all three axes.

In a flat, skidding turn with the wings level, for example, the aircraft is only yawing. But, in a coordinated turn while maintaining altitude, the airplane is yawing *and pitching.* In the extreme case of a 90° banked turn, the airplane is only pitching. But in a normal gliding or climbing turn, the airplane is yawing, pitching and *rolling.*

In a gliding turn, the airplane rolls inward, which causes the inside wing to have the larger angle of attack. Similarly, in a climbing turn, the airplane rolls outward which causes the outside wing to have the larger angle of attack.

Here's another way to look at it. During the descending turn, the inside wing is turning on a smaller radius, which means it is descending in a steeper spiral than the outside wing. The air, therefore, must "rise" to meet the inside wing at a larger angle (of attack) than it does the outside wing. Similar logic explains why the outside wing has a larger angle of attack during climbing turns.

When an airplane is made to stall while turning *and* maintaining altitude, the bank angle should not change one way or the other. The

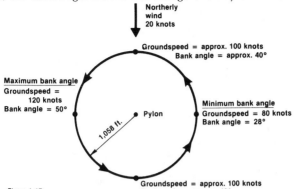

Figure 1-17

exception occurs when one wing stalls before the other because both wings are not physically symmetrical.

The effect that wind has on turning flight while performing ground track maneuvers is not always appreciated. (Remember, flying a rectangular traffic pattern is a ground track maneuver.)

For example, assume that a pilot is attempting to fly a perfect circle around a pylon. Unfortunately, a strong northerly wind is doing its best to foil the pilot's plans. To fly a perfect circle during such a condition, bank angle must be varied during the 360° turn. At what part of the circle should the turn be the steepest? Where should it be the shallowest?

Most pilots believe that the steepest bank angle is required at the southerly part of the circle to prevent the northerly wind from blowing the aircraft away from the circular ground track. Similarly, the logic continues, the shallowest bank angle is needed on the northerly side to prevent drifting into the circle. This sounds logical, but is wrong.

Figure 1-17 shows a 100 knot airplane flying counter-clockwise about a pylon; a 20 knot breeze is blowing from the north. During no-wind conditions, a constant 40° banked turn would result in a circle with a radius of 1,058 feet. But because of the northerly wind, in this case, the

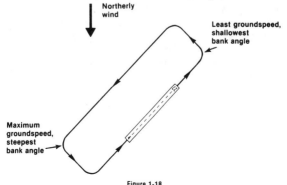

Figure 1-18

31

bank angle must vary as shown in the diagram.

Notice that the steepest bank is required when flying downwind along the western edge of the circle, not at the southern edge. This is because *the steepest bank is required when groundspeed is at a maximum.* The airplane is flying so rapidly that the rate of turn must be increased to remain on track.

Similarly, the shallowest bank is required when flying upwind on the eastern side of the circle, not when flying crosswind at the northern edge. Groundspeed here is at a minimum. The airplane is flying so slowly that more time is available to turn a given number of degrees. Hence, a shallow bank angle is required.

The same logic applies when flying the traffic pattern. Notice in Figure 1-18 that, because of a northerly wind, the turn from downwind to base leg results in the fastest groundspeed and therefore requires the steepest bank angle (assuming that airspeed is held constant around the pattern). Similarly, turning onto the crosswind leg (after takeoff) results in the slowest groundspeed and suggests a shallower bank angle.

As we have seen, there are numerous circumstances calling for executing steeper than anticipated turns while at low altitude. And unless a pilot is very adept at such maneuvering *and* has a sufficiently powerful engine, such turning can be foolhardy indeed.

It is doubtful that there lives a pilot who hasn't lost altitude inadvertently while practicing steep turns. At altitude, this is not a serious problem. But when near the ground, there may not be sufficient time to apply the proper corrections.

Instructors teach three basic ways to arrest an undesirable sink rate when in a steep turn. One way is to raise the nose; another is to add power. If neither of these corrections is adequate, the third alternative is to decrease the bank angle and raise the nose or roll out of the turn entirely.

Unfortunately, rolling out of a turn to arrest an increasing sink rate usually is regarded as a sign of failure, an inability to control the aircraft. But when operating an airplane at the limits of its performance capability, rolling out of a steep turn may be the only *safe* way to maintain a healthy reserve of airspeed and power. If a steep turn gets out of hand, it is far wiser to recognize the limitations of plane and pilot than to horse back on the yoke and risk stalling or creating enough of a G-load to warp a wing. Rolling out of an undesirable situation is a safe, professional technique that allows the maneuver to be repeated at the pilot's leisure; stalling at low altitude can be terminal.

But since prevention is preferable to cure, learn to recognize and avoid situations which induce an apparent need to turn sharply.

THAT SHIFTING
CENTER OF GRAVITY

Going a step further with
weight and balance

When Lindbergh guided the *Spirit of St. Louis* across the Atlantic in 1927, he endured many hours of monotony. Some of these were spent contemplating trivial aspects of the flight. At one point, for example, he calculated that his nine-cylinder Wright Whirlwind engine would have to produce 15 million power strokes during the 33½ hour flight from Roosevelt Field to LeBourget Airport. This staggering figure, he admitted later, gave him some cause for concern. After all, how could any engine endure so many punishing "explosions" without failing?

On a lighter note, Lindberg observed a stowaway housefly aboard his Ryan monoplane. He knew that when the fly was at rest, it added infinitesimally to the payload. But what about when the fly was winging about the cabin? When the housefly supports its own weight, does this relieve the aircraft of having to support the load?

"If this is so," Lindbergh mused, "then perhaps I should not allow the fly to rest and needlessly burden the *Spirit of St. Louis*." Lindbergh knew, however, that it made no difference whether the fly was airborne or at rest on the instrument panel. When flying, the insect's wings deflected air downward. Eventually, this minute quantity of air pressed against the cockpit floor with a force equal to the weight of the fly. The only way to eliminate such a "load" is to eject the stowaway bug through an open window.

A few years ago, the Lufthansa airline magazine, *Jet Tales*, posed a similar problem:

"If a Lufthansa 747 freighter is loaded with 50 tons of live doves and if all of these birds were to fly around in their containers at the same time, would the jumbo jet lose 50 tons of weight?"

Obviously not. There would be, however, a record number of midair collisions and busted beaks.

This problem, however, leads to another. If all of the birds were to suddenly fly from the floor to the ceiling, would this have any effect on the jumbo's center of gravity? Absolutely.

Assume that the dove-loaded aircraft is cruising at 41,000 feet and all the birds are at rest. When the birds fly toward the ceiling, the CG is displaced *vertically* to a higher location in the aircraft. The new CG could, for example, be 10 feet above the original CG. Now, would this have any effect on the 747's flight path?

It may not be immediately obvious, but the reaction of 50 tons of cargo rising to the ceiling causes the aircraft to lose as much altitude as is gained by the center of gravity (10 feet, in this case). Everything else being equal, it is the center of gravity that maintains a constant altitude, not the aircraft. If this were not so, then a drowning swimmer could lift himself out of the water by pulling up on his own hair.

When the birds tire of such folly and return to the cabin floor, the CG returns to its original location and the aircraft gains the altitude previously lost.

It is also interesting to note that the three motions of an airplane—pitch, roll and yaw—all take place about the center of gravity. In other words, when the CG changes location, so does the airplane's aerodynamic pivot point.

Most pilots aren't particularly concerned about the center of gravity's vertical movement, but they do (or should) regard seriously its longitudinal (fore and aft) travel. When CG limits are violated, both plane and pilot may be in jeopardy. But even when specified limits are observed, the location of the CG can significantly alter performance.

For example, does an airplane fly faster with an aft CG, a forward CG, or does this have no effect on airspeed? Initially, the answer seems illogical, but once understood provides some insight as to the effects of CG movement.

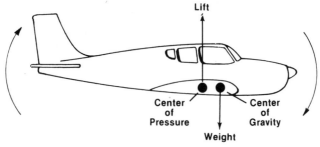

Figure 1-19

If the average pilot were to guess, he might suggest that the CG location has no effect on airspeed. He'd be wrong. Next, he might speculate that a forward CG improves performance because this helps to keep the nose down. An aft CG, he might reason, causes the tail to sag resulting in a nose high attitude and mushing flight. Wrong again. Generally speaking, an aft CG results in the fastest airspeed; a forward CG reduces airspeed.

Figure 1-19 shows a 4,000 pound airplane in cruise flight at a constant airspeed. Notice that the center of gravity is forward of the center of pressure, a theoretical point at which all wing lift appears to be concentrated. For most light airplanes, this is the normal relationship between lift and weight.

If wing lift and gross weight were the only vertical forces present, the airplane would have an overwhelming urge to pitch earthward.

Figure 1-20 introduces another factor: the horizontal stabilizer. This surface is called upon to produce "negative lift," a downward force on the tail that prevents the nose from pitching down. The wing, therefore, must not only overcome aircraft weight, it also must generate enough additional lift to offset the downward force on the tail. To maintain equilibrium in this case, wing lift must equal the sum of aircraft weight (4,000 pounds) plus the negative tail load (200 pounds, for example) or a total of 4,200 pounds.

Figure 1-21 shows the same airplane after the center of gravity has been moved aft to a point vertically aligned with the center of lift. Since lift and weight are in balance, a download on the tail is unnecessary. As

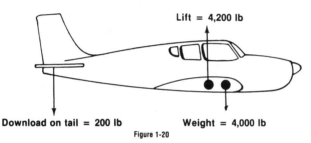

Lift = 4,200 lb

Download on tail = 200 lb   **Weight = 4,000 lb**

Figure 1-20

a result, the wing needs to produce only 4,000 pounds of lift compared to 4,200 pounds when the center of gravity was forward.

Since the wing does not need to produce as much lift when the center of gravity is aft, it is flown at a smaller angle of attack. As a result, drag is reduced and airspeed increases. Or, the same airspeed can be maintained at a reduced power setting.

When speed is important, a few knots can often be gained with aft loading. By placing heavier baggage and passengers as far rearward as is *legally allowable*, tail loading is reduced, which allows the wing to be flown at a smaller angle of attack. Several air carriers use this technique on cargo flights. Aft loading saves considerable fuel (and increases range) because cruise speed is achieved with slightly reduced thrust.

When operating some aircraft, a similar result can be achieved by burning fuel from forward tanks. As the flight progresses, the center of gravity moves gradually aft and a slight increase in airspeed can be detected.

Since the wing carries "less weight" when the center of gravity is aft, it might be concluded that stall speeds are reduced at such a time. That's true. And, as the center of gravity moves forward, stall speeds increase.

At least one major airframe manufacturer has been known to take advantage of this little-known fact. Stall speeds shown in operating handbooks often are valid only for when the center of gravity is at the extreme aft limit. At other times, when the CG is more normal, stall speeds are greater. This, however, cannot be found anywhere in the pilot's handbook. Very sneaky!

It is beneficial, therefore, to fly with an aft center of gravity. But it is possible to get too much of a good thing.

Figure 1-22 shows an airplane with its center of gravity *behind* the center of lift. To keep such an airplane in balance, it is necessary for the horizontal stabilizer to develop *positive* lift. This takes even more

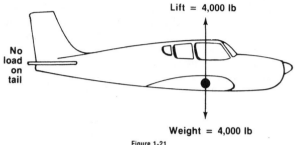

Figure 1-21

load off the wing, which further decreases the necessary angle of attack and reduces wing drag. But there's a catch. Since the stabilizer is generating lift, it also must create additional drag. As a result, very little may be gained.

In terms of performance, therefore, the best place for the center of gravity is at or very close to the center of lift. The stabilizer is unloaded (with no induced drag of its own) and the wing carries only the airplane's gross weight.

Most of the time, however, the center of gravity is forward of the center of lift, requiring the horizontal stabilizer to produce a balancing and inefficient (in terms of performance) download.

One way to resolve this problem is to move the horizontal stabilizer from the tail to the nose of the airplane. When configured in such a manner, the horizontal stabilizer becomes a small, or auxiliary wing because it is called upon—like the main wing—to produce positive lift, a necessity if the airplane is to be kept in balance. This configuration

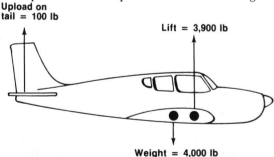

Figure 1-22

is referred to as a canard airplane and the forward located horizontal stabilizer is called a canard surface.

There is nothing new about a canard; it has been applied to various airplane designs for more than 75 years (beginning with the Wright

Flyer). Although the canard surface is generally more efficient than a conventional horizontal stabilizer, inherent difficulties with longitudinal stability have prevented popularization of the concept. Interest in the canard, however has been revitalized. Burt Rutan, who designed the VariEze, VariViggan and Defiant, seems to have overcome some of the canard's critical design aspects.

But for those of us who must be content to fly with conventional tail surfaces, we'll simply have to compensate as much as possible by maintaing an aft center of gravity.

There is nothing wrong with an aft center of gravity as long as it is kept within limits designated by the airframe manufacturer. Violating an aft CG limit, however, can result in an unacceptable decrease in longitudinal (pitch) stability, something far more dangerous than most pilots understand.

Simply stated, longitudinal stability is the ability of an airplane to return to its trimmed angle of attack (or airspeed) if disturbed from that angle of attack (or airspeed).

There are many forces created by an airplane that contribute to longitudinal stability, but the horizontal stabilizer generally is the most influential. In a crude manner of speaking, an airplane's tailfeathers really are like feathers, the feathers of an arrow. Without them, a conventional airplane would wallow and wobble uncontrollably.

The stabilizing role of the horizontal tailfeathers can be appreciated by visualizing an airplane flying steadily at a given angle of attack. Suddenly the plane is assaulted by an updraft, which momentarily increases that angle of attack. The stabilizer also would be flying at a larger and possibly positive angle of attack. As a result, the tail would temporarily create more lift (or less download). Since the horizontal stabilizer is situated way behind the center of gravity, this forces the nose to pitch down, tending to return the aircraft to its original angle of attack. This is longitudinal stability.

Like a wing, the horizontal stabilizer performs only when supplied with a healthy diet of airspeed. Reduce that life-supporting flow of air across the tail and the forces produced by the stabilizer can change dramatically.

Consider the balanced aircraft as shown in Figure 1-20. The forces are aligned normally and the engine is developing cruise power. Propwash flowing across the tail, therefore, is helping the stabilizer to do its job: create negative lift.

Assume now that the pilot suddenly retards the throttle. The amount of propwash flowing across the horizontal stabilzer decreases, which causes a decrease in the negative lift produced by this tail surface. In other words, the download produced by the tail is reduced. As a result, the nose drops.

Conversely, when power is added, the negative lift produced by the stabilizer increases and the aircraft nose rises. (Other factors also are responsible for these pitching reactions to power changes, but the action of the stabilizer is usually most influential.)

Now let's consider the potentially critical situation as shown in Figure 1-22, where the center of gravity has been shifted beyond its aft limit to a point behind the center of lift. To maintain balance, obviously, the horizontal stabilizer must produce upward lift.

If power is reduced at such a time, the horizontal stabilizer receives less propwash and is unable to produce as much lift and the tail descends. Imagine such a situation! Retard the throttle and the nose goes up.

Perhaps the converse would be even more disastrous. By applying power (such as during a missed approach), the nose would plunge earthward . . .

(The lofty horizontal stabilizers of some T-tailed aircraft are above the propwash and do not react as abruptly to power changes.)

The trend is clear: as the center of gravity moves aft, longitudinal stability decreases. Eventually, instability sets in. Flying such a machine would be a fatiguing, full-time, dangerous operation. And this is why airplanes have center of gravity limits that must be strictly observed.

Additional problems created by an excessively aft CG include potentially violent stall characteristics, a tendency for normal spins to develop into flat spins (from which recovery may not be possible) and a reduction of control wheel forces that make it easier for a pilot to overcontrol and overstress the airplane.

On the other hand, an excessively *forward* center of gravity introduces another set of adverse flight characteristics. These include faster stalling speeds, decreased performance and excessive longitudinal stability that increases the control wheel forces required to control pitch. So much up-elevator may be required to maintain equilibrium that there may not be enough left over to safely flare during landing. This can result in an overly stressed nosewheel or prevent a taildragger from making a three-point landing (which is why you should not solo a Piper J-3 Cub from the front seat).

Since the vertical and longitudinal shifting of the CG has been considered, it would be unfair not to at least mention lateral movement of the center of gravity.

If fuel is improperly managed and is consumed unevenly from wing or tip tanks, it is possible to notice a lateral shift of the CG by the tendency of one wing to fly lower than the other.

Can this affect performance? Yes, because having to continuously deflect the ailerons (with or without trim) creates unnecessary drag. In extreme cases, so much aileron might be required to hold up a heavy wing that insufficient roll control may be left to counter a strong crosswind during landing.

While it might be nit-picking to consider the weight of a housefly or the effect of doves hovering in the cockpit, an improperly located center of gravity could have serious consequences.

UP, UP, AND AWAY

*There's more to climbs than pushing
the power and pointing the nose*

For unscrupulous characters, it's not how you climb to the top that's important . . . as long as you get there.

For scrupulous pilots, however, it's precisely *how* you make the climb that *is* so important.

Often, climbing is regarded as a necessary evil, a slow flight maneuver to be tolerated until the euphoria of cruise flight is attained. Usually, a pilot simply honks back on the yoke and patiently awaits the top of climb. He rarely considers the available techniques and knowledge that not only can increase the efficiency of flight, but also the longevity of engine and pilot.

There are various climb techniques, each satisfying a specific need. But before these can be explored, it would be helpful to understand some background theory.

Figure 2-1 shows the relationship between climb rate and airspeed of a typical lightplane being flown at maximum power. Notice that at 180 knots, the aircraft is neither climbing nor descending. This is the maximum possible cruise speed (for a given altitude) and requires all available power. When faster than 180 knots, the aircraft is obviously in a dive and the climb rate is negative.

Similarly, at 40 knots the aircraft is maintaining a constant altitude. The angle of attack is so large, and results in so much drag, that—even with full power—the aircraft is unable to climb. When decelerating below 40 knots, the aircraft may actually descend prior to stall.

Flight between 40 and 180 knots, in this case, results in a positive climb rate. This is because more power is available than is required to maintain any of these intermediate airspeeds while at a constant altitude. The excess horsepower will, of course, produce a climb.

Inspection of the climb curve reveals the maximum possible climb rate of 1,000 fpm occurs at only one airspeed—100 knots. This is known as the best rate of climb airspeed or, more simply, Vy. It is at this indicated airspeed that minimum power is required to maintain altitude; a maximum excess of horsepower, therefore, is available to produce the maximum rate of climb.

It is important to note that a climb at *any other airspeed* results in a reduced climb rate. Pulling the nose higher and decelerating to less than Vy may result in temporary "ballooning," but the long-term result is diminished climb performance brought about by the increased drag at the larger angle of attack. Conversely, an increase in airspeed to above Vy increases drag and decreases climb rate.

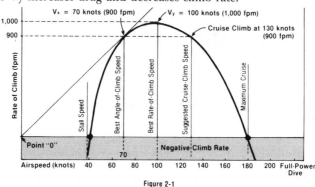

Figure 2-1

The climb curve also provides the best angle of climb airspeed, or Vx. This is found by plotting a straight line from the origin of the graph (point 0) so that is barely touches (or is tangent to) the climb curve. This point of tangency with the curve reveals Vx which, in this case, is 70 knots. When climbing at Vx, the climb angle is at a maximum, even though the rate of climb is only 900 fpm. This is an often confusing aspect of climb performance that is clarified in Figure 2-2.

Notice that when Aircraft A is climbing at Vy (100 knots), it gains 1,000 feet in one minute. Simultaneously, it flies 1.67 nm forward. In other words, the airplane gains 599 feet of altitude during each mile of flight. (The actual climb angle is 5.6°.)

Aircraft B, however, is climbing at Vx, or 70 knots, and has a reduced climb *rate* of only 900 fpm. At the end of one minute, this aircraft has gained 900 feet while covering a horizontal distance of only 117 nm. This is equivalent to an altitude gain of 771 feet per nm of forward flight. In other words, this aircraft is climbing more steeply (at an angle of 7.2°) even though its rate of climb is less.

The best *angle* of climb airspeed (Vx) is used when trying to overfly an obstacle, when it is necessary to gain the maximum altitude in the *minimum distance.*

The best *rate* of climb airspeed (Vy) is used when it is desirable to gain the maximum altitude in the *minimum amount of time.*

Fortunately, Vx and Vy are usually specified in the pilot's operating handbook. However, these critical airspeeds vary with gross weight and altitude, factors which often are not taken into consideration, especially in the older handbooks.

For example, consider a Cessna 310R. At maximum gross weight and while flying at sea level, Vy is 107 knots. Elevate the aircraft to

20,000 feet and Vy decreases to 91 knots. Reduce the gross weight by 800 pounds and Vy drops another 6 knots to 85 knots. This represents a substantial, 22 knots difference between one Vy and the other. Unless the indicated airspeed is appropriately adjusted for variations in weight and altitude, climb performance can suffer dramatically.

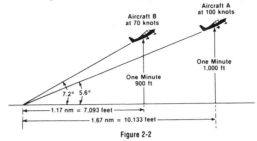

Figure 2-2

Fortunately, there are some reliable rules-of-thumb which can be used to approximately determine Vy at various gross weights and altitudes. Even when the variability of Vy is presented in operating handbooks, the following rules are often easier to use and more immediately accessible.

With respect to weight corrections only, Vy and Vx each decrease about one knot for each 100 pounds less than maximum allowable gross weight. An aircraft that grosses at 3,800 pounds with a best rate of climb airspeed of 91 knots, for example has an adjusted Vy of 86 knots when loaded to only 3,300 pounds (500 pounds = a 5 knot Vy correction).

The second rule: Reduce Vy (but not Vx) by 1% for each 1,000 foot increase in density altitude. Consider the 3,300 pound aircraft mentioned above. Its revised Vy (because of reduced gross weight) is 86 knots at sea level. At 10,000 feet, Vy for this aircraft would be only 77 knots (86 knots − 10%).

In actual practice, reduce Vy by one knot during each thousand feet of climb and this will result in very nearly the most expeditious ascent possible. These rules are valid, however, only for lightplanes with naturally aspirated, reciprocating engines.

Now let's discuss Vx, the best angle of climb airspeed. Believe it or not, this performance figure is often unavailable. Oh, yes, operating manuals do specify Vx for the *flaps down* configuration, but rarely is Vx specified for a steep, *flaps up* climb.

Vx (flaps up) is the speed to use when a steep climb gradient is required to overfly an enroute obstacle (such as a cloud or mountain) or to reach a minimum, IFR crossing altitude in the minimum forward distance. Why flaps up for a maximum climb angle? Simple—most airplanes climb best with flaps retracted.

Flaps usually are recommended *only* to overfly an obstacle at the departure end of a runway. This is because flaps help to increase the *net* climb angle, as measured from the takeoff end of the runway to the impending obstacle. With flaps extended, the takeoff roll is reduced and the aircraft can begin its climb sooner. Also, valuable distance isn't wasted while accelerating to the faster Vx (with flaps up).

Considering takeoff obstacles only, flaps do augment steep climb angles. Otherwise, the steepest climb angle usually results when the flaps are retracted.

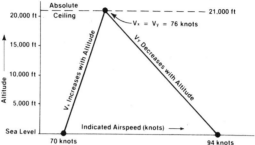

Figure 2-3

Figure 2-3 shows the relationship of Vy to Vx (clean) for a P-model Bonanza. Notice that Vy decreases from 94 knots at sea level to 76 knots at the aircraft's absolute ceiling of 21,000 feet (a decrease of nearly 1 knot/1,000 feet). The chart also shows that, at the absolute ceiling, Vy (best rate) and Vx (best angle) are identical.

This destroys a myth about high altitude flying. Most pilots believe that upon reaching the absolute ceiling, the aircraft is just about ready to stall. Not so. In order to reach the absolute ceiling, the aircraft would have to be climbing at Vy, otherwise the aircraft would never get there. At this airspeed (which is 26 knots *above* the Bonanza's stall speed of 50 knots), all available power is required simply to maintain the absolute ceiling. No excess power (or thrust) is available. If the nose were raised or lowered—even slightly—the resultant drag rise would cause a sink rate to develop. There simply isn't enough power available to maintain the absolute ceiling at speeds slower or faster than Vy. Therefore, when at its absolute ceiling, an aircraft is not in danger of stalling unless handled improperly.

From Figure 2-3, notice that Vx varies differently than Vy. Instead of *decreasing* 1% per 1,000 feet, Vx (flaps up) *increases almost ½%* per 1,000 feet. For the P-model Bonanza, Vx increases from 70 knots at sea level to 76 knots at 21,000 feet.

The industrious reader can utilize the example in Figure 2-4 in combination with the rules-of-thumb offered previously to construct a geometrically similar climb speed chart for his own aircraft. All that is needed is Vy and Vx (flaps up) at sea level and the aircraft's absolute ceiling (the service ceiling will suffice.)

Figure 2-4 is a typical example of how climb rate varies with altitude. Notice that the decrease in climb rate is linear. In other words, the rate of climb decreases by a constant amount during each 1,000 feet of climb. This is true of all lightplanes (sans turbochargers) being flown at maximum power *and* at the proper Vy.

If such a chart is unavailable for your aircraft, don't fret; it's a simple matter to construct one. All that's needed is the maximum rate of climb at sea level and the aircraft's service ceiling, data available in all operating handbooks and sales brochures.

Simply plot the sea level rate of climb on the horizontal line, as shown in Figure 2-4 (point A). And since an airplane's service ceiling (by definition) is the highest altitude at which a 100 fpm climb can be achieved, this point on the graph is located at the intersection of the appropriate altitude and the vertical line representing a 100 fpm climb rate (point B in Figure 2-4, for example). Then simply connect points A and B with a straight line. Next, extend this line until it terminates at the left side of the graph. The termination point of this line indicates the aircraft's *absolute* ceiling (point C in Figure 2-4).

With such a chart, a pilot has a very accurate method of predicting maximum climb performance at any given *density altitude* when the aircraft is fully loaded.

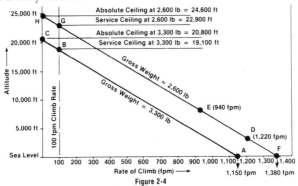

Figure 2-4

After determining the approximate gross weight of your aircraft, enter a full-power climb while maintaining Vy. Then determine the rates of climb at any two altitudes at least 5,000 feet apart. (A stopwatch is usually more accurate than the VSI).

Assume that the rates of climb at 3,000 and 8,000 feet are 1,220 and 940 fpm, respectively. Simply plot these points (D and E) as shown in Figure 2-4. Then, connect these points with an extended straight line that should very closely parallel the original line A-C. This new line (defined by the points D and E) will provide reasonably accurate predictions of the maximum climb rate at sea level (point F), the revised service ceiling (point G), the revised absolute ceiling (point H) and all intermediate climb rates for the reduced weight configuration.

This climb performance, however, is predicated on the use of maximum available power, something most pilots use only for takeoff and initial climb. This raises an interesting point. Unless otherwise required by the engine manufacturer, why reduce power prior to reaching cruise altitude? Factually, there isn't much of a reason to retard the throttle after takeoff. Most of us do it because of habit or "to save the engine," neither of which is a valid reason.

If the throttle is left untouched after takeoff, climb performance can be downright startling. Besides, during each 1,000 feet of climb, the free-breathing engine naturally loses about an inch of manifold pressure, a form of automatic power reduction.

Leaving the throttle wide open during climb is not injurious to the engine (unless *specified* in the operating handbook), increases low altitude climb rates dramatically, and usually results in *less fuel burn* and time to reach a given altitude (when the airspeed is held at Vy).

Also consider that—statistically—the most likely time for engine failure is during the first power reduction after takeoff. So why be in a hurry to retard the throttle? If the power is available, use it.

Does a full power climb increase aircraft noise for those who live beneath departure corridors? Probably not. The increased climb rate raises the noise footprint which seems to result in a quieter departure. The airlines once employed a power reduction technique shortly after takeoff, but the climb performance suffered and the noise footprint beneath the aircraft was simply held down longer. Now the jets use maximum power and pitch angles to scramble to altitude as quickly as possible, a technique which seems to reduce substantially the noise footprint beneath the aircraft.

Climbing at Vy does result in the most rapid climb to altitude, but it is not the most efficient in terms of getting from A to B. For this, a cruise climb is required. The question often asked is, "What is the most efficient airspeed to use?" The best rule-of-thumb suggests using a climb speed that is as much faster than Vy than Vx is below Vy.

An excellent example is found in Figure 2-1. Notice that Vx is 70 knots and Vy is 100 knots, a difference of 30 knots. Now, *add* this difference to Vy to obtain a reasonably efficient cruise-climb speed of 130 knots (Vy + 30).

When climbing at 130 knots, in this case, the airspeed is 30% greater than Vy while the climb rate is decreased by only 13% from 1,000 to 900 fpm, an advantageous compromise. The "cruise-climb" speed should be reduced 1% after each 1,000 feet of climb.

For those who are in a hurry and don't need to reach altitude quickly, climb at full power and the shallowest climb rate consistent with safety.

The most efficient cross-country climb in terms of saving fuel results from selecting a fairly fast climb speed, a shallow climb rate and no more than 75% power. The reduced power setting allows the engine to be leaned during the climb.

But irrespective of the climb technique used, always maintain a sharp eye on engine operating temperatures. If the oil or cylinder heads become excessively warm, increase airspeed and/or reduce power to cool the engine.

Upon reaching cruise altitude, don't be in a hurry to reduce power. Otherwise, the airplane will take forever to pull itself out of the mushing attitude and accelerate to cruise speed. Instead, leave the throttle alone. Use climb power to accelerate to a few mph *faster* than cruise and *then* reduce power. The aircraft will decelerate and more easily stabilize at the target airspeed.

One final note of caution. Be constantly aware that any climb—especially a steep one—reduces forward visibility from the cockpit. While climbing, occasionally execute shallow S-turns or dip the nose gently to see what or who might lie ahead. A mid-air collision can seriously erode climb performance.

SOMETHING FOR NOTHING

*Using soaring techniques to get
more out of your airplane*

Charles Lindbergh was known to many for more than his historic flight
to Paris. To some World War II Navy pilots, he was also the maestro
of long-range cruise control.

On several occasions, Lindbergh took off from an aircraft carrier
and returned with considerably more fuel than others who had flown
the identical mission. This happened often enough to rule out luck or
a particularly efficient airplane.

One of Lindbergh's techniques recognized the advantages of flight
through rising air and the penalties paid when flying through descending air. He skillfully used convective (vertical) currents to extract energy
from the atmosphere, free power than can supplement lift, reduce fuel
consumption, increase airspeed, or achieve exhilarating rates of climb.

Of course, none of this is particularly earth shaking to sailplane
pilots. They began developing similar skills before the Wright Brothers
had ever heard of Kitty Hawk. A few have accomplished some truly
extraordinary feats. Consider Paul Bikle, who soared to 46,267 feet msl
in his Schweizer sailplane, or Hans Grosse of West Germany, who flew
his ASK-12 for a non-stop, straight-line distance of 789 nm (908 sm).

No, there was nothing new about Lindy's ability to take advantage
of the rising currents of air, but he was one of the first to successfully
and dramatically demonstrate the feasibility of applying these techniques to *powered* flight. The lessons he taught to Navy pilots are even
more valuable to those who fly light, general aviation airplanes.

There is a fascinating, enjoyable method by which soaring can be
practiced in your own airplane (without shutting down the engine).
But before the fun (described later), some time needs to be spent in the
classroom.

Since the atmosphere is three dimensional, a pilot needs more than
a working knowledge of horizontal air motion (wind). Vertical currents
also should be considered. It is important not only to know when and
where to expect rising air, but also how to avoid sinking air, something

that can seriously erode performance.

For practical purposes, air rises only when it is heated from below (convection currents) or when it is lifted mechanically (orographically) by a mountain slope or other obstacle to the wind. (Although sailplane pilots also utilize mountain waves and frontal slopes, these sources of lift are not as useful to powered flight.)

Most pilots are aware of thermals, those columnar bubbles of relatively warm, rising air that usually produce a turbulent ride. When a thermal is sufficiently strong and contains sufficient water vapor, it results in a cumulus cloud, a visual signpost usually representing the thermal's uppermost limit. As every sailplane pilot knows, a rich column of lift usually can be found between the source of the thermal and the cloud base. But one cumulus cloud (or thermal) is normally not of value to a power pilot.

Fortunately, because of Mother Nature's propensity for order and symmetry, cumulus clouds frequently occur in long, parallel rows (called "cloud streets") extending for many miles. By flying along the street (below the clouds), a pilot can experience and take advantage of considerable lift for surprisingly long distances. To prevent gaining undesirable altitude, a power pilot simply lowers the nose and picks up additional airspeed. An increase of 5, 10 or 15 knots is not unusual. Or, if he desires, a pilot can reduce power, save fuel and maintain normal cruise speed.

Pilots tend to fly under the clear sky *between* cloud streets, although this is self-defeating and is like seeking out headwinds because the result is the same—reduced groundspeed. This is because air between cloud streets is generally sinking. Maintaining altitude here requires either additional power (and fuel) or an increased pitch angle and subsequent airspeed loss.

Lindbergh knew about the up- and down-draft activity in the vicinity of cumulus clouds and often altered his flight path to take advantage of the beneficial currents. Little wonder that he often returned with more fuel than did other pilots not so well informed.

The buoyant air feeding cumulus clouds does not always rise vertically, however. If there is a wind, a flight two or three thousand feet below the cloud base might miss the rising current entirely.

Figure 2-5 demonstrates that when the wind is blowing, the flight path should be downwind of the thermal's source and upwind of the cloud base. When uncertain of wind direction (or speed), simply spend a moment observing the movement of the cloud's shadow. (None of this is meant to imply that pilots should fly under the base of a thunderstorm or even a massive and towering cumulus cloud; this discussion deals with fair weather cumulus.)

If thermals do not contain sufficient water vapor, the vertical currents can be used even though cumulus clouds do not develop to point the way. Instead, thermals must be located at their sources such as small towns and factories that radiate considerable heat. In open country, look for contrasts in soil and fly over (or near) those areas that appear driest (moist soil, areas of vegetation and bodies of water usually do not generate significant thermal activity). Over mountainous or hilly terrain, the south-facing slopes exposed to the sun generally breed thermals better than north-facing slopes or valleys.

Sometimes, such as when overflying a desert or vast plain, it's impossible to tell where the thermals originate. It's simply a matter of flying from lift to sink to lift, etc. At such times, improved performance (or reduced fuel burn) still can be achieved. When flying through

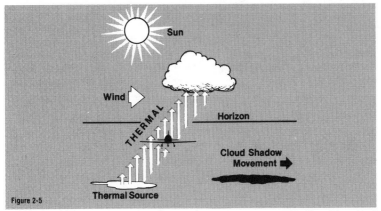

Figure 2-5

updrafts, take advantage of them by accepting altitude gains and reducing airspeed slightly to remain longer in the surges of lift. When in a downdraft, resist the urge to raise the nose to avoid losing altitude. This prolongs travel through the sink. Instead, accept the altitude loss (and possibly increase airspeed) to get out of the area as soon as possible to minimize the negative effects. This technique also can be used when *crossing* cloud streets.

If the air is smooth and stable or the day is characterized by strong winds or stratiform clouds, forget about thermal assistance and wait for another day . . . or . . . try flying the ridges.

Lift can be found on the windward side of mountains and hills when the wind direction is within 30° to 40° of a line perpendicular to the ridge (Figure 2-6). The wind speed required to generate sufficiently strong lift depends, of course, on the slope of the mountain or hill. The steeper the slope, the better.

Conversely, flight in the lee of a ridge should be avoided. This is an area of steady downwash which can erode performance subtly and make pilots wonder what is going on. Often, the condition is attributed to factors of little or no significance. The difference in airspeed between flying on the upwind and downwind sides of a ridge can be 10 to 30 knots, depending on wind velocity, slope steepness and the proximity of the aircraft to the ridge.

To maximize the benefits, fly relatively close to the upwind side of the ridge at a position approximately 45° above the ridge line (Figure 2-7). A pilot can experiment and find the area of maximum lift by slightly adjusting altitude and position relative to the ridge. Also, follow the ridge contour as closely as possible unless, of course, this necessitates unnecessarily large course changes. The additional time required to fly the longer distances may outweigh the advantages.

If any large breaks occur in the ridge, fly across these as rapidly as possible to avoid probable sink.

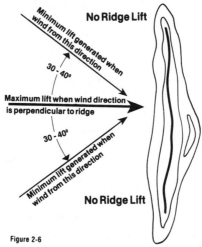

No Ridge Lift

Minimum lift generated when wind from this direction

30 - 40°

Maximum lift when wind direction is perpendicular to ridge

30 - 40°

Minimum lift generated when wind from this direction

No Ridge Lift

Figure 2-6

Soaring principles can be applied beneficially not only during cruise flight, but also after taking off in a heavily loaded (or under powered) airplane at high density altitude. Instead of pointing the nose randomly and accepting a sickly climb rate, check the surroundings to make sure you're not in an area of sink. Then, fly toward sunlit slopes or other areas where convective lift can be expected. With respect to the wind, fly to and remain on the windward sides of any nearby slopes.

The intelligent pilot will decide on the most efficient departure route (with respect to help from rising air or hindrance from sinking air) *prior* to takeoff. A working knowledge of the atmosphere's third-dimensional movement can improve climb performance dramatically, to say nothing of avoiding excessive and potentially damaging engine temperatures.

Although mechanical and thermal lift can significantly increase flight performance, the benefits often are difficult to observe. This is due primarily to the camouflaging effect of engine power and the average pilot's inability to visualize the undulating currents of air. On a given day, for example, a pilot might say this about his airplane: "Wow, she's really fulla spunk today." Is the airplane really feeling its oats or is a gently rising air mass lending a helping hand? Often, it is the latter.

A sailplane pilot (don't ever call him a glider pilot), on the other hand, depends on outside sources of lift. Every nudge of air must be correctly interpreted. Otherwise, his flights are short-lived.

His task is simplified, however, by flying his craft at relatively slow, aerodynamically efficient airspeeds. He knows the rate of descent to expect in still air. Any variation of this rate represents the presence of lift or sink.

But a sailplane is not required in order to learn similar lessons;

soaring can be practiced in an airplane without the risk of running out of lift and having to suffer the sailplane pilot's embarrassment, an enroute, off-airport landing.

Now for the rules of the game. On a smooth, stable day and while maintaining altitude, reduce airspeed to some arbitrarily chosen slow, efficient airspeed. For the purpose of this exercise, it is satisfactory to use the airspeed recommended for optimum glide.

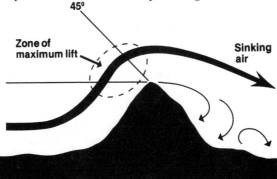

Figure 2-7

If this airspeed/power combination results in an uncomfortably nose-high attitude, extend the flaps no more than 20%. Although additional power probably will be required to maintain the same airspeed, the aircraft body angle will be reduced (in most airplanes) which increases over-the-nose visibility.

Once the required power setting has been determined (flaps up or extended partially, your choice), either wait for a day of good thermal activity or proceed toward an area where ridge-induced lift can be expected.

The idea is to precisely maintain the best glide speed and a constant power setting while paying careful attention to the vertical speed indicator (VSI), the altimeter and the seat of your pants. If a climb is detected, you're soaring; if a descent is noticed, you're in sink. With practice and the proper conditions, you'll find it possible to gain considerable altitude without varying airspeed or power. The goal, however, is not simply to taste the exhilaration of soaring, but to learn where and under what circumstances lift can be used to advantage and to confirm in a very realistic manner the workings of the atmosphere and its effect on flight.

Once a pilot has a feel for soaring, he then may desire to accept the ultimate challenge: trying to remain aloft or fly given distances *without* sufficient power to maintain altitude. This is, after all, the problem faced by every sailplane pilot. It is an exciting safe, rewarding contest that pits plane and pilot against the elements.

The contest rules remain essentially unchanged. The same airspeed is to be used with or without partially extended flaps, as desired. But this time, a pilot needs to determine the power setting that results in a glide ratio (or descent angle) similar to that of a popular single-place sailplane such as the Schweizer 1-26. The 1-26 has a glide ratio of

23:1, meaning the aircraft can glide 23 feet forward while losing only one foot of altitude. In an airplane flying at 60 knots, this translates into a 264 fpm rate of descent. At airspeeds between 60 and 80 knots, a 300 fpm sink rate is suitable.

Once such an airspeed/power/sink rate combination is established, the glide performance of the airplane will very nearly simulate that of a true soaring machine.

Now head for an area of suspected lift and, once there, see just how long you can remain aloft or how far you can travel without changing the pre-determined airspeed/power configuration. With practice and under the right conditions, this exercise can prove beyond a doubt the extent to which vertical currents can influence performance.

Any discussion of up- and downdrafts invariably leads to the question, "Can a strong downdraft force an airplane to the ground?" After polling 27 instructors about this, I found that 21 (including two FAA examiners) believed this to be impossible.

Their reasoning was, in essence, that as a descending column of air approaches the ground, it is forced to spread horizontally (Figure 2-8). In other words, the vertical component of the downdraft weakens rapidly near the ground and affords the airplane an opportunity to escape the grip of involuntary descent.

Downdraft

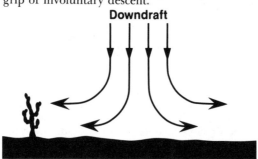

Figure 2-8

Sound logical? Of course. But is the answer correct? No. And the following helps to explain why.

An automobile is cruising along the highway. The relative wind deflecting off the windshield and over the roof is horizontally analogous to the downdraft. Enter a large bug. Does the unsuspecting insect follow the deflected airstream to safety or does it go splat?

The bug is incapable of changing its direction of travel so rapidly because the doomed creature has inertia. And this explains why an airplane can indeed be thrust into the arms of Mother Earth by a sufficiently powerful downdraft.

Understanding the forces responsible for the downdraft can help a pilot to select a heading that leads to safety and possibly an updraft that can expedite the return to a safer altitude.

THE FINE ART OF DESERT FLYING

How to be safe, not sorry, when flying across desert areas

Historically, man has avoided the desert, a sun-seared, windswept, forbidding wasteland. There have been exceptions, of course, such as bedouins, aborigines, and a few other desert dwellers who long ago adapted to the perils and discomfort of desert life. But those from moister climates have chosen to stay away—until recent times.

Airways and highways have made accessible the desert and its breathtaking geological formations, spectacular sunsets, and countless other displays of Nature's splendor. Resorts such as Palm Springs and Las Vegas thrive in areas that not long ago were considered uninhabitable. Recreational areas and national parks beckon visitors in ever-growing numbers. Even that stretch of scorched isolation known as Death Valley in California has become alluring to pilots wanting to escape the beaten path.

Those planning to fly the desert, however, should be aware of unique problems. Even when the destination is elsewhere, it's difficult to fly in the Southwestern U.S. without crossing a part of the North American Desert. Of the world's 13 major deserts, it is the fifth largest and occupies more than a half million square miles.

The word "desert" comes from Latin, means "abandoned," and is not a totally inaccurate description of much of the Southwestern U.S. The desert contains numerous pockets of population, but these are fairly widespread, as are desert airports. Because of this and the hostility of the desert toward careless pilots, flight planning should be conducted with exceptional care.

Victor Airways, for example, are often established without regard to the landscape. Blindly obeying VOR deflections can lead you over some of America's most rugged and inhospitable terrain. It is often wiser to follow major highways and railroads. This adds distance to a flight, but is navigationally more reliable. Also, a long and lonely highway is a welcome sight if an emergency landing becomes necessary.

Additionally, desert VORTACs often are few and far between.

Because of this and the nature of the desert's often mountainous terrain, there are many areas where VOR signals cannot be received. To place all navigational eggs in this basket is risky. Stick to the well-travelled ground routes.

While cowboy movies have led us to believe the West consists of wide-open spaces, such is not the case for general aviation pilots. The military has absconded with large chunks of desert airspace, leaving behind a proliferation of restricted areas. These areas must be respected because within them lurk all manner of undetectable health hazards such as ground-to-air artillery, missile activity, etc.

One restricted area, R-2502, is only 6.1 nm (7 sm) from the centerline of the popular Los Angeles–Las Vegas airway (V8N) and is uniquely dangerous. The area overlies Fort Irwin, Calif. from which such potent radiation is transmitted that flying too closely to the antennas can be harmful to both pilots and avionics.

The fact that a restricted area is printed on the chart doesn't mean that a pilot can't fly through it. If detouring is undesirable, check with a nearby FSS or military facility to determine if the area is "hot." When it is not in use, permission may be given to penetrate it without restriction.

During the summer, it is preferable to fly the desert in the early morning or late afternoon, when thermal activity is nil or at a minimum. On a hot day, the desert floor can spawn teeth-rattling convective turbulence rising to 15,000 feet or more.

There are some useful techniques to employ when you're in the clutches of moderate or greater convective turbulence. Most pilots react improperly to vertical currents and only aggravate the problem.

First, airspeed should be reduced to the aircraft's maneuvering speed to minimize the possibility of structural damage.

When you're in a strong updraft, do not lower the nose to maintain altitude. This could result in dangerously excessive penetration speeds. An updraft is beneficial; it gives something for nothing—altitude. So take advantage of the updraft and accept the gift graciously. This extra altitude may soon be needed because, just as night follows day, downdrafts follow updrafts.

When the updraft weakens and the pilot finds himself sinking helplessly in a downdraft, he should—again—not try to maintain altitude. The result of a climb attitude is an airspeed loss that could place the aircraft in jeopardy of stalling. Also, the application of climb power when flying slowly in the hot desert air can result in excessive oil and cylinder-head temperatures.

Trying to outclimb a strong downdraft is usually an exercise in futility because these downdrafts frequently have sink rates considerably in excess of an airplane's ability to climb. Also, the airspeed loss resulting from an attempted climb only delays passage through the downdraft and prolongs the agony.

When you're caught in a strong "sinker," resist habit. Accept the altitude loss and either maintain airspeed or lower the nose slightly to increase airspeed. This prevents engine overheating and enables passage through the downdraft in minimal time.

During the summer it is wise to fly reasonably high, not only to escape low-level turbulence, but also to keep the cabin cool and comfortable. Since it is not uncommon for desert surface temperatures to exceed 120°F (in the shade), it might be necessary for you to fly at least 14,000 feet agl to maintain a cabin temperature of 70°F—which is another argument for avoiding a midday flight. Parenthetically, the highest temperature ever recorded in the United States was 134°F (Death Valley, 1913).

Since there is so little moisture in the desert air to retain heat, surface temperatures can drop 60° between midday and midnight. But don't allow this to lure you into the night-clad desert without an IFR ticket in your hip pocket. After sunset, the desert floor can be the blackest black you'll ever experience, with ground lights few and far between. Combine this with a high overcast and it can be impossible to tell where the ground ends and the sky begins. Even some experienced pilots avoid flying the night desert unless the moon is available to illuminate the way and ease the strain of a VFR flight.

During their first desert flights, Easterners are often confused when trying to correlate terrain features with symbols on a sectional. Rivers and lakes never seem to appear as advertised. This is because newcomers incongruously expect to see water. Since the desert—by definition—receives less than 10 inches of rain annually, most desert lakes and rivers are dry 9 to 10 months of the year; others are perennially arid.

Otherwise, a topographical chart is a pilot's most reliable navaid, especially if he can translate contour lines on the map to those below, an essential skill when airways and highways are unavailable. Striking out across the desert without having something to follow requires either the instincts of a camel or some skillful dead-reckoning and an abundance of fuel.

A side note about dry lakes. Some can be used as emergency landing sites, but others may be too soft, too rough, or occasionally too wet. If the surface has a dark or brown complexion, the lake is probably wet. The safest place to land is near the edge of the lake. It's drier there, and adjacent terrain features (sagebrush, cacti, etc.) provide peripheral reference for judging height above the ground.

Rogers Dry Lake in Southern California may qualify as the world's longest runway. Adjacent to Edwards AFB, it is 10.4 nm (12 sm) long and is used regularly by NASA's experimental aircraft.

Desert weather is generally severe clear, but when a relatively moist, unstable air mass visits the summer desert, the result is a widespread forest of mushrooming, violent thunderstorms. Although summer storms can reach massive proportions, they are generally scattered and circumnavigable. Extreme caution, however, is required when threading through the desert under these conditions.

Early morning flying precludes the pilot's having to do battle with the cu-nims because they usually don't develop fully until shortly before noon. Once full-grown, desert thunderstorms can remain quite vigorous until well after midnight.

Fortunately, tornadoes are a rare desert occurrence, but the desert does have "twisters." Although dust devils are considerably smaller and less violent than tornadoes, they must be regarded with caution.

A tornado is born in the belly of a thunderstorm and grows downward. Dust devils, on the other hand, are not related to thunderstorm activity. They are caused by intense surface heating and grow from the ground upward.

Dust devils have the appearance of small tornadoes but are usually only 50 to 100 feet tall. It is not unusual to see a half dozen or more dancing across the desert, and during the summer they are so common as to seem a part of the landscape. On rare occasions, a desert twister matures into a full blown "sand pillar" that can extend up to 1,000 feet agl (or higher) and must be avoided.

Since dust devils are usually small and hug the ground, they are a problem primarily during arrivals and departures. Flight through a desert twister can place an airplane instantly out of control, but the difficulty usually is over before a pilot realizes what has happened— unless the encounter occurs during takeoff or landing. This can be disastrous and explains why some desert fliers prefer to land on unpaved runways where twisters can be more easily noticed. When dust devils play tag on the runway, delay takeoff or landing until their frivolity takes them elsewhere.

Dust devils should be avoided while taxiing, too. Should one head your way, taxi in another direction, *pronto!* If an encounter is unavoidable, head the aircraft directly toward the twister and take it head on. Never allow one to overtake you from behind, since this can lift the tail of the aircraft and flip it on its back. This is rare, but happens.

Another desert phenomenon is the sandstorm, a widespread affair that occurs when blusterous surface winds lift enough sand to darken the skies. A sandstorm can extend for hundreds of miles and generate dense clouds of sand to heights of 10,000 feet or more. This type of storm obviously should be avoided because of turbulence, less-than-VFR visibility, and the damage that sandblasting can do to an airplane and its engine.

Desert flying requires an intimate familiarity with the erosion of aircraft performance resulting from increased density altitude. Mountain fliers are aware of this problem because of the elevations at which they operate, but desert visitors frequently overlook the need to compute and compensate for density altitude because of the comparatively low elevations usually involved. But this oversight can be dangerous in the simmering heat of the summer desert.

Consider departing Las Vegas, Nev., for example. The elevation of McCarran International Airport is only 2,200 feet msl, but when the mercury hits 120°F, the density altitude exceeds 6,400 feet, doubling takeoff roll and decreasing rate of climb by almost 50%.

Some desert airports are above 5,000 feet. Combine this with 120° of sizzling Fahrenheit and density altitude shoots up to 11,000 feet.

The accompanying chart (Table 2-A) shows the relationship between density altitude, pressure altitude, and ambient temperature. But for those who prefer rules-of-thumb, there is a mental exercise that can be used to determine density altitude without computers or charts.

It is first necessary to determine the standard temperature for the elevation under consideration. As an example, consider an airport with a pressure altitude of 4,000 feet msl and an OAT of 105°F. The standard temperature at sea level is 59°F, and since the standard temperature decreases 3½°F per 1,000 feet, the standard temperature at 4,000 feet must be 59°F − (4 × 3½°), or 59°F − 14°F, or 45°F.

DETERMINING DENSITY ALTITUDE

Standard Temp.	Temp. Elevat.	80° F	90° F	100° F	110° F	120° F	130° F
59° F	Sea Level	1,200'	1,900'	2,500'	3,200'	3,800'	4,400'
52° F	2,000'	3,800'	4,400'	5,000'	5,600'	6,200'	6,800'
45° F	4,000'	6,300'	6,900'	7,500'	8,100'	8,700'	9,400'
38° F	6,000'	8,600'	9,200'	9,800'	10,400'	11,000'	11,600'
31° F	8,000'	11,100'	11,700'	12,300'	12,800'	13,300'	13,800'

Table 2-A

Now compare the standard temperature at 4,000 feet (45°F) with the actual temperature (105°F). The difference between them is 60°F.

Now the rule. For each 10°F that actual temperature exceeds standard temperature, add 600 feet to the elevation. In this case, actual temperature exceeds standard temperature by 60°F, meaning 3,600 feet (6 × 600) must be added to the field elevation (4,000 feet) to arrive at a density altitude of 7,600 feet.

This rule-of-thumb is reasonably accurate and produces a result rarely more than 200 feet in error. But once density altitude is determined, it is absolutely meaningless unless used to derive realistic performance data from the aircraft manual.

If a novice desert flier were to consult a grizzled veteran about desert operations, he would most likely be given the following tips about landing in the desert:

• Be careful about sloped runways. The desert is chock-full of them. A runway with an uphill gradient gives a pilot on approach the illusion of being too high, and the result is a tendency to undershoot. Conversely, a downhill gradient gives the pilot the illusion of being too low, and there's a resultant tendency to overshoot.

• On a hot day, strong thermals encountered during the approach can lead to an overshoot.

• But, on the other hand, an airplane tends to settle more rapidly in hot, thin air.

• As density altitude increases, true airspeed increases for any given indicated airspeed. So be careful about faster touchdown speeds.

• Crystal-clear desert air makes objects seem closer than they really are and can lead to premature descents.

• On windy days, be careful about sudden wind shifts, a desert trademark.

• When the air is hot and dry, resist the urge to use carburetor heat, especially during touchdown and rollout. It is unnecessary and allows damaging, sand-filled air to enter the engine without being filtered.

• Don't refuel after landing; wait until you're ready to leave and know what the temperature will be and how it will affect performance. Then refuel and load accordingly.

• Secure the aircraft firmly, even during very short visits; the desert is notorious for sudden increases in surface wind.

• If you are using a portable tiedown kit, beware of screw-in devices that are incapable of getting a firm grip in the soft desert soil (sand).

• When surface temperatures exceed 100°F, the temperature in the cockpit of an aircraft exposed to the sun can exceed 180°F. Park in the shade whenever possible. If parking in the shade is not possible, hide plastic computers and plotters from the direct rays of the sun.

Regarding departures, the desert pro might offer this advice:

• Prior to boarding, open all cockpit doors and windows and allow the cockpit to cool; otherwise, controls, switches, and seatbelt buckles may be so hot that operating them without gloves may be impossible.

• When you're departing from an airport that does not have paved surfaces, avoid extending the flaps of a low-wing airplane until immediately before takeoff; extended flaps are easily damaged by pebbles.

• Avoid prolonged runups that can overheat an engine.

• Be skillful at soft- and short-field takeoffs; these are frequent desert requirements.

• On hot days, it may be necessary to climb at faster than normal airspeeds to keep cylinder-head and oil temperatures within reason.

• If thermals are available, take advantage of them to gain altitude.

• If avionics fail to operate properly, the problem may be caused by transistors that have become too hot while parked in the sun; give them a chance to cool off.

Two of the most frequently neglected desert necessities are a survival kit and an adequate supply of supplemental water. This point cannot be overemphasized, and sometimes it is necessary to resort to shock to drive home the point.

A most gruesome and painful death is caused by dehydration. Without water, a man stranded in the summer desert has a life expectancy of two days. But before being relieved of his misery, he resorts to drinking anything available—no matter how nauseating—including engine oil, fuel, and urine. A supplemental water supply and a filed flight plan are a desert pilot's best insurance.

The survival kit should contain at least a solar still, chapstick, a signal mirror, emergency rations, a first-aid kit, whistles, hats, sunglasses, sunburn lotion, salt tablets, clothing to protect against cold nights, matches, a knife, nylon rope, a flashlight, a survival manual, water, water, and more water.

Although this article emphasizes the problems unique to summer flying, pilots should realize that the desert tames considerably during the rest of the year. Spring and autumn are delightful seasons in which to enjoy and explore the magnificent desert. It is Nature's kaleidoscope of wonders to see and things to do.

THE ONLY WAY TO GLIDE

How to stretch your chances
when the rubber band breaks

The sectional chart isn't thought of as a lethal weapon. But to those of us who learned to fly in tandem-seat trainers, the sectional was something to fear.

The instructor sat behind the student in many of those rag-covered taildraggers. And since soundproofing had yet to be discovered, cockpit communication varied between limited and impossible. Rather than yell and scream over the engine and air noises, the CFI often found it more convenient to indicate his displeasure with a student's performance by simply beaning him from behind with a rolled-up sectional. The student worked hard to please his mentor, if for not other reason than to stave off this dreaded assault.

According to my instructor, Mike Walters, a chart would last for 6 to 8 hours of dual instruction before losing its rigidity. But on October 3, 1954, I proved that the 25¢ charts simply weren't as good as they used to be. On that memorable day, Mike lost his cool and "totaled" a brand-new chart with unmerciful blows to my cranium.

Mike was giving me post-solo dual in 180°, power-off approaches. My airspeed varied from less than 45 knots (when I was low) to more than 80 knots (when I was high). But despite and because of these sloppy efforts, I never came closer than 500 feet to the elusive touchdown target. Consequently, I was earning about four whacks per approach which did little to bolster my confidence. Once, when I turned to ask Mike a question, I caught a blow on the nose and learned not to argue with Mike.

During the last circuit of the day, Mike screamed a dialogue that can't be quoted here. Every other sentence, however, contained the term "normal glide," but I was too busy nursing my wounds to pay much attention.

The post-flight briefing was short and to the point. "Look, Barry," began Mike's abbreviated tirade, "One of these days that little 'four-banger' under the cowling is gonna quit. Your cork will unplug and down you'll go. And unless you learn something about glide path control, you can forget about being able to glide safely into a small landing area."

Totally embarrassed, I paid for the lesson and lowered my head in shame, hoping that Mike would notice the welts on the back of my neck and offer a rare word of kindness. No such luck. Mike turned away disgustedly, walked to the filing cabinet and withdrew a new sectional chart in preparation for his next victim.

As the log books began to pile up in the closet corner, I learned to appreciate Mike's exhortation (its bluntness notwithstanding). It took me a long time to fully understand gliding flight, but since misery loves company, I was delighted to find that I wasn't alone. There are numerous misconceptions about optimum glide performance which prevail in even the most sophisticated quarters. Perhaps even more misunderstood are some of the techniques required to achieve it.

The normal, optimum, or maximum range glide is simply a power-off descent during which the airplane flies a maximum forward distance over the ground from any given altitude. The ability of an airplane to do this is indicated by its glide ratio, a number that simply specifies how many feet forward an aircraft can glide for every foot of altitude lost.

For example, one of the world's highest performance sailplanes, the German Schleicher AS-W 12, has a glide ratio of 47 to 1; it can glide 47 feet forward during each foot of descent. To put it another way, from an altitude of one mile (5,280 feet), this exotic craft can glide 41 nm (47 sm). Powered airplanes aren't quite that efficient.

To determine the glide ratio of a Cessna 150, for example, it is necessary only to divide the (air) distance flown in one minute by the altitude lost during the same time period. The Cessna 150 has an optimum glide speed of 61 knots, which is equivalent to 6,181 feet per minute. Its sea level rate of descent at this airspeed is 725 fpm. Dividing 6,181 by 725 results in the 150's glide ratio of 8.5 to 1.

If the pilot of a 150 were faced with an engine failure while flying one nm (6,080 feet) agl, he could glide 8.5 nm miles in any direction, giving him a choice of landing sites anywhere within a 227-square-mile circle. But from twice the altitude (two nm or 12,160 feet), the choice of landing areas is not doubled, it is *quadrupled.* From this altitude, the 150 has a 17 nm glide range and can touch down anywhere within a 908-square-mile circle. This certainly proves the adage that altitude is like money in the bank.

The optimum glide speed is usually found in the pilot's operating handbook and has much more significance than is generally appreciated. This is the *only* speed resulting in the optimum, or maximum range glide.

Some pilots, however, refute this. They claim that if an aircraft is low while on final approach, the glide can be "stretched" by raising the nose and reducing the sink rate. True, the rate of descent decreases, but so does the airspeed. It takes longer for the plane to get to the runway and more time is available for it to lose altitude. Glide performance suffers.

An example of this is shown in Figure 2-9. By reducing the airspeed of a Cessna 150 to 50 knots for example, the rate of descent reduces to 640 fpm. The glide ratio at this airspeed, therefore, is 5,067 fpm (forward speed divided by 640 fpm (downward), or 7.9, somewhat less than the 150's ability to glide at 8.5 to 1.

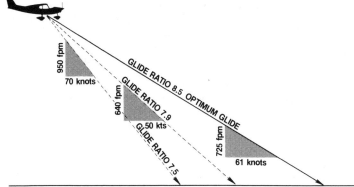

Figure 2-9

Other pilots insist that glide range can be extended by increasing airspeed, the theory being this gets you to the runway sooner and the aircraft has less time to lose altitude. Not so.

If the 150 is flown at 70 knots (one and one-sixth nm per minute, or 7,093 fpm), its rate of descent is 950 fpm. The glide ratio at this faster airspeed is, therefore, 7,093 divided by 950, or 7.5 to 1, a 12% reduction in glide performance.

It must be recognized that if flight at the optimum glide speed does not enable an aircraft to reach the runway, no amount of airspeed variation can help. There is no recourse other than to add power (if available) or choose a closer landing site.

Another hazard of attempting to stretch a glide at reduced airspeed is this may place the aircraft dangerously close to a stall; low altitude maneuvering is risky and less reserve airspeed is available to counter an unexpected wind shear. Also, there may be insufficient airspeed with which to flare. Consequently, the aircraft could simply mush into the ground at a high sink rate, a maneuver known to decrease the lengevity of both landing gear and spinal column.

The urgent need to maintain a safe and efficient gliding airspeed, especially after engine failure, cannot be overemphasized. It is much preferable to fly into the trees while under control than to allow the aircraft to choose its own method of crash landing.

There is one glide-stretching technique which can be used as a last resort. If the engine is dead, really dead, with absolutely no hope of a restart (such as after fuel exhaustion), raise the nose and reduce airspeed (but only at safe altitude) until the propeller comes to a halt. A windmilling prop creates considerably more drag than one at rest and has a negative effect on glide performance.

During tests conducted by Cessna, it was determined that stopping the prop of a Cessna 172 *increased* the glide ratio by 20%. A similar increase occurs in the Cessna 150 (and most other light aircraft) which boosts the glide ratio from 8.5 to 10.2, added gliding distance that could convert a potential disaster into a safe landing.

Once the prop is stopped, however, lower the nose and accelerate to the normal glide speed.

When power-off approaches are practiced using the optimum glide speed, a pilot learns to visualize the glide path of his aircraft. With experience, he can predict just where on the runway (or off of it) the aircraft will touch down. The astute pilot can vary the airspeed while on a long final approach to learn just how these changes affect the glide path. Also, he can learn that reducing airspeed slightly decreases glide range, a useful technique to lose surplus altitude.

Assume now that two identical aircraft are cruising side by side at 10,000 feet. One aircraft is loaded heavily, but the other is loaded lightly. Simultaneously, both pilots reduce power and begin gliding. Which aircraft will glide the farthest, the light one or the heavy one? Surprisingly, both aircraft will glide the same distance.

The gliding characteristics of an airplane are determined strictly by its lift and drag *characteristics* (Figure 2-10). Since neither of these is affected by aircraft loading, weight has no effect on glide range or ratio.

Weight, however, does have an effect on the airspeed that must be used to achieve the maximum glide. The Cessna 150's optimum glide

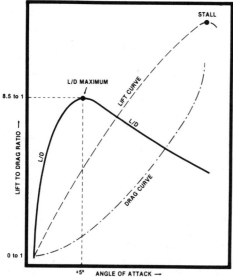

The graph shows how the lift and drag of a typical lightplane increase with angle of attack. The *ratio* of lift to drag (L/D) for any given angle of attack is shown by the heavily curved line. It is this characteristic of an airplane (or sailplane) that defines glide performance. As a matter of fact, the lift/drag ratio and the glide ratio of an aircraft are equal at any given angle of attack. Therefore, an airplane glides most efficiently when flown at that angle of attack where "L over D" is at a maximum which, in this case, is 5°. If the aircraft is glided at an angle of attack that is either smaller (faster airspeed) or larger (slower airspeed), both the L/D and glide ratio are reduced accordingly. This is why an airplane has only one optimum glide speed. When gross weight is either increased or decreased, the optimum glide still occurs at the same angle of attack (where L/D is at a maximum), but the airspeed required to achieve this will vary.

Figure 2-10

airspeed of 61 knots, for example, is valid only when the aircraft is loaded to its maximum allowable gross weight of 1,600 pounds. A gross weight decrease requires a corresponding airspeed reduction to maintain the 8.5 to 1 glide ratio. At 1,400 pounds, the 150 should be glided at 57 knots; at 1,200 pounds, the best glide speed is 53 knots. As a rule-of-thumb for most light aircraft, reduce glide speed 5% for each 10% decrease in gross weight.

Does altitude have an effect on glide performance? Absolutely none. The same indicated glide speed should be used at all density altitudes. This may sound a bit incredible because at 12,000 feet, for example, the Cessna 150 has a more rapid 870 fpm sink rate while being glided at 61 knots. But consider that this is an indicated airspeed, not a true airspeed. At 12,000 feet, a 61 knot IAS is equivalent to a 73 knot TAS. Both the true airspeed and sink rate, therefore, are 20% greater than at sea level. Since these figures increase proportionately, the glide ratio remains the same.

EFFECT OF WIND ON THE GLIDE RATIO OF A CESSNA 150 AT 5000 FT. MSL.

WIND CONDITION	BEST GLIDE SPEED (IAS)	GLIDE RATIO	RATE OF DESCENT
30 KNOT TAILWIND	55 knots	13.4	680 fpm
20 " "	56 knots	11.7	700 fpm
10 " "	58 knots	9.9	740 fpm
CALM	61 knots	8.5	780 fpm
10 KNOT HEADWIND	64 knots	7.1	850 fpm
20 " "	69 knots	6.1	900 fpm
30 " "	75 knots	5.2	990 fpm

Table 2-B

Does wind affect glide performance? Absolutely. Gliding with a tailwind obviously extends glide range; a headwind shortens it. To maximize the effect of a tailwind, an airplane should be glided somewhat slower than usual. This has the effect of reducing the rate of descent, and allows the aircraft to remain in the air longer. This increases the time during which the tailwind can be used to advantage.

When gliding into a headwind, airspeed should be increased some-what. Although the rate of descent also increases, the extra airspeed is necessary to maximize forward progress against the headwind. An extreme example is flying into a headwind equal in strength to the airspeed; the aircraft is motionless over the ground, yet it descends vertically at its normal sink rate. The glide ratio is zero. But if the airspeed is increased, at least some forward progress can be realized. When gliding with a 10, 20, or 30 knot tailwind, a reasonably valid rule-of-thumb suggests decreasing airspeed by four, six or eight knots, respectively. Against a headwind, increase airspeed by 50% of the headwind component (Table 2-B is a more accurate example of how various winds affect the glide ratio of a Cessna 150.)

The effect of wind raises an interesting point. If a pilot is faced with an engine failure and a choice of two landing sites, he should favor gliding to the one downwind of his position (everything else being equal). Remember, tailwinds increase glide range; headwinds destroy it.

Although the normal glide is the most familiar, there is another type which can be equally important: the *minimum sink* glide. This is used when gliding range is not important, such as when flying directly over the landing area. At such a time, a pilot needs time more than anything else, time to attempt an engine restart or to simply gathers his wits. By reducing to slightly above the minimum controllable airspeed, sink rate is substantially decreased. Contact with the ground is postponed. But be careful. When 1,000 feet agl (or higher), resume the optimum glide speed to increase maneuverability and to fly a reasonably normal glide path to touchdown.

The Cessna 150, for example, has a 725 fpm sink rate when flown at the normal glide speed of 61 knots. From an altitude of 10,000 feet, such a descent would last 14 minutes. But when airspeed is reduced to near 43 knots, the rate of descent is only 600 fpm. Such a glide from 10,000 feet would require 17 minutes. This increases glide *endurance* by three minutes. And three minutes to a pilot in distress can be of considerable value.

It is true that whatever goes up must come down, but *how* an airplane comes down is of prime importance to those inside. If it is without power, there are only two ways: accurately and with a plan of action, or sloppily and with a surprise ending.

WHEN SEEING IS NOT BELIEVING

Some tips on keeping out of trouble
when visual clues are misleading

The world of flight can be strangely deceptive, offering many misleading clues that should not be believed even though they can be seen.

Take the classic example of the VFR pilot flying above an inclined cloud layer. Because he is not disciplined in the skills of instrument flying, the pilot perceives the sloped cloud layer as the natural horizon. Influenced by this illusion, he tends to fly askew unless able to rationalize the deceptive visual reference with the less conspicuous, contradictory display of the attitude instruments.

Many pilots have difficulty flying over desolate terrain on a moonless, VFR night. Even though there are no ground or celestial references, they attempt to fly visually in conditions clearly requiring instrument flying techniques.

The situation is complicated by the introduction of a single light on the horizon, a target toward which a pilot can aim his craft. If the pilot stares at this beckoning beacon for any period of time, it may soon appear to move from side to side in wide, irregular arcs—a phenomenon known as autokinetic motion, or "stare vision."

In the absence of other outside references, a pilot's senses often interpret this apparent movement of light as a change in aircraft heading or attitude. As a result, the pilot—without realizing it—maneuvers the aircraft so as to keep the light positioned in his windshield. In the meantime, his senses provide the erroneous sensation that the aircraft is on an even keel. The instruments contradict this sensory illusion, but a confused pilot may choose to ignore them. A sufficiently bewildered pilot could encounter vertigo and possible loss of aircraft control.

Autokinetic motion can be duplicated by sitting in an otherwise dark room and staring at a pinpoint of light. After a short while, the light can be observed drifting in various directions, a most perplexing phenomenon.

The U.S. Air Force has blamed numerous night VFR accidents on autokinetic motion and teaches its pilots to never stare at a single light source in an otherwise dark flight environment and to frequently glance at the more trustworthy message spelled out on the instrument panel.

In 1952, Capt. Prosper Cocuyt of Sabena Belgian World Airlines prepared an award-winning paper describing another dangerous illusion with respect to night flying and a light on the ground. Unfortunately, this profound information never reached the general aviation audience even though this sensory "deception" has been, in part, the probable cause of many night accidents.

The problem deals with VFR night flying at a relatively low altitude (such as when approaching or departing an airport), when the natural horizon is not visible.

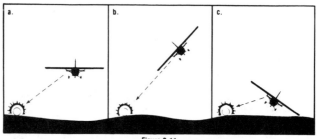

Figure 2-11

Figure 2-11a shows a wings-level aircraft flying abeam a light on the ground. The pilot senses he is at a safe altitude because the light appears below the aircraft (as it should). But consider Figure 2-11b, a situation where the pilot inadvertently allows the aircraft to bank to the left. (Remember, the horizon is not visible.) By glancing at the light, which is sighted by looking parallel to the wing, the pilot perceives that the aircraft and the light are at the same altitude—ground level. This produces the erroneous sensation of an urgent need to climb. The illusion received when a pilot has inadvertently banked toward a light is considered a "safe-side" illusion because altitude is perceived to be less than actual and the pilot, by climbing, will err on the safe side.

The dangerous illusion is shown in Figure 2-11c, a situation where the aircraft is inadvertently allowed to bank away from the light. The pilot has no sensation of being too low because he thinks he is looking down at the light, when in fact, he is not. Unless the pilot sees the silent warning of the artificial horizon, he might be the victim of a fatal shock.

Inadvertent excursions in pitch also can have serious consequences. Figure 2-12a shows an aircraft approaching a light (or group of lights) on the ground. Since the aircraft is maintaining a constant altitude, the pilot must look down at an angle to see the approaching lights. If this angle is sufficiently large, the pilot senses that he is at a safe altitude. But suppose that he inadvertently allows the nose to rise slightly while at a dangerously low altitude as shown in Figure 2-12b. The pilot senses being at a safe altitude because he appears to be looking down at a large angle when, in reality, he is looking primarily forward.

Such an illusion is most likely to occur during a nose-high departure at night toward gently rising terrain especially when there are no visible landmarks between the aircraft and the light(s) toward which the aircraft is heading. A pilot can be easily deceived into believing he will clear an obstacle.

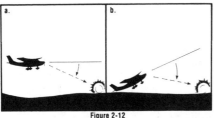

Figure 2-12

A night approach toward an airport can create an equally dangerous illusion if there are no visible landmarks between the aircraft and the airport. Under these conditions, a pilot can be totally unaware he is being lured into the ground.

The departure problem can be prevented by climbing in the traffic pattern until a safe altitude is reached. Arrival difficulties are best resolved by avoiding straight-in approaches when the approach corridor is dark or by utilizing a steep descent path toward the airport.

An additional illusion is often encountered during a straight-in approach at night when the visibility is unlimited, a condition frequently found in the desert and mountain areas of the West. Approach and runway lights appear brighter than usual at such times and cause a pilot to believe that he is closer to the airport than he really is. The result is often a premature descent toward intervening obstacles.

For this reason, experienced mountain pilots often delay a descent until safely within the confines of the traffic pattern. They use another interesting technique, which although quite logical when you think about it, is something that most pilots are unaware of.

When descending toward a distant city, for example, keep a sharp eye on the lights at that edge of the city closest to the aircraft. Should any of these lights disappear, then something (such as a ridge) has risen to block the view and dictates an urgent need to arrest the descent and recapture altitude until the lights are once again visible. As long as these lights remain in sight, the aircraft is above all enroute obstacles.

Restricted visibility also can be deceptive because of the dimming effect it has on airport lights. When approaching an airport on a hazy night, for example, a pilot unknowingly interprets his altitude as being higher than actual. This phenomenon results in the common tendency of a pilot (when first sighting the runway during an ILS approach) to reduce power and drop below the glideslope, an extremely hazardous reaction.

During daylight hours, the effect is similar because visibility restrictions dilute shadows normally used as an aid to depth perception.

Moisture on the windshield can produce unpredictable illusory effects because of the irregular refraction of light caused by the droplets. Depending on the moisture pattern and the shape of the windshield, a pilot may perceive significant glideslope and/or localizer deviations even though the ILS needles are centered.

Experienced pilots never completely abandon the "cross-pointers" during the final, visual phase of an ILS approach. Instead, they monitor the needles to confirm that outside clues are not leading them astray.

Variations in runway and approach lighting intensity can also be misleading. When these lights are set to maximum intensity, the airport appears closer than it is. Conversely, when the lights are dim, the airport appears farther away.

During the preparation of this article, I flew with a friend who was asked to approach an airport at night while maintaining 3,000 feet agl. He was instructed not to descend until intercepting what seemed to be a normal, 3°, visual-approach slot. The ILS needles were hidden from his view and, unknown to him, I had prearranged with the tower controller to vary the runway and approach lighting intensity during the experiment.

As we began the long, straight-in approach, the airport lights were set to minimum intensity and, predictably, the subject pilot was considerably above the glidescope before initiating descent; he sensed being farther out than he really was. I clicked the mike button twice, which signaled the controller to gradually increase the lights to maximum brilliance. As the lights "came up," I noticed a gradual increase in sink rate and power reduction until, finally, we were literally diving toward the airport.

Although well above the glidescope at the beginning of descent, we were now uncomfortably below it. This became more apparent as we neared the approach lights, causing the confused pilot to add considerable power and back pressure to prevent the impending undershoot.

Although a pilot is not likely to experience such gross variations in lighting intensity during any given approach, this experiment did verify (and exaggerate) the illusory effects which can be expected when airport lights are unusually dim or bright.

Although most illusions occur at night, daylight operations also offer some fascinating deceptions.

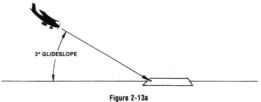

3° GLIDESLOPE

Figure 2-13a

Figure 2-13a shows an aircraft in a normal, 3°, visual descent toward a level runway. The pilot can maintain this "3° slot" quite accurately because he has spent his flying career practicing approaches that "feel" comfortable. He approaches a runway so that the visual glideslope "seems" neither too shallow nor too steep.

A visual illusion develops when approaching a runway with a pronounced upslope (Figure 2-13b). If a pilot establishes a 3° approach slot relative to the horizontal, while approaching a runway with a 2° upslope, for example, he would feel he is descending too steeply. This is because he would be aware of descending at a 5° angle with respect to the runway. As a result, the pilot automatically compensates by "dropping down" until the runway "looks right." In other words, he settles onto a 3° glidepath with respect to the runway, as he always does. Unfortunately, this results in a dangerously low, flat approach.

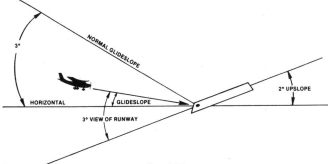

Figure 2-13b

One popular southern California resort airport, Catalina, is reputedly hazardous because the first half of the runway has considerable upslope. Unsuspecting pilots are affected by the illusion and approach this airport at dangerously shallow descent paths. Numerous aircraft have made impressions (literally) on the bluff at the approach end of Catalina's Runway 22, causing the FAA to install a set of VASI lights. When followed religiously, Catalina's VASI prevents the previously common undershoot accident, but pilots must resist the urge to fly below the red-and-white glidepath, which does appear steep but, in fact, is not.

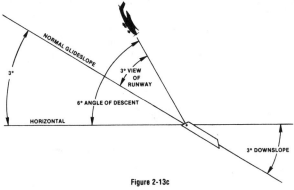

Figure 2-13c

The downslope runway (Figure 2-13c) leads to overshoots. The runway shown in the diagram has an admittedly steep (3°) downslope, but illustrates the illusion associated with shallower downslopes.

When in a 3° approach slot relative to the horizontal, a pilot can only see the approach edge of the runway, leading him to believe he is extremely low. As a result, he levels off until the runway can be viewed at a normal, 3° angle. This, of course, produces a steep, 6° descent path with respect to the ground and substantially increases the likelihood of an overshoot.

The terrain surrounding an airport often has a slope comparable to that of the runway, which makes it difficult to determine in advance whether a given runway is sloped or level. Often, the only clue afforded the observant pilot is the abnormal sink rate required to maintain what appears to be a normal slot.

When approaching a bowl-shaped runway with a pronounced dip in the middle, the proper procedure would be to use only the first half (the downslope portion) of the runway to establish a visual glidepath. By maintaining what then appears to be a somewhat flat approach, you'll be close to the proper slot.

Conversely, if the runway is convex (a hump in the middle), refer only to the first, *uphill* portion of the runway and establish what appears to be a slightly steep approach path.

Runway geometry also can be deceiving. Without realizing it, a pilot usually assesses the runway before him by comparing it with the runway to which he is most accustomed. Assume that a pilot is conditioned to landing on a 4,500 by 150 foot runway (which has a length-to-width ratio of 30:1). From above and afar, a longer runway with the same proportions (6,000 by 200, for example) has an identical appearance. But because the runway is larger, the pilot is led to believe that he is closer and lower than he really is.

The more hazardous illusion occurs when approaching a shorter runway with those same, familiar proportions (2,250 by 75, for example). When on final to this smaller runway, the pilot perceives being farther from the runway and higher above the ground than he really is.

Runway width, irrespective of length, can adversely affect judgment during flareout. Whether or not he realizes it, a pilot uses peripheral vision to help determine when he is at the proper height above the runway to initiate the landing flare. He does this during the last several feet of descent by subconsciously waiting for the edges of the runway to spread laterally beneath the aircraft until reaching the angle (Figure 2-14) to which he is conditioned.

PERIPHERAL ANGLE

Figure 2-14

When descending toward an unusually wide runway, this peripheral angle forms while considerably higher than usual above the ground. By yielding to the subconscious suggestion that he initiate the flare at this time, a pilot may run out of airspeed while several feet in the air.

Conversely, when descending toward a narrow runway, the lateral spread of the runway edges may not be sufficient for the peripheral clue to form and can result in the failure of a pilot to flare in time to avoid a hard landing.

The problems posed by wide and narrow runways are particularly acute at night when it is more difficult to judge height above the ground. This is because of the lack of contrast between the runway and the surrounding terrain. All is in blackness, a condition that decreases depth perception. Similar loss of depth perception occurs during daylight hours when there is little or no contrast between the runway and the adjacent terrain, such as when the entire airport is snow or water covered, when landing on open areas of dirt or grass; and when approaching hard surface runways surrounded by similarly colored sand. Visibility restrictions aggravate the problem by further reducing color contrast.

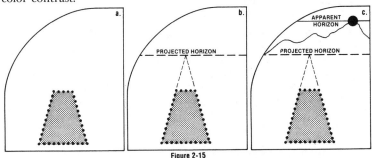

Figure 2-15

During the late 1960s, The Boeing Co. instituted a comprehensive research program to determine those factors adversely influencing a pilot during visual, straight-in approaches at night. The practical aspect of this program involved 12 senior jet instructors who were asked to execute several simulated approaches to an airport at the near edge of a sprawling matrix of city lights. Furthermore, each pilot was advised that the city (not the airport) had a pronounced upslope. Not only did most of the test pilots fly considerably below the normal glideslope, but many flew their simulators below the elevation of the airport.

One major problem of a straight-in approach at night is the frequent lack of a natural horizon. But by practicing the following technique, a pilot can learn to create an imaginary one.

Figure 2-15a displays the runway as seen from the cockpit on a night when the horizon is not visible. Since the parallel rows of runway lights, when extended, intersect at the horizon (Figure 2-15b), the pilot can project an imaginary horizon on his windshield.

This is a particularly useful technique when hilltop lights beyond the airport (Figure 2-15c) elevate the apparent horizon to a confusing height. When such a false horizon is used instead of the real one, a pilot is led to believe he is on a normal glideslope when he is actually far below.

When a pilot passes over the approach lights at night, the runway lights occupy a large portion of the windshield area (Figure 2-16a). But when sliding down the electronic banister to very poor visibilities (4,000 feet RVR or less), a pilot breaks out of the overcast and sees only the lights in the touchdown zone (Figure 2-16b). These appear in the lower portion of the windscreen and create the illusion of being too high. It is a natural tendency under these conditions for a pilot to tuck below

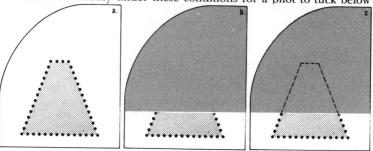

Figure 2-16

the glideslope in a subconscious effort to fill more of the windshield area with lights, as is usually the case when visibility is good. To call this dangerous is an understatement—it is the direct cause of numerous undershoot accidents following ILS approaches.

If all the runway lights are not visible when breaking out of an overcast, attempt to mentally extend those which are visible to create the image of a full-length runway (Figure 2-16c). I have practiced this technique when shooting Category I and II approaches in a Boeing 727, and it works surprisingly well.

The National Transportation Safety Board is responsible for determining the probable causes of all fatal aviation accidents. In many cases, the epitaph at the end of a report often states, with obvious simplicity, that the pilot failed to maintain adequate altitude or airspeed.

What is not so obvious are the reasons why a pilot might have been misled in the first place. Often, he has been the victim of one or a combination of sensory illusions, which prove that seeing should not always be believing.

A DIFFERENT APPROACH TO CROSSWIND LANDINGS

The kickout method offers better control and more precise touchdowns— but it must be practiced

Perhaps I'm a sadist. One of my favorite spectator sports is watching inexperienced pilots enter into combat with a blustery crosswind. Their performances are like excerpts from a Laurel and Hardy movie. A dancing windsock plays the background accompaniment and tire crunching lends an occasional percussion effect. The end of a particularly dramatic sequence is punctuated by the nasty sound of scraping metal.

The most entertaining scenes include either a wheelbarrow ballet, a groundlooping pirouette or the more unusual love sequence that concludes when the tires softly kiss the concrete.

Developing the skill necessary to make consistently good crosswind landings is not easy. One reason is that we are infrequently confronted with the challenge; the opportunity to practice is rare. At the other extreme are those who avoid crosswind landings whenever possible. While this may seem like an example of safe flight planning, it is not. Such misguided wisdom can backfire. Eventually, such a pilot is confronted with having to land in a strong crosswind at a single-runway airport. Lacking proficiency, can he now muster the skill necessary to handle a 20 knot component? Perhaps not.

There are two other reasons why many pilots are inept at crosswind landings. One is that they fly aircraft considerably different from the one in which they received their initial training. Making a cross-controlled landing in a Cherokee Six, for example, is not quite the same as in a Cessna 150.

Also, many pilots get their certificates without ever having made a difficult crosswind landing. The reason for this is that a crosswind simply may not present itself during the course of a pilot's training. It is entirely possible for a pilot to encounter his first stiff crosswind with

71

a hundred hours under his belt and a planeload of nervous passengers buckled under theirs. Such a situation is not uncommon. Amuse yourself at the airport on a windy day and you'll see the consequences: an endless parade of rock-'n-roll landings. And if you happen to be an aircraft sheet metal worker, you might even pick up some business while you're there.

The solution to the crosswind landing problem is painfully simple, obvious to the point of being ignored. Wait for one of those days when the windsock points across the runway, hire a proficient instructor and spend an hour or more honing crosswind skills. And what a thrill it will be to have the traffic pattern to yourself; everyone else will be on the ground, avoiding the crosswind as if it were carrying a dose of the swine flu.

Once a pilot learns to touch down without drifting and with the airplane lined up with the runway, then he might be ready to learn another way to make crosswind landings. Yes, there is another, perhaps better way than slipping to touchdown. But before a pilot is introduced to this somewhat unorthodox method, he should be reasonably proficient in the conventional time-honored technique. And, he should know his airplane well. So, if you don't meet these qualifications, perhaps you should stop reading and save this article for another day. But if you think you're sharp—and what pilot doesn't?—then read on. To keep my conscience clear, however, may I suggest that no one practice what you are about to read without the assistance of a competent instructor. Once this "new" technique is mastered, you may find that it is superior to conventional crosswind methods.

A well executed crosswind landing requires that at the instant of touchdown on the upwind tire, the aircraft must be heading parallel to its direction of motion. Drift is prevented by banking into the wind, a maneuver that requires cross-controlling the aircraft. For example, a left crosswind is countered by applying left aileron to keep the left wing down and right rudder to prevent yawing toward the lowered wing. Technically, this maneuver is a sideslip. Were it not for the drifting effect of the crosswind, the aircraft would slip toward the left side of the runway while maintaining a heading parallel to the runway.

This sideslip configuration is usually established a few hundred feet above the ground, presumably so the pilot has sufficient time to establish just the amount of slip necessary to offset the drifting effect of the crosswind component. Too much slip and the plane drifts into the wind; not enough and the aircraft drifts downwind.

The only thing wrong with this preparatory philosophy is that wind velocity often is quite variable at altitudes near the ground on a windy day. In addition to the effects of ground friction on wind, the influence of large hangars and buildings causes gross variations in local conditions. This was dramatically illustrated by a classic photograph published years ago in one of CAA's (now FAA) training publications. It showed three windsocks equally spaced along the edge of a long runway. The middle sock was almost limp. The other two stood out like howitzers but they were pointed in opposite directions.

Since the degree of slip required to offset drift must frequently be varied with a change in altitude, the argument in favor of establishing the slip at 200 to 300 feet agl is weakened.

Two additional major disadvantages of the slipping descent deal with a loss of roll control which can result in a damaged wingtip . . . or worse. Consider a low-wing plane being slipped a few feet above the runway. The upwind wing is being held down to prevent drift. The pilot is about to begin the landing flare when the upwind (lowered) wing suddenly is assaulted by a strong, downward gust. This increases the bank angle farther and involuntarily. If a correction is not made quickly enough, both the wingtip and the pilot's pride are vulnerable to damage.

On the other hand, consider a gust that tends to right the aircraft. The pilot may have insufficient aileron control remaining to hold the upwind wing down because he is already using considerable aileron pressure in that direction just to maintain the slip.

Also consider that a slipping descent results in a slight loss of the vertical lift component produced by the wing. To compensate for this loss, a slightly faster approach speed is required. This is in addition to the extra speed needed to compensate for gusts. (To protect against losses of airspeed caused by gust-induced wind shear, it is recommended practice to add one-half of the reported gust value to the normal approach speed. For example, if the wind is reported at 20 with gusts to 34 knots, then at least half the gust value—or seven knots—should be added to the normal approach speed.)

But there is another way to combat the crosswind. It is a method used by the airlines because of the difficulty of slipping a Boeing 707 or Douglas DC-8 to a landing.

A close look at a jetliner with low-slung, pylon-mounted engines reveals why this is so: the engine pods hang too close to the ground. Landing in a bank to prevent drift has caused more than one embarrassed airline captain to write a letter explaining how he managed to drag an engine pod along the concrete. Also, the jetliner's swept wings cause the wingtips to be relatively far aft. When the nose is raised to the takeoff or landing attitude, the wingtips (which are well behind the main landing gear) move down toward the ground. Banking the aircraft at such a time jeopardizes the wingtips and could even scrape the inboard-flap sections.

The jetliner's geometry insists that conventional crosswind landing techniques be abandoned in favor of a better method, one developed for early jet bombers. This method not only eliminates the need to slip down the glideslope, but also enables a pilot to more precisely land on the touchdown target.

A modified version of the airline method is adaptable for use in light aircraft and, when proficiency in it is developed, offers improved safety, controllability and passenger comfort during crosswind landings. Additionally, this technique allows a pilot to increase his personal crosswind limit. Parenthetically and because of the technique about to be described, the Boeing 707 has a *direct* crosswind limitation of 30 knots which, when you think about it, is a monstrous wind for an aircraft of that size and complexity.

Now that you are sitting on the edge of your seat in breathless anticipation, the time has come to relieve the suspense. The "better" way to make a crosswind landing is called the "kickout" method, for reasons that will soon become obvious.

The landing scenario goes like this. While on final approach, offset the effects of wind drift by *crabbing* into the wind. Vary the crab angle as necessary during the descent according to variations in the crosswind component that occur during the approach.

As the aircraft nears the runway, *retain* the necessary crab angle. Do not transition to a slip. Maintain the crab angle with wings level until the flare has begun and the aircraft is only inches above the runway at a near zero sink rate. Immediately prior to touchdown—and here's where some skill comes in handy—lower the upwind wing and push the upwind tire onto the pavement so as to make a firm, positive touchdown on that wheel. The idea is to plant the upwind gear on the ground, eliminating the need to enter a steep bank angle to prevent drift. Ground contact, in combination with the resulting bank angle prevents the aircraft from drifting askew.

Simultaneous with the application of aileron, it is necessary to kick the aircraft out of the crab with firm application of opposite—or downwind—rudder. This straightens the aircraft so it is aligned with the runway at the instant of touchdown.

Once the upwind tire is on the ground, increase aileron pressure to keep it there. Continue to apply rudder as necessary to maintain runway heading.

The next step is familiar. Allow the other main landing gear tire to touch down, followed by the nosewheel or tailwheel.

The kickout method is surprisingly similar in execution to a conventional crosswind landing, the difference being that the slip entry is delayed until an instant before touchdown. Banking the aircraft, however, is the manner in which touchdown is accomplished. The pilot doesn't have to sit and wait for the aircraft to plop down while he hovers above the runway with one wingtip dangling ungracefully and dangerously close to the ground. By lowering the upwind wing while the aircraft is only inches above the runway, the upwind tire is forced to descend and make firm contact with the ground.

It's a simple matter to determine when the aircraft has been banked sufficiently: just listen or feel for ground contact. Simply stated, the kickout method is a slip entry *interrupted* by a landing.

I experimented with this technique in a Cherokee 140 one day while the wind was gusting across Santa Monica's Runway 3 at 35 knots. The conventional method of landing failed because I couldn't lower the upwind wing sufficiently to offset the drift. After three unsuccessful landing attempts, I altered my technique and tried the kickout method for the first time in a light airplane.

On final, I maintained a tremendous crab angle to the left and concluded how fortunate it is there is no limit to the crab angle which can be maintained by an airplane in flight. There is, of course, a very definite limit to the degree of slip which can be maintained in any given airplane (depending upon its control effectiveness). And since I didn't have to cross-control and force myself against the cockpit sidewall, I felt relatively comfortable and at ease.

I held the crab to a point only inches above the runway and checked the rate of descent with a touch of back pressure on the control wheel. When the tires were only a second or two from scrubbing sideways against the surface, I simultaneously lowered the left wing and added right rudder; the left tire plunked cooperatively onto the concrete. The simple act of banking forced the aircraft to land. Because of the brutality of this particular wind, I simply pushed the aircraft over onto all three legs and braked to stop.

To confirm that this landing wasn't just a fluke, I made two more landings much to the chagrin of the tower controllers who thought they had a runaway lunatic in the pattern. The other two landings were equally successful. I was able to land in a crosswind that was almost insurmountable using conventional methods.

CROSSWIND COMPONENT CHART
ANGLE BETWEEN RUNWAY AND WIND DIRECTION

	10°	20°	30°	40°	50°	60°	70°	80°	90°
5	1	2	3	3	4	4	5	5	5
10	2	3	5	6	8	9	9	10	10
15	3	5	8	10	11	13	14	15	15
20	4	7	10	13	15	17	19	20	20
25	4	9	13	16	19	22	24	25	25
30	5	10	15	19	23	26	28	30	30
35	6	12	18	22	27	30	33	34	35
40	7	14	20	26	31	35	38	39	40
45	8	15	23	29	34	39	42	44	45
50	9	17	25	32	38	43	47	49	50
60	10	20	30	38	46	52	56	59	60
70	12	24	35	45	54	61	66	69	70

TOTAL WIND SPEED (MPH OR KNOTS)

Table 2-C

There are two mistakes common to the kickout technique. One is to begin slip entry at too high an altitude, negating the purpose of the maneuver. In such a case, however, the pilot is no worse off than had he elected to make a normal crosswind landing in the first place. He can opt to continue the landing conventionally or execute a go-around and try again.

The second and more serious error is to allow the aircraft to touch down while crabbing. Such neglect would punish the landing gear unmercifully. But this is where skill is required. Beginners should not attempt such a landing.

The kickout method is somewhat unorthodox and no one should adopt this technique without first practicing it during relatively mild crosswind conditions. As skill increases, then stronger winds can be challenged. During the progress to these more difficult conditions, a pilot should keep track of the crosswind components encountered and mastered so he'll know how proficient he's becoming. (See Table 2-C) Remember, it is the crosswind component, not the total wind speed, that determines the drifting effect of the wind. The accompanying chart provides the crosswind component during all wind conditions.

Perhaps equally helpful is a rule-of-thumb used to accurately determine the crosswind component at any point along final approach (or in cruise). This rule is especially convenient when landing at uncontrolled airports where wind velocity reports are unavailable. It is based on the "one-in-sixty" angular relationship used in off-course navigation.

When flying at 60 knots TAS, each degree of crab necessary to maintain a given course indicates the presence of a one knot crosswind. Similarly, at 120 knots, each degree of crab represents two knots of direct crosswind, etc.

If an airplane has an approach speed of 90 knots, for example, each degree of drift correction offsets one and a half knots of crosswind. A 12 degree crab, therefore, would indicate the presence of an eighteen knot crosswind component.

The next time you encounter a strong crosswind that necessitates an uncomfortable, awkward, sideslipping descent, remember—there is another way.

DEAD RECKONING NAVIGATION

*Are you ready to fall back to
the lost art of compass and clock
if your electronics fail?*

It is generally agreed that the compass is a pilot's primary navigation tool. But when it comes to specifying the second most valuable such device in the cockpit, there is often some difference of opinion.

New pilots generally favor the VOR receiver. But those with more experience vote for the clock. After all, when a fuse blows or the left/right needle behaves like a metronome gone berserk, a pilot must resort to basics. The reliable compass and clock become his primary weapons in a battle of wits against the elements. The compass indicates where he's going and the clock tells him how far. Without either of these allies, a pilot can get very lost, very fast, especially when above clouds or when over terrain where checkpoints are confusingly few and far apart.

Compass-and-clock, or dead reckoning navigation, however, is slowly becoming a lost art as increasingly more reliance is placed on electronic guidance. Although no one can deny that VOR navigation has simplified cockpit workloads, pilots must avoid becoming too complacent.

Some, for example, don't keep track of their forward progress while navigating along a radial. They simply wait for the to/from flag to drop, which may provide the first positive fix since passing the previous station. But shouldn't a pilot always know his position relative to the nearest airport?

Dead reckoning, or DR navigation, is a relatively painless procedure that can and should be combined with radio navigation so a pilot is aware of his approximate position at all times.

According to popular definition, dead reckoning is short for "deduced reckoning" or, as the old-timers used to say, "you're *dead* if you don't *reckon* right." In truth, however, the term originated with maritime navigation and refers to "reckoning or reasoning (one's position) relative to something stationary or *dead* in the water." Simply stated, DR navigation is a method of predicting enroute progress based on the direction of flight and the estimated groundspeed since the last known position.

Unfortunately, the mere mention of DR often makes a pilot uncomfortable with memories of FAA written examinations, wind triangles, and E-6B "confusers."

But DR doesn't have to be laborious.

Consider, for example, Jack Chrysler, an ATP who flies his Aerostar 601 all over North and South America. Chrysler has so simplified his dead reckoning procedures that he feels they are not only fun to use, but frequently result in reduced flight time because he is not confined to the often dog-legged dictates of Victor airways. Also, he claims to be more relaxed holding a constant heading than reacting to the semaphore-like movements of a VOR needle.

Prior to a VFR flight, Chrysler simply uses a yardstick and a VFR planning chart (JN charts outside the United States) to plot a direct course between the departure and destination airports (assuming that intervening terrain and other restrictions do not pose a threat to safety or legality).

He then uses the forecasted winds aloft together with Tables 3-A and 3-B to determine the true heading and groundspeed. Assume, for example, that the measured true course is 040° and the winds aloft are expected to be from 010° at 40 knots. In other words, the wind will be blowing from 30° to the *left* of his *nose*. Using Table 3-A, he determines that this is equivalent to a 35 knot headwind component and a 20 knot, left crosswind component.

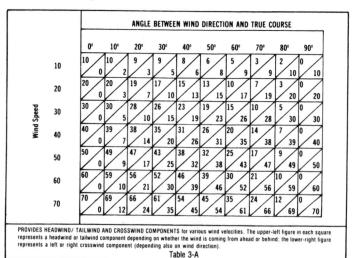

PROVIDES HEADWIND/ TAILWIND AND CROSSWIND COMPONENTS for various wind velocities. The upper-left figure in each square represents a headwind or tailwind component depending on whether the wind is coming from ahead or behind; the lower-right figure represents a left or right crosswind component (depending also on wind direction).

Table 3-A

Since the planned true airspeed is 220 knots, he expects the enroute groundspeed to be 185 knots (220 − 35 = 185).

Next he consults Table 3-B and determines that a 20 knot, left crosswind component combines with 220 knots of airspeed to require a 5° (left) wind correction angle. The true heading for the proposed flight, therefore, is 040° less 5°, or 035°.

End of problem . . . without a wind triangle.

If more than one wind condition is to be encountered enroute, they

		TRUE AIRSPEED								
		80	100	120	140	160	180	200	220	240
Crosswind Component	5	4°	3°	2°	2°	2°	2°	1°	1°	1°
	10	7°	6°	5°	4°	4°	3°	3°	3°	2°
	15	11°	9°	7°	6°	5°	5°	4°	4°	4°
	20	14°	12°	10°	8°	7°	6°	6°	5°	5°
	25	18°	14°	12°	10°	9°	8°	7°	7°	6°
	30	22°	17°	14°	12°	11°	10°	9°	8°	7°
	35	26°	20°	17°	14°	13°	11°	10°	9°	8°
	40	30°	24°	19°	17°	15°	13°	12°	10°	10°
	45	34°	27°	22°	19°	16°	14°	13°	12°	11°
	50	39°	30°	25°	21°	18°	16°	14°	13°	12°

PROVIDES THE CRAB ANGLE necessary to compensate for a given crosswind component when flying at a given true airspeed and is valid for knots or mph. CAUTION: crabbing, or turning into the wind, results in some loss of groundspeed but this loss is not significant when the crab angle is less than 10°. A chart showing the groundspeed loss associated with various wind correction angles can be found in Chapter Six.

Table 3-B

may be arithmetically averaged with reasonable accuracy if wind directions don't vary by more than 90° and wind speeds are within 15 knots of each other. For example, assume that the winds aloft for each of three flight segments along the direct route are forecast to be 080°/15 knots, 100°/30 knots and 150°/30 knots. The average wind direction is (080° + 100° + 150°) ÷ 3 = 110°. Similarly, the average wind speed is 25 knots. This technique should not be used, however, when maximum accuracy is required (such as on a long, overwater flight).

Enroute, Chrysler keeps track of his progress visually or uses elapsed time and estimated groundspeed to plot a "DR position." Often, he doesn't turn on the dual VOR receivers until within range of the destination . . . if at all. (When necessary, he applies a midcourse correction to compensate for an errant wind forecast.)

Dead reckoning works and it's reasonably accurate. Ask the man who pioneered the 2,000 mile, Newfoundland-to-Ireland route in 1927 as well as the thousands of pilots who have flown in his wake . . . with little more than a compass and a clock.

(Lindbergh was luckier than is generally realized, however. According to John P.V. Heinmuller, one of the official NAA observers for the New York-to-Paris flight, a freak wind condition existed over the North Atlantic on May 20–22. The pressure patterns were arranged in such a way that the *net* drift acting upon the Spirit of St. Louis was zero, the first time this had ever been recorded by weather experts.)

If an aircraft maintains its predicted groundspeed and track, then a positive fix obtained at any time during the flight will agree with the aircraft position as determined by DR methods. More likely, however, an actual fix (using radio or pilotage or both) will disagree with the DR position. Usually, this is because one or more variables have been appraised incorrectly. In other words, there is an element of uncertainty surrounding every position determined purely by dead reckoning.

A rule-of-thumb states that 90% of the time the maximum dead reckoning error (per hour of flight) is 20 miles plus 1% of the estimated distance flown during that hour.

Figure 3-1, for example, shows where the pilot of a 150 knot aircraft has computed his position to be at the end of one hour. The radius of the circle of uncertainty is equal, therefore, to 20 nm + 1% of 150 which equals 21.5 nm. In other words, there is a 90% probability that the pilot is actually within 21.5 nm of where he thinks he is.

It also can be shown that 50% of the time the aircraft is located within a circle with only one-third the radius of the larger circle. In this case, the pilot has a fifty-fifty chance of being within 7.2 nm of the DR position.

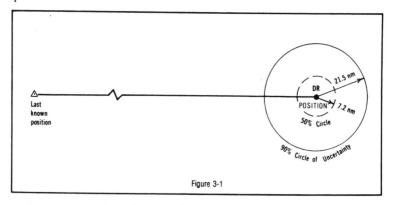

Figure 3-1

One way to reduce the size of the dead-reckoning errors is to make sure the compass deviation card is reasonably accurate. The FAA doesn't require a periodic compass swing, but pilots would be wise to perform this check at least annually. Deviation errors can change significantly over a period of time.

Also, make it a habit to glance at the compass whenever lining up on a runway of *known magnetic direction*. Remember, however, that the runway number usually represents the magnetic direction *rounded off* to the nearest 10°. Some runway numbers disagree by more than 10° with the actual magnetic directions. Tucson's Runway 11L, for example, has a magnetic direction of 122°.

None of this should be interpreted as an argument against VOR navigation in favor of DR. But it is nice to know there is an alternate, reliable way to get from one place to another when VOR is unavailable and pilotage is difficult. All that is required is some common sense reasoning. The idea is to be aware of the wind and its effects and to maintain a running score of flight progress either on a flight log or by making marks on the chart and labeling each position (estimated or actual) with the time of passage.

Not only can DR be used to compute progress along a radial, it can also be used in conjunction with VOR to arrive at a "running fix."

Consider the pilot flying from A to B in Figure 3-2. He's not necessarily lost, but it has been a while since the last positive fix. He's also having trouble correlating contour lines on the chart with those on the ground.

At 1 p.m. the aircraft crosses a railroad track, an excellent line of position (LOP). But one LOP does not establish a fix. Eighteen minutes later, the pilot is within range of a VOR station and determines that he is on the 230° radial. Again, the pilot has a single LOP, not enough to establish position . . . or is it?

A fix *can* be obtained by advancing the 1 p.m. LOP (the railroad tracks) toward the second LOP (the radial). This is accomplished by first estimating the distance flown since crossing the first LOP.

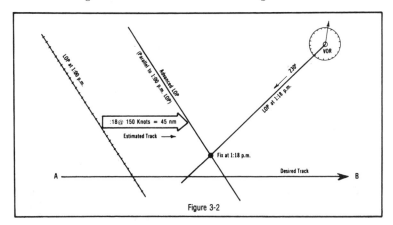

Figure 3-2

Assume, for example, the estimated groundspeed of the aircraft in Figure 3-2 is 150 knots. In 18 minutes, therefore, the distance flown is about 45 nm. The first LOP is then *advanced* (parallel to itself) 45 nm in the direction of the estimated track being flown. The point where the advanced LOP intersects the VOR radial (the second LOP) is the fix for 1:18 p.m. and shows the aircraft to be north of course.

A running fix can be obtained using any two LOPs as long as they cross at a reasonably oblique angle. They may be highways, rivers, or even a pair of radials crossed at different times.

Another combination of DR and VOR navigation is called the "single-line approach." This technique can be life saving and is illustrated in Figure 3-3.

A pilot is endeavoring to fly a true course of 090° toward the Chutzpah Airport which is on the 170° radial of a VORTAC (far to the north of course). The pilot estimates arriving over the airport at 2:55 p.m. Unfortunately, he has been unable to obtain a reliable and recent fix and isn't sure that he's on course. So, what should he do if, upon intercepting the 170° radial, the airport cannot be found? Should he fly north or south along the radial to find the destination? Since he is running low on fuel, he can't afford to turn in the wrong direction.

Dead reckoning (or common sense) navigation offers a logical solution. About 45 minutes prior to ETA, the pilot should make a sufficiently large turn and purposefully intercept the radial north (or south) of the airport.

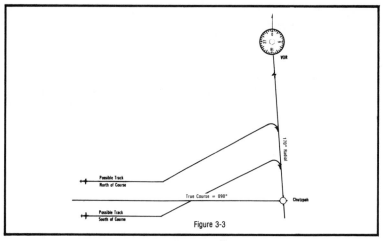

Figure 3-3

When the 170° radial is finally intercepted, the pilot knows with reasonable confidence which way to turn. By turning off course intentionally, he eliminates the likelihood of turning, searching, and wasting fuel in the wrong direction.

This procedure is also known as the "landfall intercept" and doesn't require that the destination be on a VOR radial. The airport could be situated on a river, shoreline, highway, railroad, or anything else that is easily identifiable and is approximately perpendicular to the true course. Nor does the single-line approach have to be reserved for locating a destination. It can be used with equal effectiveness to find a needed enroute checkpoint.

DR teaches another valuable lesson—how to avoid a midair collision.

In pre-radar days, one of the techniques a fighter aircraft could use to intercept another airplane required that the two aircraft remain on a "line of constant bearing." In other words the direction of one aircraft from the other must remain constant (as long as each aircraft maintains a constant heading and airspeed).

The same is true of two aircraft on collision courses. Visually, this means that if an aircraft remains fixed at a specific point on your windshield and he is at your altitude, you may expect an encounter of the wrong kind. To avoid such an unpleasantry, change heading so that the "bogie" appears to move across your windshield. When this happens, the two aircraft are not maintaining a constant bearing from one another and an "intercept" is impossible.

DR offers much to the pilot willing to expend a little extra effort. And it won't take him long to learn that DR really stands for *Darned Reliable*. He'll learn also that the big three in navigation aren't Collins, King, and Narco; they're Rate, Time, and Distance.

PRESSURE-PATTERN NAVIGATION

Perk up your long cross-country
flights with a different navigation system

Every once in a while a pilot becomes utterly bored with the prosaic
chore of navigating a long cross-country trip. So there he sits, watching
for the timely flip-flop of a to/from indicator, or mesmerized by the
hypnotic wig-wagging of a left/right needle. Ho hum!

When this happens, it's time for a change of pace. Perhaps experi-
menting with a different method of navigation will liven things up a
bit.

For the most part, pressure-pattern navigation techniques (aerolo-
gation) have been set aside for use by professionals in their long range
aircraft. But this needn't be so. The same procedures can be applied
to cross-country navigation in light aircraft. It's not only a challenging
method of navigation, it's also refreshing to learn that expensive, heavy
black boxes are not required as part of the deal. All that's needed is a
rate-time-distance computer, a compass, and a flair for something new.

Most pilots have heard of a technique allowing deviation from a
direct course to take advantage of favorable tail winds or to evade
strong head winds. This has become standard procedure on most
airline flights of two hours or more. For example, when a high pressure
system sits over the central United States (see Figure 3-4), eastbound
jets fly north of the high, while westbound jets deviate south of it. In
both cases the courses, though many miles longer than a direct straight-
line course, will take appreciably less time. Such an off-course track is
called the minimum time route (MTR). It is a classic example of the
goal of pressure-pattern navigation: to make the most of existing
pressure and wind conditions.

Euclid, father of modern geometry, may have been right when he
said the shortest distance between two points is a straight line, but he
certainly didn't have the pilot in mind. The shortest flying time enroute
is generally achieved by following along the often curved and devious
MTR.

Many pilots attempt to employ this technique although few are successful at it. How far off course should a pilot go to put the prevailing winds to advantage? Obviously, a pilot should not fly 100 nm off course during a 200 nm trip even though strong tail winds would be gained.

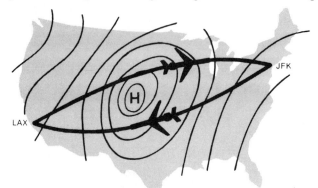

Figure 3-4

Determining the minimum time route cannot be done through hunches or guesswork. Most of the time, a pilot is better off flying the direct course rather than guessing. The forbidding grid side of an E-6B computer could be used to determine the MTR, but that would be too much like work. Fortunately, there is a far simpler method available.

Not too long ago, a Chicago scientist, Dr. John C. Bellamy, devised a rather simple formula that caused a navigational revolution. He stated that no matter what wind conditions exist along a given route, the trip can be flown with a single heading. His formula led to what is now the basis for pressure-pattern navigation. By using the Bellamy formula, a pilot can depart on any flight with one—and only one—wind correction and this correction ultimately will lead the pilot to his destination, despite the wind shifts (speed or direction) encountered enroute. And the track established by an aircraft flying a single route heading to the destination later will prove to approximate closely the minimum time route.

The magic key to successful pressure-pattern navigation was expressed by Bellamy as follows:

$$\textbf{Drift} = \frac{(P_2 - P_1)\,K}{TAS}$$

In the formula, P_2 is the actual barometric pressure at cruise altitude above the destination airport and P_1 is the actual barometric pressure at that same altitude above the departure airport. These pressure values generally can be obtained from the National Weather Service prior to departure. Should they be unavailable, destination and departure altimeter settings can be substituted with negligible accuracy loss with cruising altitudes of less than 10,000 feet msl. If the flight is to be conducted above 10,000 feet, the pilot will require access to a constant pressure chart covering his route of flight.

The true airspeed (TAS) must be expressed in knots. K is a factor dependent upon the average latitude of the trip to be flown and may be determined from the following table:

Latitude Range	K Factor
22°–25°	540
25°–28°	480
28°–31°	440
31°–34°	400
34°–38°	360
38°–43°	330
43°–50°	300
50°–55°	270

Now for a hypothetical problem. A pilot is about to embark on a trip from San Francisco to Los Angeles. The average latitude between SFO and LAX is quickly determined from the aeronautical chart; it's about 36° N. The K factor of 360 will be used, therefore, in the formula. A cruise altitude of 7,500 feet is selected and the pilot determines (from the Weather Service) that the barometric pressure at 7,500 feet is 22.75 inches above SFO and 22.95 inches above LAX. The TAS of our Firebang Special is 100 knots. The known values are now plugged into the Bellamy formula to obtain the drift.

$$\text{Drift} = \frac{(2295 - 2275)(360)}{100} = 72 \text{ nm}$$

Notice that (1) the decimal points in the pressure values are omitted and (2) the drift is shown in nautical miles. This simply means that if no correction were made for enroute winds, the aircraft would have drifted 72 nm off course by the time it should have arrived over LAX, the destination airport.

A question now is raised as to whether the 72 nm drift will be left or right. Think carefully; think of the wind circulation about high and low pressure areas. Pilots have to learn this before being licensed; it's basic knowledge for all flyers. Since destination barometric pressure is higher than that of departure, the flight is being made, effectively, out of a low pressure area into a high. Would the pilot expect left or right drift? Careful now! If you would anticipate a left drift, proceed to the head of the class.

If you're not interested in using logic to determine the direction of drift, just remember these simple rules. When P_2 is larger than P_1 ($P_2 - P_1$ is positive), a left drift can be expected. When P_2 is smaller than P_1 ($P_2 - P_1$ is negative), a right drift can be expected. In the example, P_2 is greater than P_1. The aircraft therefore can be expected to have drifted 72 nm to the left of Los Angeles if no correction for wind were made.

The left drift of 72 nm (83 sm), as determined by Bellamy's dandy arithmetical computation, is easily convertible to a drift angle through a simple flick of any time-speed-distance computer. Set up the amount of drift (72 nm) on the outer scale opposite the distance to be traveled on the inner scale. For purposes of this example, the distance from SFO to LAX is approximately 300 nm. Opposite 60 (57.6 for those who want greater accuracy) on the inner scale, read the drift angle of 14° on the outer scale. Since drift is left, the 14° wind correction angle must be added to the true course. The true course from SFO to LAX is about 145° plus a 14° wind correction, which provides a true heading of 159° to fly the intended route. This is the one and only heading that corrects for all wind conditions between SFO and LAX when the given pressure values exist. The track resulting from flying this heading represents a close approximation of the minimum time route between those two points.

In the example, it was determined that the drift for the intended trip would be 72 nm to the left. This does not mean that only a left drift would be encountered during the trip. The Bellamy formula only states that the net drift at the end of the flight will be 72 nm to the left if no correction for wind is made. Indeed, during the course of the flight, the aircraft may drift both right and left of course, depending upon actual winds encountered. The net result of *all* winds acting upon the aircraft will cause a 72 nm left drift.

At first it may be difficult to believe this one drift correction will provide for arrival precisely over destination. Although it appears that no compensation has been provided for high-velocity winds which may exist enroute, this is not true. The pressure differential between any two points will determine the *net* effect of all winds between them.

Figure 3-5 is only one of many possible situations which could exist between SFO and LAX when differential pressure is .20 inches Hg

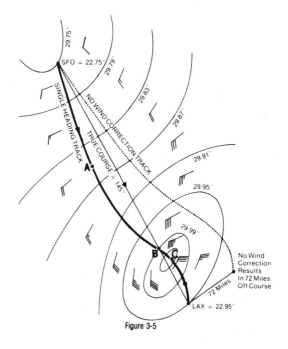

Figure 3-5

(22.95″ – 22.75″). SFO is located under a low pressure system and a pilot would experience a slight right crosswind as he began his trip. The wind is so weak that the 14° crab would be considered an overcorrection and the aircraft would fly slightly right of course. Upon reaching point A, the winds have picked up in strength and begin to blow the aircraft back on course (point B). As the flight progresses toward the high pressure area, greater drift is encountered and the ship drifts considerably left of course. At point C, the aircraft is abeam the high and the wind shifts from a right crosswind to a left. Now the aircraft drifts toward the original straight-line course. If everything has gone according to Hoyle (or Bellamy!), the reinterception of the direct route should take place above the LAX airport.

Actually, there are an infinite number of pressure patterns which could exist between SFO and LAX, but as long as the pressure differential between them remains the same, the average crosswind or net drift also remains the same.

The dotted line in the example represents the course which would have been followed had no wind correction been made. Note that the aircraft would have arrived 72 nm to the left of LAX, the net effect of all drift encountered enroute.

Single heading flight reduces time enroute for a very simple reason. During a normal flight along a fixed course, a pilot may have to crab right or left as he progresses in order to maintain a constant straight-line track. Each time he crabs into the wind, his groundspeed is lessened, increasing the time required for the flight. Using a single heading allows the aircraft to drift right and/or left of course without the loss of groundspeed caused by variable crab angles. The actual track flown may be a few miles longer, but it definitely takes less time to fly. It is also easier to execute a flight with one heading than to compute and fly the various headings often required for a straightline course with variable winds aloft.

By a quick glance at Dr. Bellamy's formula, it should be apparent that if the pressure values at the destination and departure airports are the same, then P_2-P_1 will equal zero and the net drift for the entire flight will also be zero. Under these conditions, you could take off with absolutely no wind correction and expect to arrive over your destination in minimal time, despite the winds aloft. You may encounter drift enroute, but the net drift effects of all winds encountered will be nil—and you will have flown the minimum time route. This, too, at first may be a bit tough to swallow, but Figure 3-6 should dispel any confusion. A flight conducted between any two points of equal pressure will encounter as much left drift as it will right. And voila! No wind correction is necessary to fly the MTR.

The main advantage of pressure-pattern navigation is obvious. It provides a method of flying from A to B in minimal time without having to fool around with wind triangles and their resultant and time consuming crab angles. It's also easier for the Weather Service to forecast accurate barometric pressure values than winds aloft.

But there are some problems. The accuracy of single heading flight diminishes as the pressure values at the terminal points of the flight

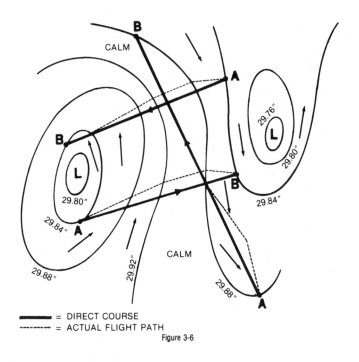

= DIRECT COURSE
------- = ACTUAL FLIGHT PATH

Figure 3-6

change. If they both go up or down, the flight will be unaffected as long as the difference between them remains relatively constant. But if one value should rise while the other drops (not too likely on trips of less than a few hundred miles), then the net drift encountered will change accordingly. The shrewd Magellan-type can counter these barometric pressure changes by determining new wind correction angles with the Bellamy formula as the flight progresses.

Another disadvantage arises when the pilot attempts to plot the MTR on his chart. After all, it's nice to have some checkpoints for reference. Unless an upper-air chart is available, this really isn't too easy. The Weather Service might frown on an attempt to plot courses on one of its beautiful charts, so always ask for one of your own. As a last resort, the wind triangles can be plotted on a conventional sectional or WAC chart. First, plot the true course (TC) on the chart, as in Figure 3-7. Then draw a line representing the true heading (TH) from the departure point. The angle between the TC and the TH is obviously the single heading correction angle. Then measure a distance along the TH line equal to one hour's worth of TAS and mark an X. This is where the aircraft would wind up under no-wind conditions. From this point draw a wind vector representing the average wind to be encountered during this first segment of the flight. Winds aloft information can be obtained directly from the upper-air chart or from a conventional forecast. The end of the wind line (Point A) represents the expected position of the aircraft at the end of one hour of cruise flight. From point A, draw a new true heading line and repeat the process over and over until the destination is reached. By connecting all of the "one-

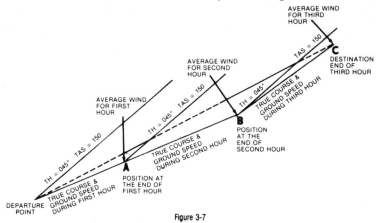

Figure 3-7

hour" positions with a smooth curving line, a close approximation of the MTR will be reached.

On the other hand, those less inclined to pencil, plotter, and chart and more prone to adventure might decide to chance it, not really knowing where the winds will blow them until arrival over the destination. Have faith that the single heading technique will work, but it is advisable to monitor the path of flight with at least a sectional chart. We don't want anyone to get lost.

Pressure-pattern navigation doesn't lend itself too well to airway flying. The FAA simply won't cooperate by laying out its route structure according to the daily whims and dictates of the wind. But a modification of the single heading technique can prove beneficial if VOR to VOR flight is desired. Using the techniques previously described, obtain a plotted MTR. Then select the VOR stations most closely aligned with it and prepare an airway-modified MTR. The results may be surprising. An airway ordinarily considered out of the way might fit pleasantly into the scheme of things.

Determining precisely how long the trip will take also creates problems. The ambitious pilot can continue with the wind triangles to obtain various enroute groundspeeds. A simpler but not-so-accurate technique involves obtaining an estimated time enroute by conventional methods and then saying to himself: "Using the MTR, I know it'll take somewhat less time." Half the fun is finding out precisely how much time is saved. The results may be surprising.

One further word of caution. Pressure-pattern navigation can be used only when the chosen enroute altitude is above the altitude below which wind speed and direction are modified by the frictional effects of the terrain. This takes place generally at 2,000 feet agl and below. Above 2,000 feet above the terrain the winds are governed almost exclusively by the direction and spacing of the isobars, i.e., winds flow parallel to the isobars and the speed is inversely proportional to the distance between them.

Pressure-pattern navigation works like a charm on long distance flights. Its benefits have been known for many years. This technique may never replace VOR navigation for light aircraft but it is sure a lot of fun to play with. And who knows? If you become good enough at it, you may want to look into pressure lines of position, or PLOPS, as they're so ungracefully called.

ADF — A GOOD, FAIR-WEATHER FRIEND

Not-so-old-fashioned navigational aid can still help you get from A to B

If the automatic direction finder (ADF) were human, it would deserve considerable compassion. Poor bird dog, the ignored orphan of avionics, the forgotten stepchild of navigation. It is used more to entertain passengers with news and music than the purpose for which it was designed.

Pilots shy from ADF tracking because of the frequent mental computations usually required. They are discouraged by the way textbooks and instructors elaborate on the mathematical relationship between relative bearings, magnetic bearings and magnetic headings. Besides, it's much easier to chase VOR needles when cross-track winds are strong. Or is it?

Believe it or not, ADF navigation does not have to be a mind-boggling affair. By eliminating most of the arithmetic usually required, ADF usage can be pleasant and relaxing. But reducing ADF to such simplicity requires setting aside textbook navigation.

Assume, for example, that a pilot is about to fly 100 nm to the remote community of Maryville. There are no FAA approved navaids in the area, but the town does boast a commercial broadcast station. After takeoff, the pilot tunes his ADF receiver to this station and turns the aircraft until the ADF needle points to the top of the dial indicating that Maryville is straight ahead.

What the pilot doesn't realize, however, is that a 30 knot, cross-track wind is drifting the aircraft to the right of course. As a result, the ADF needle moves gradually, yet persistently, to the left. Is this pilot concerned? Not at all. He simply turns toward the needle until it once again points straight ahead, repeating this corrective action as often as necessary. Eventually, he arrives over the station.

This is not ADF *tracking* because a specific course is not being maintained. The actual flight path consists of a curved line caused by wind drift. But this is ADF navigation, and it is called "homing."

Critics point to the inefficiency of homing because flying a curved track consumes more time and distance than the direct route. Agreed. But what they do not realize is that in most cases the additional time and distance are negligible.

Assume, for example, that the aircraft cruises at 150 knots. With the assistance of an electronic computer, it was determined that the pilot was subject to a maximum cross-track deviation of 7.57 nm. This "bulge" caused the flight path to increase by only 2.09 nm, resulting in a 102.09 nm flight that required 41.4 minutes. Flying the direct route would have taken 40.8 minutes. At a cost of .6 minutes (36 seconds), the pilot spared himself the mental gymnastics associated with ADF tracking.

When the crosswind component is less than 30 knots, the additional time required to bird dog a station is inconsequential. (And rarely do crosswind components exceed 30 knots.) Homing (instead of tracking) under the influence of a 20 knot crosswind, for example, adds only 18 seconds to the enroute time in the example. Also, homing frequently requires less total time and distance than the dog-legged routes usually associated with VOR navigation.

Purists argue, however, that homing with a crosswind guarantees being blown off course. True, but what's wrong with straying a few miles off the beaten path during a VFR flight? Besides, when the plane is more than halfway to the station, homing automatically corrects for its own error, and guides the aircraft directly to the beacon. A pilot is no more likely to get lost when bird dogging than when tracking a VOR radial without using checkpoints to determine his enroute progress.

There is a handy modification of the homing technique which can be used to offset what some consider to be undesirable, cross-track drifting. And it's as easy as child's play.

Assume that prior to his departure for Maryville, the pilot knew he would encounter a strong, left crosswind. He could home in on the broadcast station; but instead, he *arbitrarily* selects a crab angle of, say, 10°.

After takeoff, he turns toward the destination until the ADF pointer shows the station to be 10° right, which indicates the aircraft is being crabbed 10° left. For the duration of the flight, the pilot simply maintains whatever heading is necessary to keep the ADF needle pointed 10° right. Regardless of the actual wind velocity, the aircraft will pass almost directly over the station. If this sounds too good to be true, don't fight it. Accept this tip graciously and realize that ADF navigation doesn't have to be a continual exercise juggling numbers on a compass rose.

The logic of this simplified technique is shown in Figure 3-8. The dotted line would have been the pilot's track had he not used an arbitrary crab angle and merely homed in on the station. The dashed line represents the track actually maintained because of the crab angle. In this case, 10° of correction was not quite enough. Otherwise, the actual flight path would have coincided with the direct route. But the pilot did compensate for enough of the wind to prevent most of the

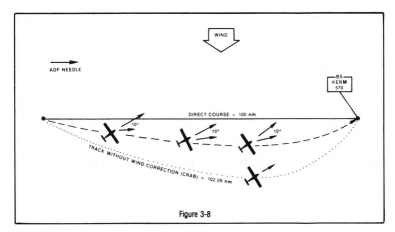

Figure 3-8

drift.

Someone is bound to say, "That sounds great, but what if the pilot crabs too much or compensates for a wind that doesn't really exist?" Good question.

Figure 3-9 shows what happens when crabbing into a nonexistent wind. Initially, the aircraft heads 10° left of course. But as the flight progresses, the ADF needle begins to move clockwise. As this occurs, the pilot turns right to maintain a constant ADF indication of 10° right. He winds up flying a curved track, but still arrives at his destination.

There are some for whom the use of an arbitrary crab angle is conceptually crude. For these pilots, there is a solution. To arrive at a more scientifically derived correction angle, it is necessary to determine the speed of the crosswind component with respect to true airspeed. For example, a 32 knot crosswind component represents 16% of a 200 knot TAS. Cut this percentage (16) in half to arrive at a crab angle of, in this case, 8°. This rule-of-thumb is accurate to within 2°, and can be used whenever a crab angle is needed and a vector computer is either unavailable or undesirable.

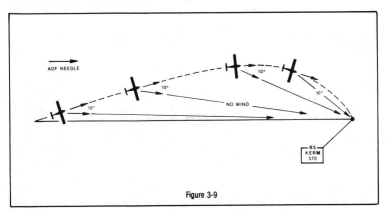

Figure 3-9

If the crosswind component is much less than 20% of the airspeed, ignore the wind entirely and keep the ADF needle pointed straight ahead. When the crosswind component is 20% of the airspeed or greater, apply the rule-of-thumb crab angle to the ADF needle. This is not necessary, but does provide for a more direct route to the destination.

Assume that a pilot is homing to a station and notices that the ADF needle has strayed from the desired position. He should not simply roll into a turn until the needle is once again in place. Because of "dipping error," the ADF needle is not fully reliable during turns. Instead, he should first note how many degrees of turn are required to reposition the needle and then execute this amount of turn with reference to the DG. Once the wings are leveled, the ADF needle will settle into place.

Tracking outbound from a radio beacon for more than a few miles is more difficult than inbound tracking and is a procedure with which most pilots are unable to remain proficient.

There is, however, a relatively effortless technique for "tracking" outbound for distances up to about 100 miles. It combines dead reckoning with drift information provided by an ADF and works reasonably well, even when the winds aloft are strong and of unknown velocity.

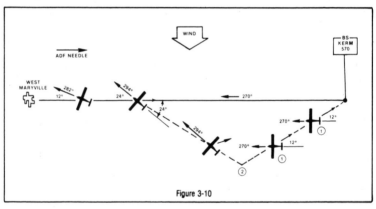

Figure 3-10

Figure 3-10 shows the broadcast station at Maryville used to help a pilot find his new destination, West Maryville. The wind is strong and northerly. The pilot overflies the station and assumes a no-wind heading of 270°. Quite naturally, this results in a southerly drift, as indicated by the ADF pointer in position no. 1. The pilot, however, is undaunted by this and maintains a heading of 270° for what he estimates to be one-third of the time required for the flight.

At approximately the one-third point (point no. 2), he glances at the ADF and notes he has drifted 12° south of course. (The ADF needle points 12° right of the tail.) He then doubles the drift angle (2 × 12° = 24°) and adds this to the magnetic heading of 270° to arrive at a new heading of 294°. This will cause the aircraft to intercept the direct route at approximately the two-thirds point.

The pilot will know he has intercepted the desired course when, on a heading of 294°, the ADF needle indicates the angle of the station "off the tail" is equal to the heading correction of 24° right. At this point, the pilot assumes the original no-wind heading of 270° *plus* the now-known drift angle of 12° to arrive at a new heading of 282°, which is used for the duration of the flight. Unless the wind changes *dramatically*, this technique will get a pilot very close to his destination.

This presentation of simplified ADF is not an argument against the use of VOR as the primary navaid. Rather, it is intended to encourage the use of ADF as a supplementary aid—or a primary aid when VORTAC stations are not in position to help. ADF usage can be maximized when flying low, below the reception altitude of the closest VORTAC stations, or when flying in remote or foreign areas where VOR coverage is spotty or unavailable.

The low and medium frequencies (L/MF) are not subject to line-of-sight restrictions and can be received at any altitude so long as the ADF is within the reception range of the station (determined primarily by power output of the transmitter). Some clear-channel, 50,000-watt broadcast stations can be received hundreds of miles away, especially at night.

Since distant L/MF signals can be received while parked on an airport situated in a valley, for example, ADF can be used as a quick-and-dirty flight planner. Simply tune to an enroute station and begin a taxiing turn until the ADF needle points straight ahead. Look out the front window to find a landmark toward which the aircraft can be headed after takeoff. It's a nifty way to become established on course.

Also, while on the ground, look at the compass. This is the no-wind heading to use once the initial landmark has been reached. By then you can probably pick up a VOR signal. If not, simply home in on the L/MF station previously tuned at the departure airport.

Quite obviously, these techniques are not compatible with IFR operations; they are strictly VFR procedures.

Relative to IFR, however, the ADF can play an invaluable role when a pilot is being radar vectored for an ILS approach. By tuning in the locator outer marker (LOM) and observing the *behavior* of the ADF needle, approach planning can be enhanced considerably.

Figure 3-11 shows an aircraft being vectored for an ILS. When flying downwind (position no. 1), a pilot with ADF awareness can sense (by needle movement) that he has quite a way to go before passing abeam the outer marker; he can keep the airplane clean and the airspeed relatively fast. The pilot should plan to reduce airspeed just prior to passing abeam the LOM (position no. 2) and prepare for a turn on to final (position no. 3) shortly thereafter. Premature or late speed reductions can be avoided by carefully observing the ADF needle and by keeping track of aircraft position relative to the LOM.

After the pilot has been turned toward final and instructed to intercept the localizer, the ADF can and should be used to verify that the intercept will occur prior to reaching the outer marker.

While maintaining the last assigned heading, the pilot at position no. 4 should observe the ADF needle moving slowly to the left. If the ADF needle remains motionless, then the aircraft (position no. 5) will intercept the localizer *at* the LOM. Or, if the ADF needle moves slowly clockwise (toward the localizer), intercept will occur inside the LOM (position no. 6). The latter two situations indicate that the assigned heading is incorrect for an intercept outside the LOM, and a revised

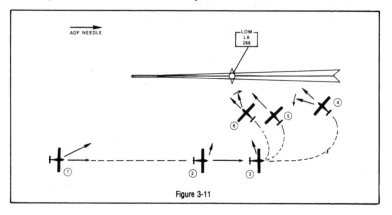

Figure 3-11

heading should be obtained from ATC. Watching the ADF needle carefully may provide the only clue to an improper vector or the presence of a strong crosswind about which the radar controller has no knowledge.

Using ADF is not always a bed of roses. The system does not have a fail flag to warn if the desired signal has been lost. On many sets, the needle will remain fixed after signal loss and will mislead the pilot into believing he is doing a marvelous job of keeping the needle in place when, in fact, the needle may be dead. If relying upon his ADF, a pilot should monitor audio output to insure that the station has not gone off the air or that the aircraft has not flown beyond the reception range of the station.

Be very careful about relying on commercial broadcast stations since these identify themselves so infrequently.

Also, be on guard for ADF errors which can be caused by nearby thunderstorms, mineral deposits, twilight effects, and the refraction that occurs when L/MF signals cross a shoreline. Be alert also for frequency interference caused by simultaneously receiving two stations on the same frequency. This is best detected by an audible whistle or hum and is most likely to occur at night. When the plane is flying in rain or snow, precipitation static can affect ADF indications and reception quality. Static can be suppressed by static dischargers (sometimes called "wick dischargers") on the trailing edges of the wings and tail surfaces. Reducing airspeed may also help.

Overall, the ADF is an outstanding navaid rarely used to its potential. Try using it more—it's a marvelous copilot.

AREA NAVIGATION (RNAV) ON A SHOESTRING

Some benefits of the system can be enjoyed with a "warm-blooded" computer—meaning you— substituted for one that is electronically fed

Area navigation is not an itch that can be scratched away or a daydream to be ignored. It is a very real concept offering so much advantage, it may someday dominate radio navigation.

RNAV proponents are quick to demonstrate the weakness of the present day VOR/DME system: Victor airways lead aircraft directly to or from VOR stations. This results in a convergence or funneling of aircraft in the vicinity of a VOR which can create the hazards associated with traffic congestion.

Area navigation, on the other hand, allows routes to be established which are not dependent upon VOR locations. Radio guidance is available along any of numerous parallel routes within reception range of VORTAC stations, thereby relieving enroute congestion along a single airway.

A typical example of an RNAV route is shown in Figure 3-12. Notice that it enables a pilot to navigate directly from Ashland to Blosser, Kan., without having to pass over a single VOR.

A fringe benefit of area navigation is that the direct RNAV route is usually shorter than the conventional, dog-legged, VOR-to-VOR route. The course shown, for example, is 22 nm (11½%) shorter. This results in a neat savings in flying time, a factor not to be ignored, especially by those who fly on rented wings or pay for their own fuel.

It all sounds great in theory and works well in practice, too, but the benefit is costly. The average RNAV system sells for more than $3500, plus installation costs. And if you don't already have a DME receiver, joining the march of progress gets to be a fairly expensive affair.

The heart of an RNAV system is an electronic analog computer. By constantly monitoring aircraft position with distance and bearing information from a nearby VORTAC station, it supplies corrections enabling a pilot to maintain a direct, preselected course between any two points. It's as easy as flying the left/right needle to or from a VOR.

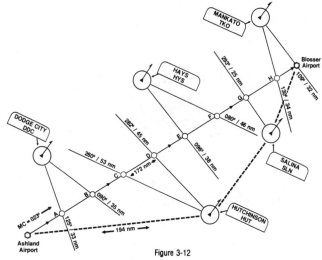

Figure 3-12

There is a prevailing notion that an analog computer can solve problems a mere mortal cannot. This is, of course, sheer fiction. The advantage of the black box is speed. Operating at near the speed of light (186,000 sm per second), it solves in a microsecond what takes you and me much longer. The point is that a pilot can perform the same chores at considerably less expense, something which should be of interest to those who haven't got a few extra "thou" salted away in the cookie jar.

Some benefits of area navigation can be had with an inexpensive plotter, an aeronautical chart, and a flair for something new. The result: area navigation on a shoestring.

The "shoestring" method still requires bearing and distance information from VOR and DME receivers. The major difference is that a warm-blooded computer is substituted for the electron-fed model. A pilot with only a VOR receiver can apply the same principles, but the procedure is so laborious that it is hardly worth the effort.

Assume that Paul P. Pennypincher wants to fly his Firebang Special from Ashland to Blosser. His first step is to plot the direct course and measure its direction, 023° magnetic. He also makes a mental note of which VORTAC stations are within reception range of his proposed routing. They include Dodge City, Hutchinson, Hays, Salina and Mankato.

Step two requires our impoverished pilot to mark off the course line with equally spaced checkpoints. The distance between each checkpoint should be equal to about one-sixth of the aircraft's normal cruising speed. This will provide an enroute position check every 10 minutes. Since Mr. Pennypincher's four-banger chugs along at 120 knots, the course is divided into 20 nm segments. The checkpoints are then labeled with consecutive letters of the alphabet.

Each checkpoint is then defined by its bearing and distance from an approximately abeam VORTAC station. Checkpoint A, for example, is defined by a point on the DDC 125° radial at a distance of 33 nm from the VORTAC.

While it might seem that this preflight planning is elaborate and time consuming, it really is not. My wife, who needs an hour to toast a piece of bread, was able to plot the radials and measure the distances in only four minutes (while the toast burned).

After takeoff, Mr. P. heads his aircraft, N22IOU, toward Blosser using a magnetic heading of 023° (no wind correction). He turns on the VOR receiver, replaces a failed fuse, and tunes in DDC. The course selector is set to 125°, the radial passing through the first checkpoint.

A few minutes later, the needle centers, indicating that Paul is crossing the DDC 125° radial. At that point, he glances at the DME indicator. If it shows 33 nm, then Paul is on course, and no right or left drift has been encountered. If the DME indicates in excess of 33 nm, Paul has drifted right; a DME indication of less than 33 nm indicates a left drift. It's that simple.

Assume that the DME reads 31 nm when crossing the DDC 125° radial, clearly indicating that a right crosswind has blown the aircraft left of course. Without getting involved in plotting drift angles, Paul guesses that a 5° right wind correction angle will get him back on course. His new magnetic heading: 028°.

Preparing for checkpoint "Bravo," Paul rotates the course selector to 090°. When the needle centers several minutes later, the DME indicator shows 35.5 nm. He is a half nm to the right of course and corrects his heading to the left by 2°, a correction based simply on educated guesswork.

To his delight and surprise, Paul crosses checkpoint "Charlie" on course. When crossing the HUT 260° radial, the DME indicator shows 53 nm.

The same techniques are repeated for the duration of the trip. Obviously, minor excursions from the course are bound to occur, but these can be held to a minimum by applying reasonable drift corrections. Even considering the extra mile or two which might be added to the total distance caused by flying a zigzag course, sufficient time and distance are still saved to warrant use of the "shoestring" method.

The accuracy with which any course can be flown depends upon the spacing of checkpoints. When they are established close to one another, say every five or ten nm, maximum course deviation is reduced. If too many checkpoints are used, however, navigation becomes burdensome, leaving little or no time to enjoy the pleasantries of flight.

This technique of comparing actual position with desired position is identical to what the area-nav analog computer does. But instead of making the comparison every 20 nm, the black box does it continuously. As a matter of fact, on any given flight, the computer makes an infinite number of course checks; the results are relayed continuously to the pilot by the indications of a course deviation indicator (left/right needle).

Needless to say, the shoestring method of area nav is not approved for IFR flight. But it can be particularly helpful when flying VFR above a solid cloud layer or when over terrain offering limited topographical checkpoints.

There are two methods of obtaining groundspeed when using the shoestring method. The first and most obvious is not necessarily the most accurate. Figure 3-13 is an exaggeration of the flight segment

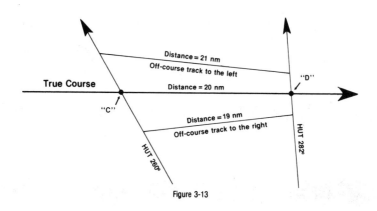

Figure 3-13

between C and D. Notice that if the aircraft tracks left of course, the distance between the HUT 260° and 282° radials is not 20 nm, but slightly greater, say 21 nm. If the aircraft tracks to the right instead of to the left, the distance between these radials may be slightly less than 20 nm, say 19 nm. This error is caused by the fact that the radials cross the true course at an oblique angle, something other than 90°. If a pilot assumes the distance to an off-course position check is 20 nm, (when it is actually more or less) an inaccurate groundspeed computation will result. The most accurate groundspeed check is determined between two checkpoints where there has been no off-course deviation or "zigzagging," or by plotting off-course fixes and measuring the distances between them.

The second method for determining groundspeed is derived from an old formula most of us have either forgotten or never learned: the wingtip bearing formula. It is used normally to determine the distance of an aircraft from a given station by measuring the time required to fly through a given number of degrees of bearing change when groundspeed is known.

The pilot in Figure 3-14, for example, is on a magnetic heading perpendicular to the radial passing through his position. In other words, the aircraft is being flown on a heading of 030° while crossing the 120° radial. The pilot then determines how much time is required to fly through, say, 10° of bearing change. Assume it takes four minutes to fly from the 120° radial to the 110° radial. If the pilot knows his

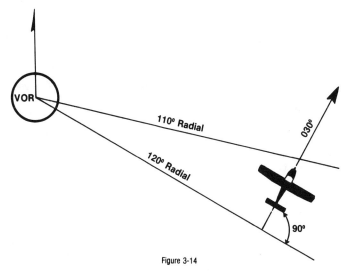

Figure 3-14

groundspeed, say 120 knots, he can determine how far he is from the station using the formula: distance = groundspeed × time ÷ bearing change, which, in this case, is $120 \times 4 \div 10 = 48$ nm.

The shoestring method takes advantage of this formula by first rearranging the terms with a bit of algebraic magic. This may sound a bit deep, but all we're concerned about is arriving at a formula to be used in determining groundspeed instead of distance to the station (which in this case is read from the DME indicator). The new formula is as follows: GS = distance to the station × the number of degrees of bearing change ÷ time.

This formula is especially useful when practicing area navigation, because the aircraft is flown abeam several VOR stations in the course of an average flight, any one of which can be used to obtain wingtip bearings.

Figure 3-15, for example, is the segment of pilot Pennypincher's flight abeam the HUT VOR. He is flying on a magnetic heading of 023°. By subtracting (or adding) 90° from the heading, Paul determines that the HUT 293° radial ($023° - 090° = 293°$) would be useful in determining groundspeed by the wingtip bearing method. When he crosses this radial, he glances at the DME and notes the distance to Hutchinson, 44 nm. Next, he rotates his course selector to 303° and waits for the left/right needle to center once again. When this occurs, he notes that 3:30 has been required to fly through a 10° bearing change. Using the formula, he determines that his groundspeed is equal to the distance (44) × bearing change (10) ÷ time (3.5), which is equal to 126 knots, or 145 mph.

While all of this may sound cumbersome, it is only intended for the purists in the crowd. Others may elect either to measure the distances between visual or radio fixes, or to forget about groundspeed computations entirely.

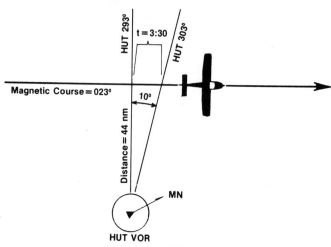

Figure 3-15

Area navigation on a shoestring can be a lot of fun for those who are bored with conventional VOR-to-VOR flight. It is certainly an inexpensive way to become acquainted with a relatively new method of navigation that normally costs much more to enjoy.

THE MAGIC OF INERTIAL NAVIGATION

*There is little to do except monitor
the system and stare at the landscape*

It has been said that "whatever the mind of man can conceive and believe, it can achieve."

If this maxim is applied to navigation, it would seem that we are approaching the zenith. Such is the miracle of inertial navigation.

To say that (inertial navigation system) INS has revolutionized long range navigation is an understatement. Airline pilots routinely use it to fly the world's oceans without needing a computer, a plotter, a pencil and paper or even a chart. A knowledge of navigation isn't even necessary. A reasonably bright office secretary could just as competently use INS to go anywhere in the world. All a pilot needs to know is where he is and where he wants to go.

INS is impractical for light aircraft, at least for now, because of its price—at least $107,000 plus installation. Since the average INS weighs 61 pounds, this places the cost at almost $110 per ounce. For the same money, you can buy a brand new, fully equipped Bonanza. A few hundred bizjet owners, however, have opted for INS for use where navaids are scarce or nonexistent.

Expensive? You bet. But the price is somewhat understandable considering that INS is 30 times as complex and several hundred times as reliable as color television. One manufacturer, however, predicts an eventual INS price tag of only $50,000, but is reluctant to speculate as to when this might come to pass.

One noteworthy installation was made in a Piper Navajo in 1971 by Flying Tiger Line Captain Elgin Long who used INS during his gruelling 28-day, 36,000 sm, solo flight around the world—via both poles—in December of that year.

It is doubtful if many general aviation pilots will have occasion to use INS to span oceans and continents in their light singles or twins, but that doesn't mean you aren't curious to know what makes it tick. In theory, INS is quite simple; in practice, simpler yet.

INS operates on the principle of inertia, a property possessed by every object in the universe. Sir Isaac Newton defined inertia best when he stated that "every object at rest remains at rest and every object in motion remains in motion unless acted upon by an exterior force."

For example, a stationary ball on a table remains at rest until some force moves it. A ball rolling along a frictionless surface continues to roll indefinitely until some force is applied to stop it. In practice, the force of friction (and some air resistance) causes a rolling ball to decelerate and eventually stop.

Since every human being has mass—some of us have a bit too much—and a brain, each of us is a crude inertial navigator operating—in principle—the way INS does.

Assume that a man is sitting blindfolded in the rear seat of a stationary automobile. He is told exactly where he is and in which direction the car is headed. His brain is now "programmed" or "loaded."

The driver starts the engine and accelerates the car to 60 mph. The man's body has mass (inertia), so the acceleration forces his back against the rear seat. Since he can approximately measure this force, he knows that his body has been accelerated to 60 mph. In the meantime, his brain counts the seconds and minutes during which time the driver maintains a constant speed. After thirty minutes, the driver slows to 20 mph, a deceleration detected by the man as his body pitches forward slightly. "Aha," he says, "I have traveled 60 mph for 30 minutes and have therefore traveled 30 miles. Now I am traveling at only 20 mph."

Half an hour later, the car stops. The man concludes that while traveling at 20 mph for 30 minutes, he has traveled an additional 10 miles, or a total of 40 miles. By carefully measuring acceleration and deceleration, the blindfolded passenger has been able to determine his speed at any given time and convert this to distance traveled.

Had the driver changed course at any time, the passenger would have detected the centrifugal force associated with a turn and could have computed the amount of turn and the new direction of travel.

The human brain, however, cannot accurately measure acceleration, keep track of time and account for the myriad of velocity changes that occur during even a short ride. An inertial navigation system does a much better job.

A major advantage of INS is that it is totally self-contained. It operates independently of ground based transmitters, the earth's magnetic field and the positions of celestial bodies. Also, it does not transmit energy as does radar and is totally unaffected by wind, sea and atmospheric conditions.

Since INS is oblivious to exterior sources, it found early military acceptance. An enemy cannot "jam," intercept or detect nonexistent signals to or from an inertially guided device. The Germans made first use of INS in the V-2 missile of World War II fame. When the preset distance had been travelled, the V-2's on-board computer sent a cutout signal to the rocket engine. The missile then fell upon its prey. Admittedly, this system was primitive. Had it been as refined as modern units, the London Blitz would have been considerably more catastrophic.

The heart of INS consists of three extremely sensitive accelerometers that measure acceleration (speed changes) in three planes: fore and aft, right and left, and up and down. These accelerometers make it impossible for any aircraft movement to go undetected.

It is difficult to appreciate the sensitivity of these accelerometers. They can measure any acceleration between .0008 and 10 Gs. Translated, this means that INS can accurately measure the acceleration of an object requiring an hour to accelerate from 0 to 2 knots. At the other extreme, it measures the 10 G acceleration of a missile that accelerates from a standstill to 60 knots in only one-fourth of a second.

All aircraft speed and direction changes—no matter how slight—are fed into the INS computer, which continuously converts this information into track and distance data. The computer knows at all times where it has been, where it is, where it is going and at what speed.

Since INS accelerometers measure speed changes with respect to the earth, they must be kept aligned with the earth's surface. This is accomplished by placing them on a small platform gyroscopically held parallel to the earth's surface in the same manner as an artificial horizon. The result is called an inertial platform but is also referred to as a stable element or "stable table."

INS gyros are so critically balanced that they are assembled under conditions ten times as sterile as a hospital operating room. A fingerprint or a speck of dandruff on a finished gyro can cause sufficient imbalance to render the gyro useless in a guidance system.

Since these gyros keep the platform so perfectly level with earth, they are used also as the reference for the pilot's artificial horizon on the instrument panel. This arrangement provides a considerably more accurate attitude display than the conventional artificial horizon. Conventional gyros provide erroneous attitude displays during turns because of gyroscopic precession. Compensation circuits prevent INS gyros from allowing precession to affect either the inertial platform or the pilot's artificial horizon.

Additionally, attitude data is fed from the inertial platform to the autopilot and used to stabilize the radar antenna on aircraft so equipped.

Operating an INS is only slightly more complicated than using a pushbutton telephone.

When the pilot enters the cockpit, he rotates a knob on the mode selector unit from "off" to "standby." He then informs the INS computer of the latitude and longitude of the aircraft by pushing the appropriate buttons on the keyboard of the control/display unit (CDU). Light-emitting diodes—like those on many pocket-size electronic calculators—illuminate to reveal what the pilot has programmed into the computer. This allows the pilot to doublecheck his entry for a clerical error and, if necessary, cancel his entry and program the computer once again.

It is not enough that a pilot load the INS with the latitude and the longitude of the airport. The computer wants to know where on the airport the aircraft is parked.

The knob on the mode selector unit is then moved from "standby" to "align." At this point, the inertial platform erects itself. Also, since INS senses the earth's rotation, it determines the direction of true north to the nearest tenth of a degree. This information is fed to the directional gyro on the instrument panel. As long as he elects to do so, a pilot can navigate with respect to true north. No longer is he concerned with the magnetic compass. Gone from his vocabulary are the words variation and deviation and those ditties about true virgins and ducks that make vertical turns.

Additionally, since INS senses the earth's rotation, it knows its approximate latitude without being told. (Remember, the speed of the earth's rotation decreases as distance from the equator increases.) If the INS senses a latitude that disagrees with the latitude programmed into the control/display unit, then "tilt!" The computer rejects the location entered by the pilot. In such a case, the pilot has made a boo-boo and he'd better doublecheck his entry.

The INS not only aligns and calibrates itself automatically but, with a seemingly braggadocio flair, also announces how well it has done by displaying a numerical performance index on the control/display unit.

The pilot then loads the computer with the coordinates (latitude and longitude) of each waypoint (if any) over which he intends to fly. Once this is accomplished and the entered coordinates are carefully double-checked, the knob on the mode selector unit is rotated from "align" to "navigate." That's all there is to it. A trans-Atlantic pilot's navigational chores have been completed. There is nothing left to do except allow the INS to inertially guide the aircraft to its destination.

The INS begins to navigate as soon as the aircraft leaves the chocks—literally. To confirm this, the pilot rotates the data selector on the CDU to TK/GS and—lo and behold—the aircraft's taxi speed (in knots) appears in the window as well as the true direction in which the aircraft is moving (to the nearest tenth of a degree). As taxi speed and direction change, so do the illuminated numerals on the CDU. If the data selector is rotated to POS (position), the pilot can observe his constantly changing latitude and longitude as he taxis about the airport. No movement of the aircraft escapes detection by the INS.

After takeoff, the pilot leaves the airport traffic area and intercepts the desired track by flying "to the needle" on a panel-mounted instrument in the same way he would intercept a VOR radial. By simply keeping the needle centered, a pilot knows he is tracking along the great circle route between Honolulu and Tokyo. It's that easy.

Enroute, the pilot can rotate the data selector to obtain a dazzling plethora of information. With the selector set to WIND, for example, the pilot can observe the existing wind velocity to the nearest degree and knot. It's incredible to watch the illuminated numbers flicker from 246°/64 knots to 245°/65 knots to 241°/67 knots, etc. Every change in the wind, no matter how slight, becomes public information. The data is so reliable that pilots are encouraged to make hourly wind reports to ground stations. This information is used to update wind reports and forecasts and assists meteorologists to detect changes in global weather patterns.

When the data selector is set to DIS/TIME, the pilot is told the precise distance and time remaining to any selected waypoint or to the destination. Imagine watching the DIS/TIME change, for example, from 1024nm/211.2 minutes to 1024nm/211.1 minutes to 1023nm/211.0 minutes.

Time to destination, however, must be regarded cautiously because it is based on existing winds, not on the winds to be encountered later in the flight.

Should the pilot elect to deviate from course because of thunderstorms along his route, the data selector is then set to XTK/TKE. The display unit then provides—continuously—the cross-track (off course) distance to the nearest tenth of a mile as well as the track angle error (the number of degrees right or left of course).

While enroute, the INS continuously performs self-tests, and should it become dissatisfied with itself, it flashes a WARNING light on the CDU. The pilot then rotates the data selector to DSRTK/STS. In addition to the desired track, which appears on the left side of the CDU, INS status appears on the right side. The coded numbers appearing there tell the pilot what's wrong with the system, what he can do to improve conditions and to what extent he can rely on the system. INS failures are rare but do occur. This is why TWA, for example, has three INS units aboard each of its Boeing 747s. In case any two units disagree, the third settles the argument.

As the aircraft gets within two minutes of a waypoint, the ALERT light on the CDU illuminates to warn of the impending turn. The INS computer and autopilot cooperate to turn the aircraft prior to the waypoint so as to cause the aircraft to "round the bend" and roll out precisely on the new course line.

Enroute, the pilot can alter course at any time by adding or deleting waypoints. Also, he can change the destination simply by inserting new coordinates. Obediently, the INS will command a turn and fly the aircraft to the alternate airport or waypoint via the great circle route.

There is a disadvantage to INS; it is boring. There is little to do except monitor the system and stare at the landscape.

Pilots occasionally take advantage of the enroute lull in cockpit activity to use the INS computer to plan flights in their privately owned aircraft. Since INS takes only micro-seconds to compute the course and distance between any two points on earth, isn't this more pleasant than plotting and measuring courses on a sectional chart?

During one particular flight, I asked the computer for the course and distance from the equator to the North Pole. I knew, of course, that the true course is 000° and the distance is 5400 nm (90° of latitude × 60 nm per degree = 5400 nm). I was curious to see if INS would agree.

After punching in the equatorial and polar coordinates, the INS display blinked and illuminated the answers: 000°/5409 nm. I was shocked. How could the electronic marvel be so wrong?

An INS engineer explained later that the distance between the equator and the Pole is 5400 nm, but only along the earth's surface. When at 37,000 feet (which is six miles above the earth), the distance from the equator to the Pole is greater by nine nm.

Using INS is a humbling experience.

Enroute, the aircraft may pass over a navaid. The prudent pilot—he never completely trusts any black box—compares the actual position of the aircraft with that advertised by the INS. Should there be a disagreement, the INS can be updated, but this is rarely needed.

Like humans, an inertial navigation system has an appetite. Its diet requires 400 watts of 26v and 115v AC and 27v DC. Should its feeding be interrupted for even a fraction of a second, the computer will lose count and throw a temper tantrum. For this reason, an INS contains its own battery that stands by and takes over automatically in case of an electrical power loss.

At flight's end, the INS computer may disagree with the actual aircraft position by a few miles. It makes you wonder if the airport is really where everyone thinks it is.

At this point, the pilot inserts the actual position into the computer. The INS will digest this error, think about it a while and take out a portion of the error during the next trip. This has the effect of increasing INS accuracy with usage. Other navaids such as VOR, DME, ADF, etc., erode in performance as soon as they're installed in the aircraft.

Considering that INS receives no enroute assistance from ground-based stations, it is very accurate. Tests conducted during 3000 flights and 14,000 hours of flying time reveal that 50% of the time INS errs less than .41 nm per hour of flight. Ninety-five percent of the time, the error is less than 1.4 nm per hour of flight. This means that at the end of a 10 hour flight, an inertially guided aircraft has a 95% chance of being somewhere within 14 nm of its destination.

The weakest link in the INS chain is the pilot who might program the computer with the wrong coordinates. To prevent this possibility, INS manufacturers have designed an INS "card reader." A pre-punched card—similar to cards with prepunched telephone numbers—is inserted into the card reader before flight. Voila! That's it. The INS computer is programmed and, when coupled to the autopilot, will guide the aircraft accurately and automatically to any corner of the world.

If you were to program the computer with the coordinates of heaven, INS probably would guide you there, too.

VLF NAVIGATION

*Long-range characteristics of
frequencies below 30 kHz are bringing global
navigation closer to general aviation*

In the beginning, there were heaven and earth. And fortunately for man (who came later), there was a useful predictability to the apparent motion of the celestial bodies. Thus was born one of the earliest methods of global navigation.

The first popular, electronic method was LORAN, an acronym derived from its formal name. LOng RAnge Navigation. An on-board receiver/processor was used to determine the difference in time between the reception of signals from a pair of station transmitters. The result was a hyperbolically curved line of position (LOP) that had to be plotted on a special chart.

The procedure was then repeated to obtain another curved LOP which resulted in a reasonably accurate fix (usually within 10 nm).

Obtaining such a fix, however, was a time consuming affair, subject to misinterpretation by the pilot/navigator and frequently impossible when needed the most because LORAN signals often did not extend far enough.

The next significant improvement was Doppler navigation, a self-contained radar system which constantly measures groundspeed and drift. Given these variables and some input from the compass, the on-board computer can "reckon" continuously the progress of an aircraft with respect to any chosen course. But Doppler is no more precise than its weakest link, the compass. Magnetic and precessional errors accumulate during flight, resulting in a loss of system accuracy.

Then came the magic of the inertial navigation system (INS), a marvelous collection of accelerometers, gyros and other electronic wizardry which brilliantly measures every change in aircraft speed and direction. An on-board computer digests these changes to keep track very accurately of enroute progress.

INS may be the ultimate navigation system—if you can afford it.

Prices range from $107,000 to $112,000 *plus* an expensive installation *plus* maintenance which averages almost $4 per hour per unit.

But a recent newcomer, VLF navigation, is arousing considerable interest in general aviation circles. It is much less expensive than INS (prices begin at $26,500), does not accumulate errors enroute (and is, therefore, often more accurate than INS), requires little more maintenance than a transistor radio, and at least one model (the GNS-500A) is approved for IFR, enroute navigation (on or off airways).

VLF navigation utilizes very low frequency radio signals in the 3 to 30 kHz band. The advantage of such low frequencies is that they closely follow the earth's surface for vast distances (depending on the amount of radiated power). A receiver situated in a Pennsylvania valley can easily receive signals originating in Norway, for example. VLF reception is not subject to line-of-sight limitations as is VHF (30–300 MHz).

VLF navigation is based on "phase measurement," a principle not difficult to understand so long as some simplification is allowed.

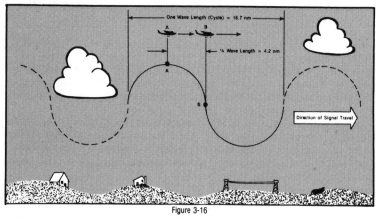

Figure 3-16

Figure 3-16 shows a 10 kHz (10,000 cycles per second) VLF radio wave traveling from left to right. Each complete wave (the solid line) is one cycle. Frequency, by definition, is the number of these cycles produced in one second. Since radio waves are known to travel at a constant 166,925 nm/second, it is easy to determine the precise length of a complete cycle. In other words, if the speed of radio wave transmission (166,925 nm/second) is divided by the frequency (10,000 cycles/second), the result is the precise length of each cycle (or wave) which, in this case, is 16.7 nm.

Now assume that at the beginning of flight, the aircraft is at point A in the diagram. The pilot turns on the VLF navigation system and, by punching the appropriate buttons, informs the computer of his known location (using longitude and latitude). In the meantime, the system very carefully measures the *phase* of the signal being received. In other words, the system determines precisely where along the wave the aircraft is situated. A minute later, the system determines that the aircraft has moved to a different phase of the cycle (point B) and knows, therefore, precisely how far the aircraft has moved either toward or away from the transmitter.

In the example, the aircraft has flown along one-fourth of a wave length and has traveled, therefore, one-fourth of 16.7 nm, or 4.2 nm away from the transmitter. This provides one circular line of position. Simultaneously, the system "phase measures" the waves from one or more additional transmitters to obtain a fix.

In reality, this process takes place constantly, thus providing a continuous, digital display of aircraft position. And by measuring the rate at which position changes, the system computer also provides instantaneous groundspeed as well as a plethora of other navigational data (described later).

One weakness of the system is its inability to determine position from scratch. To provide meaningful information, the system must be told (via push-buttons) of its starting position and be allowed to monitor aircraft progress from that point. In this respect, VLF and INS are similar.

Anyone who knows much about radio wave propagation realizes VLF signals travel between the earth's surface and the ionosphere, one of the atmosphere's numerous upper layers. And since the height of the electrically charged ionosphere is constantly changing from day to night and with the seasons, this has an effect on the *apparent speed* at which radio waves travel. This phenomenon is called the "diurnal shift" and requires compensation by the VLF system. Otherwise, unacceptable errors would accumulate.

For this reason, the pilot must tell the VLF computer (at the beginning of flight) the time of day (GMT) and date. The computer, which has been programmed with an accurate "picture" of the very predictable diurnal shift, can then correct all incoming signals to eliminate errors caused by the varying height of the ionosphere.

Figure 3-17, for example, shows an aircraft flying over Southern Nevada in the late afternoon. The airborne VLF system is receiving and processing VLF signals from Hawaii, the state of Washington, Norway and Panama. Since the computer knows the time of day, the date and the precise location of each transmitter, it corrects each incoming signal for the varying effect of the ionosphere. The Norwegian signal, for example, travels over a portion of the earth that is predominantly dark (a lowered ionosphere), whereas the Hawaiian signal travels (at this time) along a path of daylight (a raised ionosphere). The computer corrects these and all other incoming signals to a common denominator so that the apparent speed of them all is identical.

A few years ago, such a "diurnal computation" would have required a computer the size of a small house; today, that same function is completed by microcircuitry which can be held effortlessly with your fingertips.

The signals used in VLF navigation originate from two independent, global transmission networks. The first consists of nine communications stations (most of which are operated by the U.S. Navy) for the purpose of maintaining worldwide fleet communications. Each transmitter has an assigned frequency between 14 and 24 kHz and is extremely

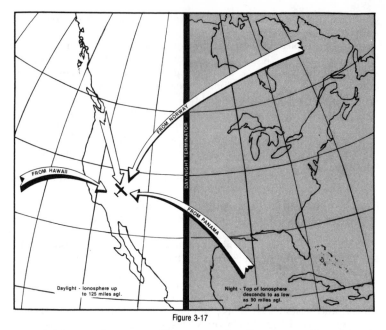

Daylight - Ionosphere up
to 125 miles agl.

Night - Top of Ionosphere
descends to as low
as 90 miles agl.

FROM NORWAY
FROM HAWAII
FROM PANAMA
DAY-NIGHT TERMINATOR

Figure 3-17

powerful (as much as one million watts of radiated power) resulting in reception ranges of more than 10,000 nm.

And since VLF navigation systems are not equipped with audio circuitry to allow eavesdropping on military communications, the Navy does not object to the use of its transmissions by civilian users. (There was some controversy about this some years ago, but that problem was resolved.)

The second VLF network consists of eight Omega Navigation transmitters operated and maintained by the U.S. Coast Guard. Originally, this system of long range navigation was developed for surface vessels and submarines, but the development of lightweight, digital computers allows the use of Omega in aerial navigation.

To the pilot using VLF navigation, there is essentially no difference between the nine communications stations and the eight Omega stations. As far as he is concerned, there is a total of 17 VLF transmitters spread around the world, any combination of which can be used for navigation.

The beauty of VLF is that the pilot is not required to tune and/or identify any of the stations. It's all done automatically when the system is activated. The GNS-500A (manufactured by Global Navigation), for example, continuously monitors all 17 stations and selects the eight most suitable signals for navigation. Every ten seconds, the system reviews the quality of all incoming signals and makes the appropriate substitutions whenever necessary, even when one of the stations being used suddenly goes off the air.

The pilot, however, is unaware of this internal search for perfection. If he desires, he can query the computer as to which stations are being received and the reception quality of each. Obediently, the coded answers will be displayed digitally on the control/display unit (CDU).

Although it might be disconcerting to know that the closest station being used for navigation may be several thousand miles away, this need not be so. The proximity of an aircraft to a VLF transmitter has no effect on system accuracy.

VLF is not without its Achilles heel: solar flares, for example. These eruptions on the surface of the sun raise havoc with VLF signals and can be responsible for errors of up to five miles. Fortunately, however, these infrequent disturbances last for only a few minutes at a time.

Otherwise, system accuracy is nothing less than fantastic. Typically, VLF errors are measured in fractions of a mile. When the FAA flew a Global GNS-500A for purposes of bestowing an STC on the installation, the error at the end of a two-hour flight was .1 nm. An Air Force VC-135, equipped with every modern form of electronic, long range navigation equipment ran extensive tests of VLF and found system errors to average .7 nm, as well as or slightly better than INS. A virtue of VLF worth repeating is that errors do not accumulate during a long flight as they do with Doppler or INS.

The CDU is the business end of a VLF system and is similar in appearance and operation to that of INS.

After the pilot turns on the system, he prepares for flight by inserting present position, time and date into the computer. If the proper keyboard buttons have been pushed, the CDU will acknowledge its readiness for flight.

The system can then be loaded with up to ten enroute waypoints to define the planned flight, or this procedure can be delayed until after departure. Like INS, VLF requires little navigational knowledge or talent to be a system "programmer."

Once underway, present position is constantly shown in the left (latitude) and right (longitude) data displays. Or if he desires, the pilot can rotate the display selector switch to obtain waypoint displays, time and distance to any selected waypoint (based on existing wind), drift angle, groundspeed, actual track, desired course, distance off course, parallel tracks, and actual wind. Virtually every navigational chore is possible.

And when the pilot gets lonely, he can even have a limited enroute conversation with the computer (really!) to obtain a phenomenal amount of data (including the direct distance between any two points on earth).

At this point, it is important to differentiate between the two types of VLF systems presently available. One type receives both the Navy's communication stations and the Coast Guard's Omega network. The other receives only Omega signals.

The combination systems (referred to as VLF/Omega) offer the greatest geographic coverage. Since 17 stations blanket the earth with VLF signals, navigational capability is virtually assured anywhere in the world.

This is not necessarily true of the pure Omega systems that rely on fewer, relatively low powered, transmitters (only 10,000 watts), each of which is scheduled for a maintenance shutdown during a specific month of the year. During July of every year, for example, when the Omega station in Norway is taken off the air, total North Atlantic coverage is questionable. But even when all eight Omega stations are on-line, there remain several large, remote areas of the world that lack adequate coverage.

The Navy's communications stations have a staggered maintenance schedule with each station going off the air several hours a week, but the loss of one such station rarely has an adverse effect on VLF/Omega navigation. (The remaining stations still offer a sufficient overlap of VLF coverage.)

Temporary loss of adequate signal coverage is not a serious problem, however; VLF systems will automatically dead reckon (based on last known wind) until signal acquisition is resumed.

Why, then, have the airlines replaced their LORAN units with only Omega instead of VLF/Omega? Simple. It's a matter of money. Since VLF has yet to be approved as a means of *primary* oceanic navigation for the carriers, this chore must be accomplished by something that has been approved, namely Doppler or INS. The Omega systems are being purchased only to replace the aging LORAN as a means of providing an occasional fix to cross-check Doppler accuracy.

Once VLF is approved as a primary method of air carrier navigation (and it soon will be), there is little doubt that many airlines will convert totally to VLF/Omega and/or INS.

In the meantime, if a general aviation operator has to choose between VLF/Omega and pure Omega, it would appear that VLF/Omega is the best choice even though—on the average—it is a bit more costly. The expanded, redundant coverage makes it a better buy.

After being exposed to VLF (or INS), it is difficult to imagine a better method of long-range navigation. (Where have we heard that before?)

But you don't have to exercise your imagination; the Department of Defense is already developing its futuristic global positioning system (GPS). Nicknamed "Navstar," this system will incorporate 24 earth orbiting satellites to provide horizontal *and* vertical positioning information to within ten meters (33 feet) anywhere on earth. In other words, Navstar will not only tell you whose house you're in, but also what floor you're on with more accuracy than most barometric altimeters.

Although the initial purpose of Navstar is to guide weapons delivery systems, there is little doubt that civilian applications will evolve. With the degree of accuracy expected from Navstar, the system could be used to establish a Category I ILS approach to every runway in the world without the need for expensive ground facilities.

Eventually, according to some experts, a soldier in the field (or a general aviation pilot) may be equipped with a GPS receiver similar in appearance to a pocket calculator. All he'd have to do is flip the switch and watch the LEDs advertise his precise location and elevation—to within 33 feet.

Now that, my friends, will be the ultimate navigation system (until something better comes along).

FLYING THE ILS

*The thinking man's approach
to the perfect approach*

Believe it or not, there is quite a similarity between romancing and the ILS approach. Not only can each be performed with mechanical movements learned by rote, but experience teaches that—in both cases—the most successful are those who have learned to execute these procedures with finesse and a certain delicate touch.

Most ILS novitiates attempt to keep the cross pointers centered by applying techniques learned while chasing VOR needles on cross-country flights. Although the localizer and glideslope are similar in principle to VOR radials, they are considerably more sensitive and demand a refined mental attitude. The large corrections used during VOR navigation cannot be tolerated during an ILS approach.

To appreciate the sensitivity of a localizer needle, consider, for example, that a VOR radial has an effective width of 20°. In other words, a pilot must displace the aircraft 10° either side of a selected radial to cause the course deviation indicator (CDI) to deflect fully.

The average localizer, on the other hand, has a width of only 4°. A displacement of only 2° from the centerline results in maximum CDI deflection. In other words, the localizer is five times as sensitive as a VOR radial at any given distance from the transmitter. (It is interesting to note that localizer course widths vary from 3° to 6°. Each is tailored so as to be 700 feet wide at the runway threshold. And since a localizer transmitter is usually just beyond the rollout end of its associated runway, it is obvious that short runways have relatively wide localizers and long runways relatively narrow ones.)

An appreciation of localizer sensitivity combined with the following suggestions can considerably improve a pilot's ability to execute an ILS approach to minimums.

Table 4-A demonstrates why localizer corrections must be so minimal. When tracking a 4° wide localizer, for example, at a distance of only one nm from the runway threshold, the chart shows that when the needle is deflected one-quarter scale, the aircraft is only 141 feet from being precisely on course.

Localizer Needle Deflection	At the Runway Threshold	Distance from Runway Threshold					
		¼ nm	½ nm	¾ nm	1 nm	2 nm	3 nm
¼-Scale Deflection	88 ft	101 ft	114 ft	127 ft	141 ft	194 ft	247 ft
½-Scale Deflection	175 ft	202 ft	228 ft	255 ft	281 ft	387 ft	493 ft
¾-Scale Deflection	263 ft	302 ft	342 ft	382 ft	422 ft	581 ft	740 ft
Full Deflection	350 ft	403 ft	456 ft	509 ft	562 ft	775 ft	987 ft
Localizer Width	700 ft	806 ft	912 ft	1,018 ft	1,125 ft	1,549 ft	1,974 ft

To find the *distance of the aircraft from the center of the localizer*, enter table with amount of needle deflection and distance of aircraft from runway threshold. (Note: This table is based on a 4°-wide localizer.)

Table 4-A

Unfortunately, to a pilot accustomed to VOR flying, a quarter-scale deflection seems like quite a bit. When between VORTAC stations, a return to course might require a 10° correction (or more) to be held for several minutes. This previous experience with the CDI has an adverse effect on the pilot because it creates the tendency to make similar large corrections when tracking an ILS.

The same correction (10°) applied to a localizer when only 141 feet off course results in such a rapid return to the centerline that over-shooting the localizer is almost impossible to avoid.

With respect to a localizer (and not a VOR radial), a quarter-scale deflection is not that big a deal. When 141 feet off course, the aircraft is only 41 feet from being lined up with the average, 200-foot-wide runway.

Putting this in proper perspective, consider how small a correction would be required when 141 feet from the extended runway centerline during a VFR, straight-in approach. Very little. The heading change would be barely noticeable. Quite obviously, the same minor correction should be made during an actual ILS approach.

This, then, is what is meant by the need to adopt the proper mental attitude. Heading changes during an ILS approach should only be a small fraction of what is normally required to center an equally displaced needle when tracking a VOR radial.

Most pilots who have difficulty keeping the localizer needle within reasonable limits are usually guilty of chasing the needle. They have not learned that the secret of a successful ILS approach is the result of logical, minimal, predetermined heading changes.

For example, assume that a pilot is intercepting the localizer. He rolls out on the ILS heading just as the needle centers in the "bull's-eye." The published magnetic course of the ILS becomes what is called the temporary "reference heading" which, in this case, shall be 095°.

Under no-wind conditions and with an error-free directional gyro, this heading theoretically would lead the aircraft precisely along the localizer. Of course, such is rarely the case.

Expecting some drift, the pilot pays careful attention to needle behavior, while flying the reference with flawless determination. *He knows that an inadvertent heading change causes the LOC needle to move and leads to the false impression that wind drift is the responsible culprit.* An accurate "picture" of the wind cannot be drawn unless the reference heading is precisely maintained.

The heading is 095° and the needle slowly moves left. There are two possible reasons for this: a left crosswind or an improperly set directional gyro (or a combination of both). But this pilot is sharp. Once on the localizer, he knows that to subsequently reset the DG can only interfere with his plans to execute the perfect ILS approach. Once the DG has been synchronized with the compass, prior to localizer intercept, he will assume that *all needle movement* is caused either by *wind drift* or *heading change*.

As the needle moves left, the pilot rolls into a shallow banked turn toward the needle. His immediate intention is not to center the needle, but simply to stop it dead in its tracks.

After 5° of turn, in this case, the needle stops and the pilot rolls the wings level. He precisely maintains the new heading (090°) and again begins his vigil of the vertical needle. If the needle remains in its displaced position, the pilot knows that this new heading (090°) is causing the aircraft to essentially "parallel" the localizer. He knows also that whatever heading "parallels" the localizer also can be used to track the localizer when the needle is centered later. This new heading (090°) becomes the revised "reference heading" and quite accurately compensates (within a degree or two) for any prevailing wind and/or any discrepancy between compass and DG.

If the needle continues to move, however, it is at a much reduced rate and the pilot can make whatever smaller correction is necessary to stop needle movement. The end result becomes the new "reference heading."

Since it is his desire to center the needle, the pilot turns farther left to a heading of 085°. Obligingly, the needle moves towards the bull's-eye. As the needle centers, does this pilot have to guess at what heading shall be required to track inbound? Of course not. He turns to the reference heading (090°) and smugly observes the captured localizer. He is now ready to intercept the glideslope and continue with this, the thinking man's approach.

This two-step maneuver of (1) turning to stop needle movement and then (2) turning farther to intercept the localizer can be accomplished by a savvy pilot in one smooth move. He turns toward the digressing needle and simply notes the reference heading at that point during the turn when the needle comes to a halt. But the turn continues briefly and without interruption to reverse needle movement. When the needle returns to the bull's eye, a turn is made to the reference heading noted during the initial turn.

As the descent begins, no one can be so naïve as to believe that wind drift will not change. We can count on it. The point is this—unless a strong wind shift (or shear) exists between the ground and 1,500 feet agl, drift change will be gradual. As the localizer needle begins to react accordingly, a pilot must similarly turn to stop the needle and establish a new reference heading, one that can be used until conditions again require a change. The idea is to fly logical headings, based on observations of needle behavior, and not to take arbitrary, random swipes at the localizer.

As the aircraft descends on the glideslope, it also gets closer to the localizer transmitter which further increases needle sensitivity. Although the same techniques are used when the localizer moves off center, heading changes must be proportionately smaller. A 2° heading change near minimums, for example, has about the same effect on needle movement as a 6° "bite" when near the outer marker.

As the aircraft approaches the decision height (DH), it becomes increasingly more important to fly a specified heading and to not chase the needle. The most urgent requirement is that the needles not be in motion because this indicates cross-tracking and is usually more responsible for missed approaches than arriving at minimums with slightly offset, yet motionless needles.

If the localizer is slightly left or right (and motionless), it is better to accept being a few feet off course than to risk initiating a cross-track correction that could result in a larger needle displacement in the opposite direction. In other words, don't be so precise that a slight needle deflection cannot be tolerated (unless you can make exacting 1° or 2° turns or are below the glideslope). The obsession to exactly center the needles can blow an approach. (This applies, of course, to Category I approaches only; the lower minimums associated with Category II approaches do require substantially more precision *and* equipment.)

The glideslope is another breed of cat, similar to the localizer but even more sensitive. It has an effective width of only 1.4°. In other words, a vertical deviation of only seven-tenths of one degree fully deflects the horizontal indicator.

Glideslope Needle Deflection	Distance from Runway Touchdown Zone					
	¼ nm	½ nm	¾ nm	1 nm	1½ nm	2 nm
¼-Scale Deflection	5 ft	9 ft	14 ft	19 ft	28 ft	37 ft
½-Scale Deflection	9 ft	19 ft	28 ft	37 ft	56 ft	74 ft
¾-Scale Deflection	14 ft	28 ft	42 ft	56 ft	84 ft	111 ft
Full Deflection	19 ft	37 ft	56 ft	74 ft	111 ft	149 ft
Glideslope Thickness	37 ft	74 ft	111 ft	149 ft	223 ft	297 ft

To find the *distance of the aircraft above or below the glideslope*, enter table with amount of needle deflection and distance of aircraft from runway touchdown zone (not runway threshold).

Table 4-B

Table 4-B graphically displays glideslope sensitivity. When 2 nm from the runway touchdown zone, for example, a needle deflected half-scale indicates that the aircraft is only 74 feet above or below the glideslope. When only one-half mile from the touchdown zone, the same needle deflection translates to only a 19 foot deviation from perfection.

To put it another way, the glideslope is 14 times as sensitive as a VOR needle and three times as sensitive as the localizer at equal distances from the station transmitters. Or consider this—when tracking a glideslope one mile from the touchdown zone, the needle has the same sensitivity as when tracking a VOR radial when only seven one-hundreds of a nautical mile from the VORTAC transmitter (if that's possible).

Such sensitivity requires thinking about the controls (or perhaps breathing on them) more than it does moving them. Tracking this ILS beam also requires the proper mental attitude.

Instead of requiring a reference heading (as does the localizer), the glideslope *demands* a reference sink rate. The vertical speed indicator (VSI) is often ignored, but is the magical key required to unlock the airport when ceiling and visibility conspire against you.

Prior to glideslope intercept, determine from the approach plate the recommended sink rate required to slide down the glideslope at the groundspeed anticipated during the approach. Table 4-C shows, for example, that a 4° glideslope (the steepest in the U.S. is actually 3.9°) requires a 709 fpm sink rate when groundspeed is 100 knots.

Usually, however, you can predict the required sink rate without referring to any table. Since most glideslopes are on the order of 2¾° to 3°, this handy rule-of-thumb can be used: "Cut the approach groundspeed (knots) in half and add a zero." When using a 3° glideslope with a groundspeed of 80 knots, for example, sink rate should be approximately 400 fpm. Table 4-C indicates a required sink rate of 425 fpm, but there aren't many pilots who can control a VSI quite that precisely.

| | Glideslope Angle | | | | |
Ground Speed	2°	2½°	3°	3½°	4°
60 knots	212	265	319	372	425
70 knots	248	310	372	434	496
80 knots	283	354	425	496	567
90 knots	318	398	478	558	638
100 knots	354	442	531	620	709
110 knots	389	487	584	682	779
120 knots	425	531	637	744	850

To find the *recommended sink rate (fpm)*, enter table with anticipated ground speed and glideslope angle (from approach plate).

Table 4-C

As the glideslope is intercepted, immediately establish and attempt to maintain the recommended sink rate. If this is done correctly *and* if groundspeed remains constant, the glideslope needle will require no further attention. But this happens only in textbooks; the glideslope undoubtedly will move off center.

Quite obviously, variations in sink rate are required to arrest a displaced glideslope needle, but it is the method and amount of correction that require emphasis.

What is about to be said is certain to raise eyebrows and attract scowls from the purists, but the best and easiest way to recapture a displaced glideslope needle is to simply apply the appropriate elevator pressure without regard to airspeed and power. Allow airspeed to vary (within reason) and to hell with power adjustments—why complicate the issue by trying to rub your tummy and the top of your head simultaneously.

Simply nudge the yoke and adjust sink rate slightly. (Do, however, keep a ready hand on the throttle in case airspeed starts to get out of hand. Unless a wind shear is present, however, airspeed usually takes care of itself rather nicely.)

The required sink rate adjustment rarely exceeds 200 fpm. So, if a 500 fpm sink rate is being used and the glideslope needle begins to rise, change the sink rate to 300 fpm and watch needle behavior. Usually, it will return toward the bull's-eye at which time the original 500 fpm sink rate (or slightly less) should be resumed.

If the needle stops or only slows a little, then reduce sink rate an additional 100 fpm. Very little change in sink rate is usually all that's necessary to recapture the glideslope. Just tickle the yoke; don't horse around with it.

Unless the glideslope needle is fully deflected upwards, don't reduce the sink rate to zero. Such an abrupt change requires subsequent abruptness (and sloppy technique) to prevent the needle from dropping rapidly toward the bottom of the instrument.

Unless wind conditions change dramatically and unless an aircraft is dangerously below the glideslope, varying sink rate by more than 200 fpm is rarely necessary.

To appreciate the finesse required to do this properly, concentrate on varying sink rate by increments of 100 or 200 fpm during a visual, straight-in approach. Learn how little control movement is required. Observe also, during a visual approach, how little the elevator is used to remain "in the (visual) slot." It's no different when the aircraft is engulfed in cloud and the glideslope is being used for descent.

So you see, flying the cross-pointers is sort of like romance. Both require the proper mental attitude, a soft touch and the ability to put it all together (meaning the localizer, the glideslope and the instrument bull's-eye, of course).

THE PRECISION OF NON-PRECISION APPROACHES

*The painless way to do without
the crutch of ILS crosspointers*

There is a strange misnomer in IFR flying called the "non-precision approach." The terms seems to suggest that there's something sloppy about an IFR approach which doesn't incorporate an electronic glide-slope.

In practice, the opposite is true. The non-precision approach is often more demanding and requires more precision and technique than the ILS or so-called precision approach.

Accident statistics seem to bear this out. Considerably more fatalities result from non-precision approaches than from ILS approaches. This is not because the VOR, ADF or LOC approach is inherently more dangerous than the ILS. Every IFR approach—irrespective of the type navaid used—is a safe procedure as long as the pilot is capable of complying with the dictates of the approach plate.

The non-precision approach is the most difficult because it requires a pilot to devise his own glideslope and use judgement to establish a visual slot, techniques requiring more skill and IFR discipline than chasing perpendicular needles. Time and again, I have observed professional pilots shooting near-perfect ILS approaches only to find that these same pilots invariably have more difficulty with VOR approaches, for example.

The reasons for this are numerous and lead to the purpose of this article—to offer suggestions that can simplify the demands of a non-precision approach.

Pre-solo pilots are taught that good landings result from good approaches. So it is that the quality of an IFR approach is related to the time spent on planning for the procedure, an activity best performed while enroute to the destination airport.

After reviewing and becoming familiar with the approach plate, check for notations warning of unusual conditions. Often, these notes go unnoticed.

The Detroit (Metro Wayne) VOR Runway 9 approach plate, for example, contains this interesting caution: "Brightly lighted street in town 1½ nm short of runway may easily be confused for Runway 9." An often overlooked notation on the Hayward (Calif.) VOR-A plate says, "Final approach course aligned 1,150 feet left of approach end Rwy 28L." And finally, this word of caution from the Santa Ynez (Calif.) VOR-A plate: "Turbulence and downdrafts in vicinity of GVO VOR."

Searching for and studying such notes can eliminate undesirable and dangerous surprises during an IFR approach.

The mental gymnastics of computing the time required to fly from the final approach fix (FAF) to the missed approach point (MAP) should also be accomplished while enroute. Unfortunately, this chore is usually left until the last minute, a practice which can result in dangerous error.

Assume, for example, that a pilot is preparing to shoot a VOR Runway 8 approach to Albuquerque (Figure 4-1). He quickly scans the

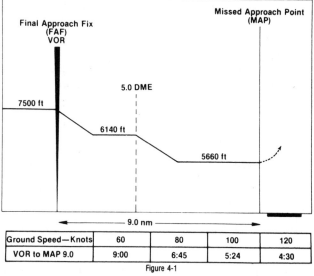

Ground Speed—Knots	60	80	100	120
VOR to MAP 9.0	9:00	6:45	5:24	4:30

Figure 4-1

bottom of the plate and notes 6 minutes and 45 seconds are required to fly from the VOR to the missed approach point (based on an approach speed of 80 knots). Sounds simple enough, but such simplicity incorporates considerable error.

This approach calls for passing over the VOR at 7,500 feet and descending to an MDA of 5,660 feet, which means the average altitude during the approach is roughly 6,500 feet. A quick spin of the computer reveals that 80 knots of indicated airspeed is equivalent to a true airspeed of more than 90 knots.

Now consider that even though the wind at the surface may be calm, the wind over the VOR could be a westerly tailwind of 10 or 20 knots which increases groundspeed to more than 100 knots.

It is the groundspeed, not the indicated approach speed, that must be used to enter the "time to MAP" table at the bottom of the plate. At 100 knots groundspeed, the time required to fly the 9 nm final approach course is 5:24 not 6:45 as calculated earlier. Without realizing it, the pilot in this example would fly beyond the missed approach point for almost a minute and a half, a potentially lethal error.

Conversely, failure to consider the effects of a headwind could result in flying an abbreviated final approach course. During conditions of minimum visibility, this would require having to execute a pullup before getting close enough to the airport to establish visual contact.

Assume that a pilot considers all factors and determines his average groundspeed on final will be 73 knots. After consulting the table, he determines it is necessary to interpolate between 60 knots (9:00) and 80 knots (6:45). The actual time required, therefore, is 7:32, a number easier to determine in your living room than while flying solo in the clouds.

Fortunately, there is a clever way to eliminate the need for laborious interpolation. In this case, for example, simply increase approach speed by seven knots to arrive at a planned groundspeed of 80 knots and read the time required directly from the table. Adjusting approach speed is simpler than juggling numbers and prevents mathematical errors from ruining an otherwise good approach.

With respect to timing the final approach course, do not use a conventional clock with a sweep-second hand because this adds unnecessary hardship.

Assume, for example, that the clock indicates 12:57:33 when passing over the VOR at the beginning of a 6:46 final approach course. Quickly now, at what time should the pullup be executed? The answer is 1:04: 19. But a pilot should not be bothered with such exercises during this critical phase of an IFR approach. Instead, use a stopwatch and fly the approach until the watch indicates 6:46.

There's an even simpler method to use, a technique which doesn't require having to remember the specific time required to fly from the FAF to the MAP. While enroute, substract the determined time (6:46) from ten minutes which results in 3:14. Then start the stopwatch and hit the stop button at precisely 3:14. When over the final approach fix, start timing again. When the missed approach point is reached 6 minutes and 46 seconds later, the stopwatch will indicate ten minutes.

If such a technique is employed prior to every timed approach, the stopwatch will always indicate ten minutes when the missed approach point is reached. This relieves the pilot of having to remember a specific time interval, one that varies from one approach to another. The effect is that of reducing all timed approaches to a common denominator. It would be marvelous if some manufacturer would develop a "backwards" stopwatch so the MAP is always at zero, for instance.

Another number that is often hard to keep in mind is the minimum descent altitude (MDA). It is usually an odd figure such as 1,620 feet or 770 feet. And since it is often necessary to fly low and slow at this altitude for up to several minutes, it is a number that is vital to a pilot's health and well-being. But there's no need to commit this number to memory either.

Before your next IFR flight, visit a stationery store and buy a box of small, red, self-adhesive arrows. Prior to an IFR approach, peel off the protective backing from one of these markers. Then place the arrow on your altimeter so that it points directly at the MDA. With this simple act, you've eliminated something else to remember. (And don't worry about removing these markers; they peel off easily.)

This technique is used by virtually every air carrier pilot. But instead of using stickers, he uses a mechanical "bug" built in to his altimeter. Frankly, I don't understand why every IFR aircraft doesn't have an altimeter (and airspeed indicator) with these extremely helpful devices.

By employing these suggestions, a pilot is relieved of having to memorize a string of unrelated numbers and is less encumbered during final approach. His mind is free to concentrate on the demands of his instruments.

There is another item to be covered during the planning stage. Glance at the circling MDA even when planning to execute a straight-in approach. Occasionally, the circling MDA is the same as the straight-in MDA. When such is the case, a pilot who establishes visual contact with the runway from too high an altitude to land straight-in has the option to circle and land (should he so desire).

Conversely, if the circling MDA is higher than the straight-in MDA, a pilot has no such option when flying at the lower minimum descent altitude.

But here's a tip. Assume that the straight-in MDA is 500 feet and the circling MDA is 600 feet. A pilot makes a straight-in approach and descends to 500 feet. He spots the airport, but is too high to land straight-in. He is also 100 feet below circling minimums. Is a missed approach necessary? Perhaps not. If the pilot can climb to the higher, circling MDA *prior* to reaching the missed approach point and can *still see the airport* at this higher altitude, he is then in a legal and safe position from which to commence a circling approach.

Fortunately, most of the preceding considerations are unnecessary during an ILS approach; the glideslope needle solves many of the problems associated with non-precision approaches, but not always.

Should a pilot encounter a glideslope failure (either the transmitter or receiver), he is suddenly compelled to either abandon the ILS or continue by executing a non-precision LOC approach. The latter, of course, requires preparation. It is extremely difficult to convert from a precision to a non-precision approach without first having become familiar with the MDA and the time required to fly from the outer marker to the missed approach point.

The prepared pilot will, prior to executing an ILS, become acquainted with the "glideslope out" requirements and begin timing his approach when passing the outer marker—just in case.

It should be obvious by now that the success or failure of a non-precision approach often hinges on the quality of preparation.

When approaching the final approach fix, airspeed, altitude and heading should be stabilized. The pilot should spend a moment reviewing what must be done once the FAF is crossed for this is probably the busiest portion of an IFR approach. To simplify a pilot's workload at this point, a system of five Ts has been developed. Each "T" represents a required action.

(1) Time. Begin timing the final approach segment when directly above the final approach fix. This step comes first because timing must commence at the FAF and no later.

(2) Turn. Turn the aircraft to the new course (if a dog-leg turn is required at the FAF). This must be done as soon as possible to remain within the obstruction-free approach corridor.

(3) Tuck. This is a cute term used to describe the beginning of descent. It is not mandatory that the descent begin precisely upon passing the FAF, but it is in a pilot's best interest to descend rapidly to the MDA (or to an intervening altitude) for reasons explaned later.

(4) Twist. Twist or rotate the course selector to the desired radial and make whatever final corrections are necessary to bracket and track the final approach course.

(5) Talk. This has the least priority because communicating with a tower controller has little to do with a successful IFR approach. Although approach control will usually ask a pilot to contact the tower when passing the FAF, don't be intimidated into conversation before the first four of the five "Ts" have been attended to. FAA should revise its procedures so that—during IFR conditions—approach control can issue landing clearance to a pilot before he reaches the final approach fix. The final moments of an IFR approach are not the time for talking.

Once the tower is contacted, however, always ask for the latest altimeter setting because this can be significantly different from the setting obtained earlier from ATC or an outdated ATIS broadcast. Remember, each error of .01 inches represents ten feet on the altimeter.

A pilot who can remember his five "Ts" (time, turn, tuck, twist and talk) has an organized method of getting lots done in minimal time. The system also helps to prevent forgetting an important step.

The method of descending to MDA is a source of controversy. Many pilots descend so as to reach the MDA just prior to the missed approach point. This results in a relaxed, gradual descent, but is illogical during minimal weather conditions.

Figure 4-2 is the profile view of a typical VOR approach. The pilot must pass over the VOR at 2,000 feet and then descend to a 600 foot MDA. The distance between the VOR and the missed approach point is six nm which, at a groundspeed of 90 knots, for example, requires four minutes.

Quite obviously, if the pilot breaks out of the 600 foot overcast immediately prior to reaching the missed approach point, he will be too high to continue and be forced to execute a pullup.

Proper planning dictates that a pilot level off at the MDA *prior* to intercepting a 3° approach slot (the dotted line in the diagram) from which point a normal, visual descent to the runway can be executed.

The problem, therefore, is to determine how soon one must arrive at the MDA in order to intercept such a slot. The solution is not difficult.

A 3° slot simply means descending 300 feet during every nautical mile of flight. To be in a normal visual slot when approaching the

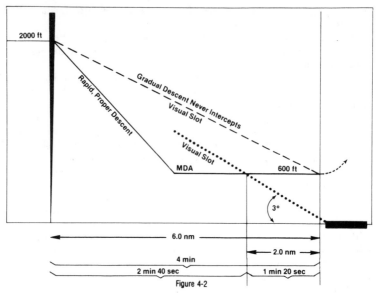

Figure 4-2

example airport, therefore, it is necessary to level off at the 600 foot
MDA when at least two nm before the MAP.

At a groundspeed of 90 knots, two nm requires a flying time of 80
seconds. This means that it is necessary to arrive at the MDA, in this
case, at least 80 seconds (1:20) prior to reaching the missed approach
point. Since it will take 4:00 to fly from the FAF to the MAP, a pilot
should plan to be at the MDA at least 2:40 (4:00 − 1:20) after passing
the final approach fix.

The suggestions offered here cannot be found in FAA manuals.
Instead, they represent a gathering of techniques developed by professionals whose survival depends on the precise execution of non-precision
approaches.

NEW APPROACH TO
NON-PRECISION APPROACHES

Familiarize yourself with instrument procedures
at far-away airports without leaving home base

How would you like to shoot a VOR approach to Zamboanga, an ADF approach to Vienna or a localizer approach to Singapore? Well, you can do just that using your own airplane and without ever leaving the local flying area.

These locations may be romantically appealing to most pilots, but the reason for suggesting such adventuresome flying is not to give vent to your wanderlust. Rather, the suggestions following, in addition to adding some spice to your flying, are methods to help a pilot become more thoroughly acquainted with the vagaries of non-precision approaches.

The ILS (precision) approach is, believe it or not, easier for the average pilot to master than VOR, ADF and localizer approaches. Once he has learned to move the cross-pointer needles slowly and keep them in place, he can feel justifiably confident about shooting a similar approach anywhere in the world. This is because one ILS approach is essentially the same as every other.

Non-precision approaches, on the other hand, are not so similar. They are like people; each has a unique personality with which to reckon, procedures that somehow differentiate one approach from another. This is one reason non-precision approaches annually claim more victims than do ILS approaches even though the latter permits a pilot to descend to considerably lower minimums.

The NDB (ADF) approach to Runway 13 at Hong Kong International Airport is an excellent example of just how unique a non-precision approach can be. Figure 4-3 is a simplified view of this approach but bears little resemblance to the actual approach plate which has such a profusion of hieroglyphic notations that it looks more like an Aresti aerobatic chart.

The approach begins when the pilot is at cruising altitude and is cleared direct to the Cheung Chau NDB for an ADF approach to

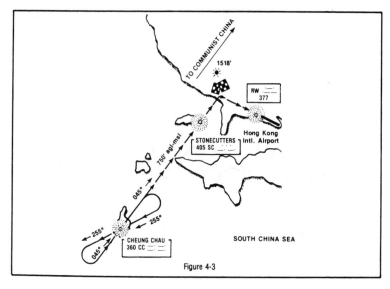

Figure 4-3

Runway 13. (English speaking pilots refer to this as the "Charlie-Charlie" approach.) Upon reaching the beacon, the pilot must descend over it in a series of precise figure eights so as to cross the beacon inbound at 1,000 feet. After passing "Charlie-Charlie," he descends to 750 feet (the MDA) and tracks across almost ten nm of the South China Sea toward the Stonecutters NDB.

After passing Stonecutters, the pilot plunges straight ahead and purposefully heads toward a 1,518-foot-high obstacle. Continuing, he should spot a hill on one side of which are two large, brightly-colored, illuminated, orange and white checkerboards. The pilot aims for these warning signs and gets as close to them as he dares. He must not overfly the checkerboards, however, because if he is fortunate enough to miss the towering obstacle nearby, he might wind up in Communist China. Instead, he banks sharply right and heads toward the RW NDB at the approach end of Hong Kong International's Runway 13. Theoretically, the pilot will then be on short final and should have little difficulty descending over (and through) the adjacent concrete canyons of high-rise buildings to a successful landing.

This is an extreme example of what can be expected during a non-precision approach, but it does demonstrate that a pilot who has learned to shoot a VOR approach at Santa Monica, for example, may not be prepared for what may await him elsewhere.

Unfortunately, the average pilot becomes proficient in executing only those approaches within a relatively short distance of his home airport. This can build false confidence because he may not be sufficiently familiar with the non-precision approach procedures used elsewhere.

But there is a solution to this problem, a new and unique approach to non-precision approaches.

Since the average VOR approach incorporates only one VORTAC, it is possible to use a local station as if it were distantly located. For example, if a pilot lives in beautiful downtown Burbank, Calif., he can practice shooting a VOR approach to Kansas City International Airport by substituting the nearby Van Nuys VORTAC for the MKC VORTAC shown on the Kansas City "VOR Rwy 27" approach plate.

A pilot can practice the Kansas City approach without ever leaving Southern California.

There is one obvious problem with this suggestion, but it is actually a blessing in disguise. After executing the Kansas City approach (while using the Van Nuys VOR), there's no way that a pilot will find a runway at the missed approach point. So, let's convert this liability into an asset. What does a pilot do when he can't find the runway? He executes a missed approach. So here's a way to practice both the VOR approach and the "pull-up" procedure.

Since a pilot knows in advance that he will have to execute a "miss," he will be forced to prepare for that maneuver, something most pilots don't do when relatively certain of finding a runway under the overcast. Learning the pull-up procedure prior to *every* IFR approach is a habit most of us need to develop further.

Another problem easily solved is that of adhering to the altitudes published on an approach plate. Assume, for example, that a Denver-based pilot wants to practice the "VOR Rwy 22L" approach to Knoxville, Tenn. while using the Denver VORTAC. According to the Knoxville approach plate, the pilot is supposed to cross the final approach fix (the VOR) at 3,000 feet (or above). There's obviously no way to fly over the Denver VORTAC at 3,000 feet msl because this station is situated more than a mile above sea level.

The solution is obvious. Simply add some convenient altitude to every altitude shown on the Knoxville approach plate. The lowest altitude shown on the Knoxville plate is 1,500 feet msl which, of course, is the MDA. The Denver-based pilot should mentally add 5,000 feet, for example, to all altitudes shown on the Knoxville plate. In this case, the MDA would be raised from 1,500 to 6,500 feet, the 3,000 foot altitude required over the VOR would become 8,000 feet msl, etc.

One must be cautious, however, to determine in advance that a practice approach of this nature will not cause the aircraft to barge through a local traffic pattern, TCA, etc. If necessary, altitudes can be raised farther so as to remain above a nearby airport traffic area during the procedure.

Conversely, if a Knoxville-based pilot wishes to use a nearby VORTAC to practice a "VOR-A" approach to Ely, Nevada, for example, he need not change the altitudes shown on the plate. The MDA at Ely is 8,800 feet, well above the relatively low terrain of East Tennessee. It might be desirable, in this case, to *lower* all altitudes by 4,000 or 5,000 feet.

One word of caution. When practicing IFR procedures, safety demands carrying a qualified safety pilot—even during CAVU conditions and when not wearing a hood. Conforming to the rigors of an IFR approach, especially an unfamiliar one, demands that considerable time be spent concentrating on the instruments. Without an additional pair of Mark IV eyeballs to scan the skies, safety is seriously compro-

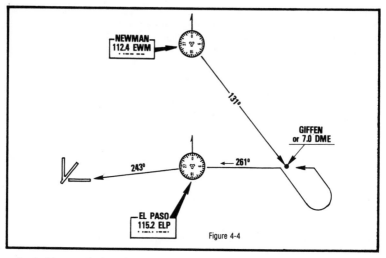

Figure 4-4

mised. To maximize the value of such practice, however, it would be wise to hire an instrument instructor.

In many parts of the country it is becoming more and more difficult to practice ADF approaches. This is because the FAA is decommissioning so many LOMs and RBNs. But for those who choose to use our "mock approach system," the lack of a local radio beacon poses no problem. Simply use a convenient commercial broadcast station and pretend it is an LOM.

When training pilots in the Los Angeles area, I usually have them tune in KMPC (710 kHz), hand them a plate for the "NDB Rwy 1" approach to West Yellowstone, Mont., and relax to the accompaniment of soothing music and an on-the-hour newscast. West Yellowstone is perfect, in this case, because the published MDA is 8,000 feet. This keeps a training flight well above the jet traffic zipping in and out of nearby Van Nuys and Burbank Airports.

Occasionally, a problem arises which could prevent using a local VORTAC station in place of the one specified on an approach plate. This occurs when a cross-radial from a second VORTAC (or RBN) is required to define a fix such as in Figure 4-4, which is a simplified display of a "VOR Rwy 26" approach to El Paso, Tex.

If a pilot wanted to practice this approach while flying in the vicinity of Hershey, Pa., for example, it's not likely that he would be able to find a pair of VORTACs in the same relative position as those used for the El Paso procedure (ELP and EWM VORTACs). So, instead of using the Newman 131° radial to define Giffen Intersection, he would use a 7.0 DME indication from the Pennsylvania VORTAC being used to practice the approach. This is a legal and more accurate method of defining the intersection.

However, if a DME distance is not authorized on the approach plate as a means of identifying a fix, then this approach could not be practiced unless actually flying in the El Paso area.

Fortunately, more than one facility is rarely required for a non-precision approach. A single VORTAC or RBN is usually all it takes to practice distantly located procedures in your own back yard.

In addition to the experience gained from practicing an assortment of non-precision approaches at altitude, there are numerous other reasons that make this technique more practical than shooting local approaches to "real" airports.

First of all, this procedure does not require working with approach control or the tower. As a result, there are no costly, time consuming traffic delays. Also, the safety pilot (or instructor) does not have to be concerned with extraneous communications and watching out for other aircraft buzzing around the pattern. Since he is not so preoccupied, the instructor can spend more time observing and critiquing a pilot's technique.

Also, the instructor can allow his student to digress from the published procedure (like descending below the MDA) without worrying about wiping out someone's chimney with the landing gear. This allows a pilot more time to recognize his own errors and take positive, corrective action. Often, this results in a more meaningful lesson as compared to one in which an instructor must terminate the deviation because of conflicting terrain and/or traffic.

The high altitude approach also gives the instructor a chance to present his student with a totally unfamiliar approach plate. Having to study a procedure while enroute (or holding) is excellent preparation for the real world of instrument flight. For many pilots, it is a shocking experience to deviate to an alternate airport and execute an approach (and possibly a miss) for which he has not planned.

Have you ever tried to practice a back-course ILS approach at a local airport only to find that the prevailing wind (and runway in use) invariably conspires against you? For similar reasons, most pilots rarely have the opportunity to shoot an approach through the "back-door" to an airport.

But that approach can be executed at altitude. After all, the localizer has virtually the same characteristics at 5,000 feet agl as it does at 500 feet. Additionally, other rarely used, "back-door" approaches (VOR or ADF) can be practiced at altitude.

Difficulties can arise also when practicing a local approach which coincides with the runway in use. Because of excessive VFR traffic in the pattern, a pilot may not be allowed to continue an approach to both the MDA and the missed approach point. Instead, the tower controller may request that the approach be broken off at some point (or altitude) which defeats the entire purpose of the flight. More frequently than not, pilots practicing approaches at a busy airport are not allowed to execute the pull-up procedure because this, too, usually conflicts with traffic in the pattern.

All such problems are eliminated by executing the procedure above the airport traffic area. It's a great way to beat the system.

When a pilot elects to use a local navaid as the nucleus for a distantly located procedure, he has the option of practicing any of thousands of approaches to "airports" all around the world. But perhaps he cannot find a published approach procedure to suit his needs. This problem, too, is easily resolved; the ambitious pilot can create his own procedure. A typical example is shown in Figure 4-5 and is a procedure which I present to a pilot about to get his instrument rating. It helps me to determine whether he knows how to prepare properly for a strange approach and how well he can execute the procedure.

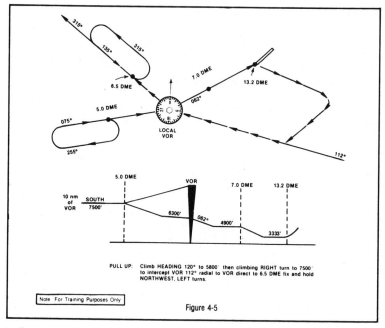

PULL UP: Climb HEADING 120° to 5800' then climbing RIGHT turn to 7500' to intercept VOR 112° radial to VOR direct to 6.5 DME fix and hold NORTHWEST, LEFT turns.

Note For Training Purposes Only

Figure 4-5

So you see you can shoot a non-precision approach to Zamboanga, Vienna, Singapore or anywhere else in the world you may care to venture—without ever leaving home.

CAUTION: CIRCLING APPROACHES MAY BE HAZARDOUS TO YOUR HEALTH

A game with a different set of rules can be a trap for the unwary

The circling approach is not an instrument approach. It is a contact approach, a maneuver used after the airport is sighted during a conventional instrument approach (ADF, VOR, ILS, etc.) in cases where the final approach course is too far off the runway heading for the pilot to make a straight-in landing.

The circling approach is not an easy—or a particularly safe—approach. An inherently hazardous procedure, it involves making steep turns about a point while slow flying under a less-than-400-foot overcast with one mile visibility. The procedure is not easy even under optimum conditions, but when attempted on a turbulent, showery night, the circling approach demands highly disciplined, sharply honed skills.

This maneuver is uniquely different because it cannot be practiced in a simulator. Although the mechanics of a circling approach may be practiced in VFR conditions, this drill bears little similarity to reality. In fact, practicing could even add to the danger of an actual circling approach because an inexperienced pilot could be misled into believing the maneuver is easier than it really is.

Several major U.S. air carriers recognize the hazards of circling approaches and have revised their policy manuals to prohibit line pilots from executing the maneuver in less than VFR conditions. There's a message in this that applies indirectly to general aviation pilots who are allowed to perform circling approaches when the weather is considerably less than VFR.

Most commonly, circling is required because the final approach course (to or from a radio facility) makes more than a 30° angle with the runway in use. This is typical of most VOR approaches and explains why corresponding approach plates contain only "circling minimums."

When the final approach course makes an angle of 30° or less with the active runway, "straight-in" minimums usually are published.

If the final phase of an IFR approach requires an abnormally steep descent (because of obstacles on final), FAA publishes only circling minimums even though the procedure would otherwise qualify as a straight-in approach. This does not mean a pilot must circle to land. If the runway is sighted sufficiently early in the approach and the pilot feels it is safe to do so, he has the option to either land straight-in or circle to land.

Most approaches that require circling are obvious. A pilot can determine from a glance at the approach plate that a circling maneuver is required. What often traps the unsuspecting pilot is the following situation—an ILS approach to Runway 18 at a time when Runway 27 is the active runway.

When preparing for an ILS, a pilot is preoccupied with setting up the radios, reducing airspeed and establishing the aircraft in an approach configuration. He expects to be cleared for an approach to Runway 18 but may not be prepared for the words that follow: ". . . circle to land Runway 27."

The pilot is suddenly thrust into a new game with a different set of rules. He must shift from a relatively low decision height (DH) to a higher minimum descent altitude (MDA). Also, he must determine the allowed flight time to the missed approach point and figure out which circling method to use.

If circling at this particular airport is an unusual experience for the pilot, he might consider requesting clearance to a holding pattern where he will have ample time to become familiar with what must be done. An unprepared pilot circling at minimums is a candidate for a catastrophe.

It's logical to ask why a pilot might be required to circle and land on a runway other than that served by the ILS (or other approach facility). There are several reasons. Sufficiently strong, adverse winds might warrant the use of another runway, or the ILS runway might be closed because of construction or blocked by a disabled aircraft. A preflight analysis of weather forecasts and NOTAMs often indicates when a pilot might be a candidate for a circling approach and its associated higher minimums and hazards.

Listening to an ATIS broadcast sufficiently far from the airport is a more accurate source of information and allows the pilot time to study the approach plate before becoming involved in the demanding complexities of an IFR arrival.

Not all circling approaches are as difficult and inherently dangerous as has been implied. Because of the unusually high circling minimums at Palm Springs, Calif. (1,712 feet agl and three miles), for example, the procedure is relatively simple—descend to VFR conditions, enter the pattern and land.

The most important aspect of any approach that requires circling is to be prepared for what must be done after establishing visual contact with the airport. Prior to initiating the IFR approach procedure, study the airport diagram and create a mental picture of the runway layout and how to distinguish the active runway from among the possible matrix of others.

Next, determine, in advance, the best circling procedure to use once the runway has been located. Those procedures recommended by the FAA are shown in Figure 4-6. Although these sketches appear logical on paper, they are in need of explanation and some criticism.

Maneuver 4-6a is used when landing opposite to the direction of the approach. But by following this recommendation, the runway winds up on the right side of the aircraft where it may be impossible to see, especially when visibility is poor. Unless the presence of obstacles dictate otherwise, plan a counterclockwise (left) circle.

Although the minimum visibility for circling approaches may exist on the ground (where it is measured), visibility at circling altitudes (the MDA) may be less. Once the runway is in sight, keep it in sight with the tenacity of a hungry cougar stalking its prey. Losing visual contact with the airport is a good excuse for an expeditious missed approach, although this is not mandatory.

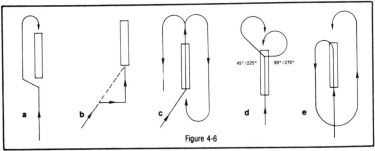

Figure 4-6

While left hand circles are strongly recommended, don't ignore notations on the chart that might dictate otherwise. A comment such as, "NA East of RWY 18-36" in the Circle-To-Land Minimums section of the approach plate is often overlooked and warns that circling must be confined west of this particular runway because of obstacles on the other side.

Figure 4-6b is used when on an approach course that intercepts the runway centerline at less than a 90° angle *and* when the airport is sighted sufficiently far away so as to allow a simple turn onto base leg.

There are times, however, when a pilot does not sight the runway until almost above it. Since he is too high to use 4-6b, it is necessary to circle as shown in 4-6c. If allowed, he should avoid the right-hand pattern and execute a left-hand circuit.

The FAA should admonish itself and delete maneuver 4-6d. Presumably, this method of course reversal to the runway is used when a pilot breaks out of the overcast when over the approach end of the active runway and is heading in the opposite direction. Whether using the 90° or 45° breakaway, as shown, the pilot temporarily severs his visual connection with the runway and trusts (to luck?) that he'll find it once again after completing the turnaround maneuver.

This technique is an invitation for vertigo and disorientation, especially at night. A better method, although not published by FAA, is shown in 4-6e. From over the approach end of the runway, make a left turn to the upwind leg and completely circle the runway until established on final.

Circling maneuvers following ILS approaches are easier than those following VOR and ADF approaches. The localizer leads a pilot to the airport with precision. VOR radials and ADF bearings frequently do not.

Most pilots appreciate that outbound ADF tracking rarely coincides with the course printed on the chart, but they probably are not aware of the sometimes deplorable inaccuracies which can be experienced when tracking a radial. It's time to set this record straight.

Every IFR pilot knows (or should know) that a VOR receiver is allowed up to a 4° error when tuned to a VOT test signal. What he may not know is that the VOT transmitter is allowed a 1° error. Additionally, a conventional VOR transmitter is allowed up to a 2.5° error. Unless exceptionally sharp, a pilot is not likely to keep the needle precisely centered throughout an approach. A quarter-scale needle deflection is an acceptable deviation and represents another 2½° error. And if this were not enough, an FAA study reveals that nondigital omni-bearing selectors are frequently up to 2° in error.

If all these potential errors were to accumulate in the same direction and conspire against an unsuspecting pilot, his aircraft could be 12° off course at any given point during a VOR approach. Curiously, FAA protects a pilot from enroute obstacles only when within 4½° of the published course.

There's more to this than chastising FAA and reviewing potential VOR-bearing errors. An error of several degrees can result in being considerably off course. Since most circling approaches are associated with VOR approaches, it is distressingly obvious that a pilot could execute a VOR approach with superhuman precision, establish ground contact and because of restricted visibility, sail past the airport without being close enough to see it.

Pilots tracking along a final approach course also should not limit their search to the left of the aircraft, for example, simply because the approach plate says that is where the airport should be. Once a pilot establishes ground contact, he should search for the airport in all directions. Many experienced, honest pilots will admit to having passed an airport and executing a missed approach simply because of psychological blinders riveting their attention in only one direction.

After passing the fix from which a descent to MDA is authorized, it is important to descend rapidly. The idea is to level off at MDA and establish a stabilized attitude and airspeed at least one mile prior to reaching the airport. This affords ample time to conduct a thorough search for the airport. If a gradual sink rate is used, the MDA and the missed approach point might be reached simultaneously. This allows no time to scan for the runway.

Another reason to descend rapidly applies primarily to straight-in, non-precision approaches but can, at times, apply to circling approaches.

Figure 4-7 shows a typical stratus overcast. At the airport, the ceiling is measured as 400 feet overcast. But this is not necessarily the height of the cloud base at any given point along the approach corridor. For example, Aircraft A descends gradually to the MDA and, because of a lower ceiling at this point, the pilot never establishes ground contact and is forced to execute a missed approach.

The pilot in Aircraft B, however, is more savvy. He descends rapidly to the MDA, levels off and eventually spots the runway.

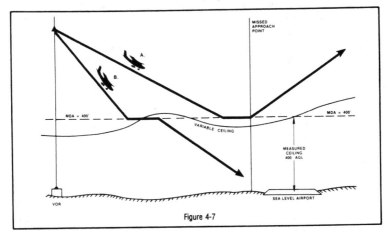

Figure 4-7

If the descent to MDA is made with full flaps, consider retracting them to the 50% position (in most light aircraft) when leveling at MDA. Circling with full flaps at a constant altitude requires considerable power. This leaves little power in reserve to compensate for inadvertently lost altitude or to initiate an expeditious pullup.

One danger associated with circling is the temptation to descend beneath the MDA simply because the airport has been sighted. Unless the aircraft is in a position from which a normal descent to landing can be made, a premature descent can be fatal.

When the FAA establishes circling minimums, it does so on the basis of providing only a 300-foot-obstacle clearance within a 1.7-mile radius of the runway (for Category A aircraft) on the circling side of the airport (if designated). Dropping down an extra 50 or 100 feet to avoid a lowering cloud base, for example, erodes this already marginal obstacle clearance. Therefore, if maintaining MDA results in cloud reentry, accept the inconvenience and execute a missed approach.

Once the airport is in sight, maneuver so as to keep the active runway on your left (unless otherwise prohibited). Plan to always be within one mile of the active runway. This guarantees adequate obstacle clearance and probably will prevent losing sight of the airport when visibility is poor.

Should a large turn be required, it might be a good idea to temporarily play ostrich. Keep your head in the cockpit and execute the turn on instruments and with precision. It is not difficult to lose control in a turn because of a visual fixation with the ground when the weather is 400 and one. An occasional glance at the airport during the turn is all right, but most attention should remain in the cockpit.

During the circling maneuver, airspeed should be stabilized at normal approach speed (1.3 Vso). This provides adequate stall protection, obviates the need to lose both airspeed and altitude when turning final, prevents the need for massive trim changes and finally, keeps turn rates relatively high. This final item is particularly important. Increased airspeed decreases the turn rate (at a given bank angle). This increases the turn radius which can result in excessively wide patterns and loss of visual contact with the airport.

Another area demanding extreme care is the missed approach. It is of paramount importance that a pilot be thoroughly familiar with the pullup procedure prior to beginning an approach. If it is necessary to consult an approach plate after inadvertently entering clouds at less than 400 feet agl, you are in serious trouble.

Since the need for a missed approach can occur at any point while circling, confusion often arises as to the method of initiating the pullup. Simply stated, turn toward the runway (even though it cannot be seen) and intercept the missed approach procedure when over the airport. This can require some imagination and again stresses the need to be familiar with the pullup procedure.

A final word of caution. The pullup procedure guarantees terrain clearance only when it is initiated at the designated missed approach point (MAP). Executing a premature pullup sacrifices this protection. So, if you're engulfed in cloud and tracking toward the airport at MDA when the tower advises that the field has just gone to zero-zero, do not abandon the approach. A climb may be initiated, but avoid turning until the MAP has been reached.

The "sidestep maneuver" is often confused with the circling approach. These procedures are related but, like brothers, should be treated individually. A sidestep maneuver follows an IFR approach to one of two parallel runways less than 1,200 feet apart. A pilot is allowed to "sidestep" and land on the other parallel runway, *provided* it is in sight when at or above the published "Minimum Sidestep MDA" and the appropriate clearance has been received.

Generally, sidestep minimums are higher than those for straight-in approaches and less than those for circling approaches.

Any pilot who considers making his first circling approach when the weather is reported as 400-and-one should either hire an experienced-pro to ride shotgun or cancel his planned flirtation with fate. There is no doubt that the circling approach can be a hazard to your health— respect it accordingly.

HOLDING PATTERNS SIMPLIFIED

How to comply without confusion
when you're sent into orbit

Murphy created two inescapable laws especially for aviation. The first states that headwinds shall increase in proportion to the pilot's anxiety to get home. The second says that when fuel reserves are low, an IFR pilot can expect to be sent to a holding pattern.

We have no choice about accepting Murphy's first law; it is merely an expression of Mother Nature's whimsical ways. The second axiom is less tolerable and more aggravating because the holding pattern is a man-made shackle. After all, an air traffic controller has to put an airplane somewhere when he doesn't know what else to do with it.

Holding clearances usually are issued when excessive traffic converges on a terminal area or when the destination weather is below landing minimums. Also, a pilot might be instructed to hold when the IFR runway is closed temporarily because of snow plowing or is blocked by a disabled aircraft. At such time, a pilot can either proceed to an alternate airport or etch racetracks in the sky while waiting patiently for conditions to improve.

The holding pattern is ATC's stop sign and is flashed whenever an aircraft cannot proceed.

A corollary to Murphy's Holding Law states that a holding clearance shall be issued only when the pilot is completely submerged in cockpit activity and is least prepared. Somehow, controllers always manage to comply with this rule. Whether he's driving a 707 into San Francisco or a Cessna into Santa Monica, the holding clearance always seems to catch a pilot off guard.

The inbound course of a holding pattern *usually* lies along the route of flight. In such a case, entering the pattern is no more complex than making a 180° turn at the holding fix. But occasionally a satanical controller sends a pilot to a pattern requiring either a teardrop or parallel entry. And that's when the suds hit the fan. The average instrument pilot hasn't had to worry about such procedures for so long that he's probably forgotten how.

After the pilot finally locates the holding fix, he usually consults that hieroglyphic holding pattern diagram on the IFR chart. But that miniscule guide looks confusingly similar to an Aresti aerobatic diagram and, if followed, can result in a teardrop entry to a Lomcevak. Desperately, the victim pilot searches the cockpit for a template or holding pattern computer to resolve his difficulties. But by the time he finds one and figures out how to use it, the holding fix has been left behind.

There is a simple way to avoid such confusion. Once a pilot earns his instrument rating, he might consider simpler ways to enter holding patterns. There is no reason to be further intimidated by the FAA's methods because they are only *recommended methods*. No regulatory muscle has been created to enforce their use.

When the FAA devised its entry procedures, it did so with the objective of confining the aircraft as closely as possible to the lateral limits of the holding pattern. Every holding pattern is surrounded by a large womb of airspace to protect the holding aircraft. The exact size of this area varies according to altitude, distance of the farthest VOR defining the fix, and the type of aircraft (propeller-driven or jet-powered).

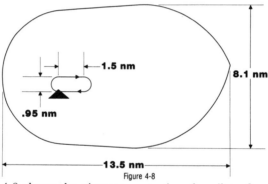

Figure 4-8

Figure 4-8 shows the airspace protecting the pilot of a propeller-driven airplane while holding at 5,000 feet at a fix 20 nm from the farthest VOR defining that fix. The pilot is offered a 14 by 8 nm area within which to maneuver his machine into a racetrack pattern that measures only 1.0 by 2.5 nm (assuming a 90 knot holding airspeed, one minute legs, and no wind conditions).

Clearly, he can use any *reasonable* method of entry without having to worry about violating the limits of protected airspace.

Figure 4-9 illustrates one extremely simple method that can be used to enter *any* holding pattern regardless of the direction from which it is approached. It is the only method to use (even during an FAA flight test) when ATC issues a holding clearance just as the aircraft passes over the holding fix. All the astonished pilot has to do (after crossing the fix) is to turn to the outbound heading of the holding pattern and remain on that heading for one minute. This initial procedure requires no mental gymnastics and is foolproof.

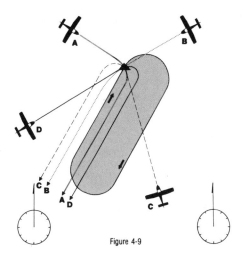

Figure 4-9

During the minute of outbound flight, set the VOR course selector to the inbound course of the holding pattern and decide which way to turn to intercept that radial. At the end of the minute, turn toward the radial, intercept it and track inbound to the fix. That's all there is to it. The airplane has been established in the holding pattern with a minimum of fuss and bother.

This technique of "turning to the outbound heading" can be used without fear of recrimination whenever a pilot is doubtful about which of FAA's three *recommended* entry methods to use. It is an easy, safe and legal technique.

(Although FAA examiners prefer that instrument rating applicants demonstrate standard entries during a flight test, they won't fail anyone who uses reasonable procedures and remains well within protected airspace.)

If a pilot desires to use the FAA's entry procedures, he can do so with much less effort by slightly modifying those techniques. The suggestion that follows doesn't require correlating those 70° and 110° relative bearings and sectors to aircraft heading and holding pattern alignment. Instead, use 90° quadrants because they are so much easier to visualize.

For example, assume that a pilot has been cleared to hold at Delay Intersection (Figure 4-10). According to the FAA's *recommendations,* there are three ways to enter the pattern depending upon the direction from which the fix is approached: the teardrop, the parallel or the direct entry.

To simplify the holding problem the pilot should draw the racetrack pattern on his chart. For some unknown reason, pilots protect their IFR charts from pencil marks as if they were priceless Picassos. IFR charts are replaced so frequently that revising the Jeppesen manuals is almost a sideline profession; there's no reason *not* to write on them.

So, when a holding clearance is received, immediately draw the pattern on the chart—with a red crayon if that helps to make the pattern stand out. Once the pattern is illustrated, half the battle is won.

Next, slash a line through the fix perpendicular to the holding radial (represented by line A-B in Figure 4-10). Then extend the inbound course of the pattern beyond the holding fix (line C). With a modicum of practice, these lines won't have to be drawn, but for now they help to visualize what follows.

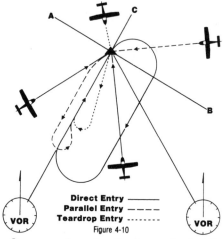

Direct Entry ————
Parallel Entry — — — —
Teardrop Entry ········
Figure 4-10

If the aircraft approaches the fix from the holding side of the perpendicular line (A-B), simply make a direct entry. In other words, turn to the outbound heading of the holding pattern upon reaching the fix. The direction of the turn should coincide with that of the holding pattern. That is, turn to the right for standard patterns or to the left for nonstandard patterns. That's all there is to it. You're in the pattern and have little more to do than patiently bore holes in the sky until ATC mercifully allows continuation of the flight (to another holding fix, no doubt).

If the fix is approached from within the quadrant bounded by lines A and C, the aircraft nose will be inside the holding pattern upon crossing the fix. So take a hint; stay inside the pattern and execute a teardrop entry.

The only other possibility is to approach the fix from within the quadrant bounded by the lines B and C. Upon crossing the fix, the nose of the aircraft will be pointed outside the holding pattern. So, take another hint; stay outside the pattern and execute a parallel entry.

This modified version of FAA's recommended entry procedures works equally well with right and left hand patterns. Happily, it requires considerably less mental wizardry.

The truth is that a pilot is free to choose whatever method of pattern entry is easiest for him. There are no requirements other than to be careful about not getting too far from the holding pattern and violating the limits of protected airspace. To preclude this possibility, maneuver into the holding pattern at reduced airspeed. Since there is ample maneuvering room for aircraft holding at 175 knots IAS (maximum allowable holding speed for propeller-driven airplanes), flying at 100 knots (or less) results in using proportionately less airspace and allows much more room for error.

Savvy instrument pilots not only know how to simplify holding procedures, they also know how to occasionally escape from having to hold at all.

If a pilot is relatively far from the holding fix when he receives the holding clearance, he should immediately advise ATC that he's reducing airspeed. He then slows to the aircraft's best endurance speed. This airspeed is very nearly the same as that used for a power-off glide and results in the use of minimal engine power.

This serves three purposes. First of all, it gives the pilot more time to prepare for the holding entry. Second, it reduces the per-mile fuel consumption and conserves fuel at a time when it might be desperately needed. Finally, reducing airspeed *consumes part of the holding delay while enroute* and reduces the amount of holding necessary at the clearance limit. It is certainly far more comfortable to cruise in a straight line at reduced airspeed than to chase your tail around a holding pattern.

With some luck, a pilot might be able to consume the entire delay while enroute and not have to hold at all. This technique, by the way, is common practice among airline pilots, and controllers have become used to it.

Once established in a holding pattern, it usually is necessary to begin timing the inbound and outbound legs. The duration of the outbound leg is adjusted so the inbound leg is one minute long (when holding at or below 14,000 feet msl). When above 14,000 feet, the inbound leg should be a minute-and-a-half long.

Timing the legs, however, is a pain in the empennage. There really is a better way, but only when holding on a VORTAC radial and when the airplane is equipped with an operable DME.

At such times, a pilot has only to request holding with 5 mile DME legs, for example. Controllers almost always comply with this request. Subsequent turns in the pattern are then made with respect to DME indications, not the clock. The procedure is considerably simplified.

If DME is unavailable, a pilot might request five or even ten *minute* legs. If approved, this eliminates the drudgery of having to hold in relatively small patterns which have only minute-long legs.

With respect to time, be very skeptical about Expect Further Clearance (EFC) and Expect Approach Clearance (EAC) times issued by controllers.

When issued the EFC, don't plan on having sufficient fuel reserves solely on the basis of this estimate. When the EFC expires, you might be issued further holding instructions with a new and extended EFC. Likewise, an EAC can be extended depending on traffic, weather conditions, etc.

In other words, don't continue holding and burning the reserve fuel needed to divert to an alternate on the basis of an optimistic EAC or EFC. When the time comes to divert, do so without hesitation. It is tempting to continue holding with the thought that an approach clearance is *probably* imminent. But the result could be an untimely and lethal case of fuel exhaustion.

Consider a pilot holding in a pattern situated at right angles to the prevailing wind. The wind causes the turn radius to increase when the turn is initiated over the holding fix. Conversely, a turn at the opposite end of the pattern is into the wind, which reduces turn radius.

Pilots often attempt to correct for this drift by using a steep bank when turning downwind and a shallow bank when turning into the wind. This is improper and makes the job of holding unnecessarily difficult. All turns in the pattern should be at the standard rate (3° per second for light airplanes) or with a 30° bank angle, whichever requires the shallowest bank angle (unless a flight director is used).

The easiest way to correct for wind drift is to first determine the crab angle necessary to track the inbound course of the holding pattern. Then, triple this wind correction angle and apply it to the no-wind heading normally used to fly the outbound leg.

For example, if the pilot uses a 5° left crab to track the inbound course, he should correct 15° to the right while flying outbound.

A final note of caution concerns the holding "stack," a situation where numerous aircraft are holding at the same fix, but at different altitudes (hopefully).

When the bottom man in the stack is cleared to leave the pattern, clearances are usually issued—one at a time—for successive aircraft to descend 1,000 feet to the next lower altitude. A problem can arise when one pilot is slow to initiate the descent while an impatient pilot only 1,000 feet above makes like a dive bomber. The result can be a near miss or worse.

To prevent such a conflict, never report vacating a holding altitude until actually doing so. Also, make descents in the stack at 500 fpm, no more—no less. These simple steps can go a long way toward preventing an encounter of the wrong kind.

Unfortunately, there is no advice available to help a pilot totally circumvent Murphy's Holding Law. Hopefully, however, some of this advice can be used to ease the burden of compliance.

FLYING THE DME ORBIT

The only way from A to B is sometimes a circle

Of all the black boxes in an airplane, the DME ranks as one of the simplest to use. All a pilot has to do is glance occasionally at the slowly changing numbers to determine his slant-range distance from a given VORTAC. But when he is confronted with having to maintain a circling track at a specific distance from the station, DME usage assumes an entirely different complexion. Tracking DME arcs can be a new and frustrating experience especially when winds aloft are strong.

A few years ago, DME arcs were relatively uncommon, and IFR pilots didn't have to worry much about them. But times are changing; the FAA has been increasing the use of DME arcs as prescribed paths to be followed during the initial phases of IFR approaches.

The Feds have even gone so far as to create an IFR approach procedure incorporating a *final* approach defined by the 24 DME arc of a nearby VORTAC. That's right, the "straight-in," VOR/DME approach to Runway 10 at NASA Wallops Station at Chincoteague Island, Va., requires flying a circular track all the way from the intermediate approach fix to the runway threshold.

Since this may be the only such approach in the world, it alone doesn't dictate an urgent need to become proficient in flying DME arcs. But the proliferation of DME arcs as "initial" IFR approaches does.

A DME arc is simply a circular course at a specific slant range (DME distance) from a given VORTAC. An arc typical of the type most likely to be encountered is shown in Figure 4-11, which is a simplified view of a back course approach to Runway 21 at Amarillo, Tex. A pilot who arrives at the initial approach fix (IAF) south of the AMA VORTAC (Aircraft No. 1) and is then "cleared for the approach" is expected to track along the 8 DME arc (a radius of eight nm from the DME) until near the localizer.

Since his only navigation receiver must be tuned to the AMA VORTAC while tracking the arc, a pilot needs to be warned when nearing the localizer to prevent him from unknowingly flying through

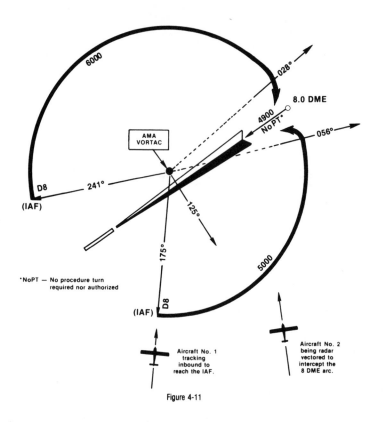

AMA VORTAC

6000

028°

8.0 DME

4900 NoPT*

056°

D8 — 241°

(IAF)

125°

175°

5000

*NoPT — No procedure turn required nor authorized

D8

(IAF)

Aircraft No. 1 tracking inbound to reach the IAF.

Aircraft No. 2 being radar vectored to intercept the 8 DME arc.

Figure 4-11

the final approach course.

This warning is provided in the form of a "lead radial," which, in this case, is the AMA 056° radial. After tracking the 8 DME arc and upon reaching the lead radial, the pilot should simultaneously tune in the ILS and turn to intercept the localizer.

It is also possible that a pilot might be radar vectored to intercept the DME arc at a point other than at an IAF. Aircraft No. 2 in the diagram has been cleared to maintain a given heading and intercept the 8 DME arc at which point he should begin orbiting the VORTAC as shown on the approach plate.

It is interesting to note that each circular initial approach, like conventional initial approaches, is provided a minimum enroute altitude (MEA). The arc northwest of the AMA localizer, for example, has an MEA of 6,000 feet while the southeastern arc has an MEA of 5,000 feet. It is imperative when tracking such an arc that a pilot does not descend to the applicable MEA unless either "cleared for the approach" or cleared to the specified altitude. Otherwise, he must maintain the last assigned altitude.

Assume that a pilot has been cleared for the approach and is tracking the northwesterly arc at 6,000 feet. Upon crossing the 028° lead radial, he begins an inbound turn to intercept the localizer. Is he then free to descend to 4,900 feet, which is shown on the plate as the MEA when inbound from the "8.0 DME" fix along the localizer course? Emphatically not! Descent must be delayed until the localizer has been *intercepted*. Crossing a lead radial is not an authorization to descend; intercepting the localizer is.

Another requirement for arc flying is shown in Figure 4-12, a

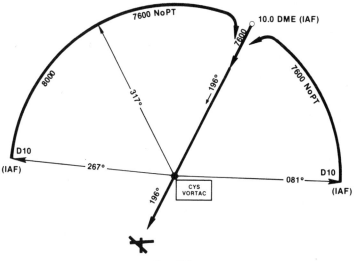

Figure 4-12

simplified view of the VOR-A approach to Cheyenne, Wyo. Lead radials are not needed to warn a pilot that he is nearing the final approach course because the same navaid (CYS VORTAC) is used throughout the entire procedure.

Pilots should be aware that when DME arcs are used as initial IFR approaches, maximum obstacle protection is provided only when within four miles of the arc. In other words, when tracking a 17 DME arc, for example, a pilot must remain between the 13 and 21 DME arcs which provide him with an eight-nm-wide band of maneuvering protection.

Additionally, as the DME radius becomes shorter and the circle becomes smaller, flying the arc becomes more difficult. To prevent imposing too much of a workload on pilots, FAA limits DME arcs to a minimum radius of seven nm (for civilian aircraft).

At first glance, tracking a DME arc appears to be a relatively simple affair. It's just a matter of flying a wide, sweeping circular track in such a way as to keep the indicated distance relatively constant.

Maintaining a *precise* track along a DME arc on a windless day theoretically requires an extremely shallow banked turn with an almost infinitesimal turn rate. For example, if a pilot were tracking an arc with a 30 DME radius while flying at a true airspeed of 100 knots, 1.9 hours would be required to fly the 188-nm circumference. To do so while constantly turning would require a turn rate of only one-twentieth of a degree per second. Only an electronic computer is capable of such excruciating precision.

In practice, therefore, tracking an arc necessitates flying a series of short, straight segments each of which spans a 10° sector of the arc. The result is a 36-side polygon that approximates a circle.

To intercept the 20 DME arc shown in Figure 4-13, for example, the pilot tracks inbound on the 140° radial (as shown). When approximately one-half nm from the arc (20.5 DME), the pilot turns to a heading perpendicular to the inbound course (either 050° or 230° in this case, depending upon the desired direction of flight).

Since the pilot in the illustration plans to fly a counterclockwise arc, he turns 90° right to a heading of 050°. This results in an initial track

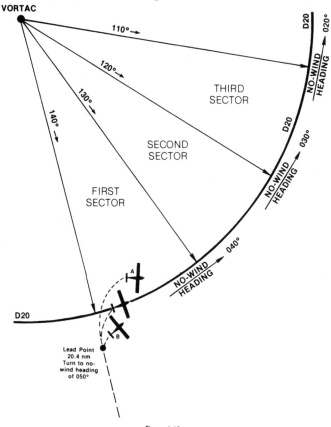

Figure 4-13

very nearly the same as the desired course. (A one-half-mile lead usually prevents overshooting the arc and is satisfactory for aircraft with airspeeds of 150 knots or less; proportionately larger leads are required for faster aircraft.)

During the latter part of the intercepting turn, closely monitor the DME. If the DME indication is something less than 20 nm (Aircraft A), the arc has been overshot and the turn should be continued beyond 90° to reintercept it. If the DME indicates more than 20 nm (Aircraft B), the arc has been undershot, and the turn should be terminated prematurely.

Upon intercepting the arc, return to the original 050° heading and make whatever small heading corrections are necessary to maintain a constant DME indication of 20 nm.

Once established on the arc, it is theoretically possible (on a windless day) to remain on track by flying perpendicular to the radial being crossed at any given instant. This, however, requires changing the omni bearing selector (OBS) in 1° increments throughout flight along the arc and is an arduous procedure. Instead, it is satisfactory to use radials spaced 10° apart.

While crossing the first sector in Figure 4-13, therefore, the pilot should rotate the OBS to 130°, which is 10° from the radial used to intercept the arc.

As this radial (130°) is being approached, an approximately perpendicular heading (040°) should be used to track the arc. This heading, 040°, is simply a guide—a no-wind reference heading. If the DME indication tends to decrease, the pilot is drifting inside the arc and should correct slightly to the right. If the DME indication tends to increase beyond 20 nm, then a correction to the left is required.

After crossing the 130° radial, the OBS should be set to 120°. The new reference heading while traversing the second sector is 030° and is perpendicular to the newly selected 120° radial.

If it is determined that a crosswind necessitates crabbing while crossing one sector, don't neglect to apply a similar drift-correction angle to the reference heading of the next sector. As progress around the arc continues, however, the effect of the wind will change gradually. A correction used on previous segments of the arc may be insufficient or excessive on subsequent segments.

Quite obviously, this is a thinking man's game and requires constant analyses of heading *versus* bearing from the station *versus* wind correction *versus* distance from the station. All these factors must be considered continuously to maintain a reasonably circular track. When the winds are strong, the mental gymnastics compound proportionately.

Orbiting in a strong wind can be simplified somewhat by flying slightly inside the arc. In this manner, the arc is constantly "turning" toward the aircraft and interception usually can be accomplished by holding a constant heading. If the aircraft is outside the arc, the curved course constantly "turns" away from the aircraft, and larger heading corrections are required to intercept.

Since the FAA is encouraging the expanded use of DME arcs in terminal areas, it is logical to assume the agency is developing a more simplified method of arc tracking. Yes, it's a logical assumption but an incorrect one. There is pitifully little information available about orbiting procedures.

After querying FAA officials about this, I was told arc flying is considered more a matter of technique than procedure and was referred to FAA's only published work regarding the subject, an Advisory Circular (AC No. 90-62), dated Jan. 23, 1973. The circular contains a noteworthy comment: "Unless the pilot is highly proficient in the use of [VOR DME] equipment and in performing [DME arcs], it is recommended that [orbits] be flown only when RMI equipment is available."

Since most general aviation aircraft are not so elaborately equipped, this places most of us between a flat rock and a hard place when confronted with the need to fly a DME arc, especially when the winds are strong.

The RMI, of course, does simplify orbiting. With a needle that points to a VOR station the way an ADF needle points to a radiobeacon, all a pilot must do is keep the needle pointed approximately toward the inside wingtip while making small heading corrections to maintain a relatively constant DME indication. The RMI is invaluable in this regard because it helps a pilot to visualize the relative location of the VORTAC station.

Orbiting without RMI is almost like "turning about a point" without being able to see the pylon. A pilot has to visualize the relationship of the aircraft to the VORTAC station by using the changing variables of heading, bearing and distance.

Flying a DME arc was once simpler than it is now. An early model Narco DME receiver incorporated an orbit indicator, a left/right needle that assisted a pilot in precisely tracking a given DME arc. But that function did not meet expectations and was quietly dropped from future models. The concept, however, was excellent, and perhaps now that DME arcs are being used more, avionics manufacturers will give thought to an improved version of Narco's orbiter.

In the meantime, most pilots are left to deal with DME arcs using only raw data. Although the difficulty of the maneuver increases in proportion to the wind velocity, it is something with which the average instrument rated pilot manages to cope, primarily because he has an eight-nm-wide band within which to bracket and maneuver.

Tracking a DME arc is one of those maneuvers which is probably easier to perform than to describe, but before it can be executed proficiently, considerable practice is required. Fortunately, this can be done in VFR conditions and requires neither a hood nor an IFR clearance. But before embarking on a practice mission, one additional piece of equipment is required: a competent observer to watch for traffic. Orbiting can be a mentally distracting affair, and the student of DME arcs rarely has time to both concentrate on the problem and watch for traffic.

Initially, a pilot should practice with a large radius arc, one at least 20 DME from the station. Arcs of large radii have relatively "flat" curves and are easier to track. Also, maintain relatively slow groundspeeds during the orbit; fast groundspeeds require more skill because of the greater rate of course deviation and correction.

After the large arc has been mastered a pilot should increase ground speed and tackle DME arcs with progressively shorter radii.

Once a pilot can accurately encircle a VORTAC along a 7 DME arc at cruise airspeed, he is ready to graduate into the exercises shown in Figure 4-14.

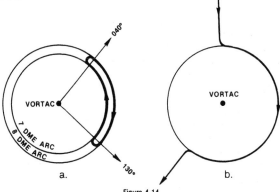

Figure 4-14

The first (Figure 4-14a) is a holding pattern used occasionally by the military and requires flying the 7 DME arc, for example, between a pair of specified radials. Upon reaching the 040° radial, the pilot in the diagram turns right to intercept and track the 8 DME arc until reaching the 130° radial, etc.

The second exercise (4-14b) is a typical entry/exit problem and consists of tracking inbound to a VORTAC along a given radial, intercepting and orbiting a specified arc and then tracking outbound along a departure radial.

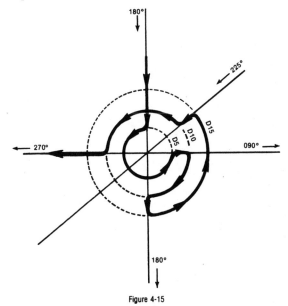

Figure 4-15

151

The final, seemingly sadistic maneuver (4-15) is an excellent exercise that not only develops orbiting skills, but also forces a pilot to simultaneously plan impending courses of action, such as might be required when orbiting a station in preparation for an actual IFR approach.

When these skills have been developed, a pilot is ready to practice under a hood on a windy day. Those who scoff at the *apparent* simplicity of orbiting have probably never flown a short-radius DME arc under the demanding and difficult conditions that can arise during an actual IFR approach.

Speaking of DME, here's a tip that can save considerable aggravation when confined to the rigors of a conventional holding pattern. Instead of timing the inbound and outbound pattern legs to arrive at a one minute inbound leg to the holding fix (when at or below 14,000 feet), ask ATC for permission to fly 3 DME legs, for example. Such a request is almost always granted in a radar environment.

Then instead of timing each leg, simply fly to the fix (which may be at 30 DME for example), execute a 180° turn, and fly outbound until reaching 33 DME, for example. Then, turn again, track inbound and repeat the process. This saves considerable mental wear and tear.

In the meantime, practice getting into orbit; flying in circles may not be the shortest way from A to B, but it could be the only way.

ENGINE FAILURE AFTER TAKEOFF

To turn or not to turn:
That is the question

It is characteristic of man to ignore certain facts of life, even though his fate may be determined by them. He is reluctant, for example, to think about cancer, syphilis, and obesity, to name just a few threats to his welfare.

Among such unpleasant and frequently avoided topics is the pilot's nightmare—an engine failure after takeoff in a single-engine airplane. But unless such problems are discussed and understood, we may never learn to cope with them.

Engine failures occur more frequently than most pilots realize. The National Transportation Safety Board states that during a five-year period (1965–1969), 4,310 accidents resulted from engine failures in the U.S. That's an average of 862 per year, or more than two *every day*. Of these 4,310 reported powerplant failures, a significant percentage occurred during or shortly after takeoff. In fact, many more engine failures occurred during this period, but did not result in either aircraft damage or bodily injury and therefore were not included in the survey.

Much has been written about *enroute* engine failure, and many techniques have been developed for dealing with such emergencies. Pilots are taught, for example, to flight plan so as to avoid hostile terrain and be always within gliding distance of a landing site suitable for an emergency landing. And the NTSB published a special study (report number: NTSB-AAS-72-3) recommending crash landing techniques for small, fixed-wing airplanes.

But what advice has been developed for the hapless pilot who finds himself behind a stilled engine shortly after takeoff? Damned little! Virtually everything taught about this potentially catastrophic event can be encapsulated in a single sentence: "If the engine fails after takeoff, land straight ahead; do not turn back to the airport."

Unfortunately, this "rule" is not so golden that it can be accepted without question or criticism. This is a controversial subject, requiring penetrating analysis, because there are times when a pilot *should* return to the airport and should *not* land straight ahead.

FAA records are full of case histories describing in hair-raising detail the often fatal results of attempts to make a 180° turn back to the airport from too low an altitude. In most cases, stalls and/or spins were entered inadvertently by frightened pilots with an aversion to flight near the ground. Many other pilots have made it back successfuly, but these events have gone unnoticed because they never became accident statistics.

Altitude seems to be the primary difference between success and failure. When a pilot has sufficient altitude, a turnaround to the airport may not only be safe, but also be his only recourse, especially when the terrain ahead is a forest of unyielding obstacles.

If the pilot does not have sufficient altitude, a turnaround should not be attempted. It is wiser to accept a controlled crash than to risk spinning uncontrollably into oblivion.

But how high is high enough? What is the minimum altitude above which a return to the airport can be executed safely?

This depends not only on aircraft glide characteristics, but also on the turnaround technique. For example, should the turn be shallow, medium, or steep? To answer these questions regarding the controversial turnaround, I enlisted the aid of two Southern California professional pilots: R. R. "Chris" Krengel, accident prevention specialist from FAA's Western Region, and aviation attorney Robert Cleaves.

We experimented with five light aircraft: a Piper Super Cub, a Cherokee 140, a Cessna 150, a Cessna 172, and Cleaves' own Cessna 185. The results were most revealing.

To simulate an engine failure shortly after takeoff, we flew each aircraft in takeoff configuration and at its best rate of climb speed. At an arbitrarily chosen altitude (usually 2,000 feet), the throttle was abruptly retarded.

The pilot flying the aircraft did nothing for four seconds. According to FAA studies, it takes this long for a pilot to recognize an engine failure and initiate action. After the four second delay, the aircraft was established in a 30° banked, gliding turn. At the completion of a 180° turn, the sink rate was arrested to simulate a landing flare. Subsequent tests were conducted using 45°, 60°, and 75° banked turns. The net altitude loss during each turnaround was recorded and compiled.

According to these findings, the minimum altitude loss (in most cases) results from a steeply banked turn. The altitude loss in a Cessna 172, for example, is 380 feet when a shallow bank is used, but only 210 feet when the bank angle is steepened to 75°.

It might seem incongruous that a shallow bank results in more altitude loss then a steep bank. After all, the sink rate during a gliding turn does increase with bank angle. The explanation involves the element of time. When a Cessna 172 is banked 30° while gliding at 70 knots, the rate of turn is only 9° per second. As a result, the time required to execute a 180° turn is 20 seconds—sufficient time for substantial altitude loss even though the descent rate is nominal.

Conversely, the turn rate increases to an astonishing 58° per second during a 75° bank. In this case, a 180° turn requires only three seconds, insufficient time to lose substantial altitude even though the descent rate is relatively fast.

The results seem to favor using a steep bank angle, but before we conclude this, another factor must be considered: stall speed. Increased stall speeds result from progressively steepened bank angles. When the pilot is flying in a 30° banked turn, stall speed increases only fractionally, from 50 knots (calibrated airspeed) to 53 knots. In a 75° banked turn, the stall speed increase is a dramatic 97%, from 50 to 97 knots. It is obvious that steep bank angles must be avoided during low altitude maneuvering to avert the deadly stall/spin.

Another argument against the steep turn is the difficulty a pilot would encounter while attempting to arrest a high sink rate near the ground. With the aircraft already dangerously close to stall, added elevator pressure is required to overcome the airplane's substantial vertical inertia. This aggravates the problem by increasing the probability of a high speed (accelerated) stall near the ground.

Test results indicate that the optimum bank angle is a compromise between the altitude-losing effects of the shallow bank and the rising stall speeds associated with steep banks. Although it is for each pilot to determine, I am satisfied that a 45° banked turn provides the best results: a moderate turn rate and altitude loss, combined with only a 19% increase in stall speed.

During this investigation, other turn methods were explored: half-spins, wingovers, and skidding turns. In most cases, these exotic maneuvers proved unacceptable and resulted in greater altitude losses than were experienced during coordinated turns. So to the hairy-chested types who envision a wingover back to the runway following an engine failure, good luck. The maneuver itself may not cause an excessive altitude loss, but the recovery may be your last. Bear in mind that a turnaround maneuver is not complete until a normal flare arrests the sink rate and places the aircraft in a normal landing attitude. Aerobatic maneuvering usually fails to allow for this final, vital necessity.

One noteworthy exception was noticed when we flew the Cessna 150: the skidding turn. It is a technique recommended *only* for highly experienced pilots who are intimate with this popular aircraft.

Once the nose has been lowered following an engine failure and normal glide speed has been attained, place the Cessna 150 in a 30° banked turn. Slowly add bottom rudder. Simultaneously, apply whatever amount of top aileron is necessary to maintain a constant 30° bank angle. Continue cross-controlling until full bottom rudder has been applied. The result is a skidding turn with a rapid turn rate and nominal sink rate. The aircraft is fully controllable and shows no tendency to stall or spin. The altitude loss after recovery and landing flare is considerably less than 200 feet. Students and low-time pilots must not experiment with this maneuver unless accompanied by a flight instructor.

The applicability of this technique is peculiar to the aerodynamics of the Cessna 150. Similar techniques would not necessarily be satisfactory in other aircraft. We experimented with skidding turns in the Super

Cub and the Cherokee 140 and experienced altitude losses of 500 and 480 feet, respectively. In these aircraft, and probably in most others, the 45° banked turn is safer and more efficient.

It must be emphasized that no two aircraft types behave or perform similarly, even though they may have similar design features. The optimum turnaround technique for any specific aircraft type must be determined experimentally and be suitable for the experience level of the individual pilot.

Consider the position of a Cessna 172 at the completion of each of three 180° turns using bank angles of 30°, 45°, and 60°, respectively. As the bank angle steepens, lateral displacement from the extended runway centerline decreases. After completing a 45° banked, 180° turn, the aircraft is displaced 854 feet from the runway. Because of this lateral offset, it is obvious that a pilot with barely enough altitude to execute a 180° turn is still in jeopardy, unable to return to the runway. Additional maneuvering altitude is required to continue the turn beyond 180°.

It was felt initially that an extra 25% of altitude, beyond that lost in the turnaround itself, would be required to return to the airport. For example, in the case of a Cessna 172 in a 45° bank, we thought an extra 25% (75 feet) added to the 300 foot altitude loss during turnaround would be sufficient to jockey the aircraft into a position from which a safe landing could be made. This assumption was wrong. Further investigation and flight testing revealed that an extra 50% of altitude is needed. Instead of 300 feet, a Cessna 172 in a 45° bank requires a minimum of 450 feet. Similarly, a Cessna 150 in a 45° bank requires 420 feet; a Cherokee 140, 525 feet.

Once a pilot learns how much altitude a particular aircraft loses during a 180° gliding turn, he should increase this figure by 50% to determine the minimum safe turnaround altitude. By adding this result to the airport elevation, a pilot has a target altitude that should be attained before a return to the runway is contemplated. If a Cessna 172 pilot were departing an airport at 1,900 feet msl, for example, he would add a turnaround altitude of 450 feet to arrive at a target altitude of 2,350 feet msl. Below this altitude, a turnaround would not be recommended. Above 2,350 feet, a turnaround would probably be safe, depending on the distance traveled during the climb, the runway length, and the wind conditions.

A turnaround normally should not be made to a short runway because the pilot is afforded little or no margin for error. And since a turnaround usually results in a downwind landing, the problem of "deadsticking" into a short field is compounded. A turnaround probably should not be attempted when the runway is less than 3,000 feet long and the wind component down the centerline is in excess of 10 knots. Proportionately longer runways would be required as wind velocity increases.

When the pilot is taking off into strong headwinds, a turnaround is extremely risky because of the possibility of overshoot and the considerable runway length required to dissipate fast groundspeeds. Under these conditions, it is advisable to lower the nose and accept the terrain ahead. If initial impact groundspeed is cut in half by a strong headwind, the destructive energy of the aircraft is reduced by 75%, increasing the probability of survival. Doubling touchdown groundspeed, however, quadruples destructive potential and proportionately increases the chance of injury.

If a turnaround results in excessive altitude on final approach, it can be dissipated conventionally by S-turning, flap deployment, slipping, or a combination of these. If, on the other hand, a pilot winds up with a slight altitude deficiency and he's not sure whether the landing gear will clear the fence or destroy it, he might wait until the last possible second to extend flaps to the takeoff position. This last-ditch effort causes a slight ballooning in most aircraft and might be what's needed in a pinch. But since you don't get something for nothing, watch out for an increased sink rate after the fence has been left behind (hopefully intact).

A turnaround should be made into a crosswind (if any). Turning into the wind decreases lateral displacement from the runway and allows the aircraft to be more easily aligned with the centerline after the 180° turn has been completed. A downwind turn, however, allows the aircraft to drift farther from the runway, decreasing the likelihood of a safe return to the airport.

If the wind is blowing straight down the runway, then turn in whichever direction is most comfortable (left for most pilots). Consider, however, that as altitude is gained in the lower layers of the atmposhere, Mr. Coriolis makes the wind veer clockwise (in the Northern Hemisphere), suggesting that a right turn is more practical.

Of course, if a pilot departs from a parallel runway, he should turn toward the other parallel and land on it. He must not have a fixation about landing on the departure runway. When a pilot's one and only engine fails, no holds are barred. If a taxiway or another runway or a clear area between seems a better choice, then by all means use your options. Put the airplane on any surface that appears survivable.

As the landing is begun, do not allow a prolonged flare to eat up valuable terrain. Put the airplane down—firmly if necessary—and stomp on the binders. If obstacles loom ahead, raise the flaps to kill lift, consider groundlooping and if necessary, allow either or both wings (but not the nose) to strike an object, assisting in deceleration.

Do anything to stop the aircraft while keeping the fuselage intact. Some experts even consider a gear-up landing when deadsticking into a very short field. That'll slow down the airplane—fast. The idea is to save you and your passengers. To hell with the airplane; that can be replaced.

Tradition claims that landing is more hazardous than takeoff. Landing, we have learned, usually requires more finesse and expertise and has been compared to threading a needle. A takeoff, on the other hand, frequently is compared in simplicity to withdrawing thread from a needle. But when it comes to relying on the structural integrity of aircraft and engine, the takeoff offers more risk. This is when the powerplant and its related systems are first put to the crucial test, and when we learn if everything is going to hold together. Maximum performance is required when engine stresses and strains are at a maximum. A pilot is not as concerned about powerplant reliability during an approach because he has been assured of structural integrity while enroute.

Once a pilot acknowledges the risk of an engine failure during takeoff and initial climb, the least he can do is prepare for the possibility. One ace up his sleeve is knowing the minimum safe turnaround altitude of his aircraft.

Having a target altitude provides a psychological advantage during a time when a pilot is burdened with an assortment of departure chores and is least prepared for an engine failure. With a target altitude in mind, he is not forced to make an immediate "turn/no turn" decision. That determination was made where it should have been made—on the ground. If he is below target altitude, the pilot knows—without guessing—the inadvisability of a turnaround. Above this altitude, he can turn with some assurance of safety and, as a result, perform more calmly and efficiently than were he to turn without knowing the probability of his survival. An engine failure after takeoff is extremely frightening and can reduce mental sharpness to pudding with the snap of a connecting rod. (Take it from someone who's been there—twice!) Armed with a target altitude, a pilot is considerably ahead of the game.

When conditions suggest using the turnaround maneuver, a pilot can ill afford the luxury of guesswork. He must know that he can make it safely or he should not attempt the turn. Once committed to a course reversal, he must perform with cool, calculated precision, turning at the desired bank angle while maintaining closely the optimum glide speed. Large variations in pilot performance can drastically erode valuable altitude.

A pilot might be advised to keep his head in the cockpit and stay on instruments, while establishing the gliding turn, to assure himself of a proper entry. Neck-craning to locate the runway doesn't do any good until he has completed at least 90° of the turn. He must firmly resist the temptation to steepen the bank and/or reduce airspeed. An excessively nose-high attitude does not avert ground contact. On the contrary, it may rush things a bit. (A 5% variation in glide speed does not cause any appreciable erosion of glide performance.)

When a pilot follows a calculated course of action, his mind is less encumbered with fear, offering him the opportunity to attempt a restart of the failed engine. Perhaps the problem can be eliminated by switching fuel tanks or adding carburetor heat. But to maneuver the aircraft and simultaneously analyze an engine failure requires a clear head. Preparation makes this possible.

As you read this, you will no doubt consider the ancient arguments against a turn after takeoff. Many of these are valid and have been reviewed, but what about the arguments favoring a return to the airport? There are many, including the most obvious temptation: the availability of a long, smooth landing surface. Also, a disabled aircraft can be handled better on an airport than off, and the airport may have firefighting equipment and an ambulance available. An off-airport crash can delay assistance, making a timely rescue difficult or even impossible.

Additionally, it is instinctive in man to want to return to the comfort and security in which he begins. Babies want their mothers; pilots want airports. Surprise a pilot by retarding the throttle during a routine departure and the chances are excellent that he will—without thinking—initiate a turnaround without regard to altitude.

To emphasize the influence of this subconscious, instinctive desire to return, it is worthwhile to draw from the crash experience of the air carriers. When an airliner makes a survivable crash landing at night, most of the passengers usually flock towards the single front door through which they entered originally. Never mind that the stewardess is urging them to leave through a closer, more suitable exit; they're not listening. Shocked passengers are often hellbent for leather to travel the entire length of the fuselage (even through an over-wing fuselage fire) to get to where it all began—the front door.

When a pilot is below the minimum safe turnaround altitude, he must fight this natural, often overwhelming instinct to return to the airport.

One procedure far superior to the turnaround maneuver is simply to avoid the engine failure in the first place. Since fuel starvation/exhaustion is more common than structural/mechanical failure, a pilot should modify his normal thorough preflight to include setting the fuel selector valve on the fullest tank *prior* to engine start. Once this is done, the valve should not be moved again until the aircraft is safely enroute.

Many pilots reposition the selector valve during runup. Wrong! Absolutely wrong! When a tank is selected so soon before takeoff, a pilot has no assurance the engine is operating on an unrestricted flow of fuel. There may be only sufficient fuel in the lines for the plane to become airborne before sudden silence stuns the pilot into quiet, unnerving reality.

By selecting the desired fuel tank *before* engine start, a pilot can test fuel-flow integrity before departure. Sufficient fuel is used during engine start, normal taxi, and runup to guarantee fuel from the tank is indeed flowing freely to the engine.

As the throttle is advanced during the initial takeoff roll, the pilot should consider the possibility of an aborted takeoff. After maximum power is stabilized, he should listen carefully for unusual roughness and judiciously scan engine gauges. Unfortunately, too few single-engine pilots are mentally prepared for an abort; they are "wired to go" and tend to either ignore or contend with abnormalities until it is too late to simply retard the throttle and brake to a safe stop.

One year I administered 24 biennial flight reviews. It became my habit to pop open the right-hand door at approximately 30 knots during the takeoff roll. Of the 24 pilots I checked, only five rejected the takeoff. The other 19 persisted with the takeoff even though more than 4,000 feet of usable runway remained ahead. This dramatically emphasizes that many pilots lack mental preparation during takeoff and fail to consider an abort might be necessary. A problem on the ground is rarely serious, but when it is taken aloft, a pilot has the devil as copilot.

After liftoff, if wing flaps are used, they should be retracted as soon as practicable, since keeping them extended hinders climb performance. The idea is to climb as rapidly as possible to the minimum turnaround altitude.

The climb should be made at the best rate of climb speed, which, contrary to popular opinion, is not a fixed number. This airspeed varies with aircraft weight and density altitude. The Cessna 172, for example, has a best rate of climb speed of 71 knots (IAS), but this is valid only at sea level when the aircraft weighs 2,300 pounds. As gross weight decreases to 1,700 pounds and density altitude increases to 15,000 feet, recommended climb speed decreases gradually to 63 knots (IAS). Pilots should review climb performance data provided in their operating handbooks to determine how these variables affect climb speeds.

The best rate of climb speed in most light airplanes is very nearly the same as the optimum glide speed. Therefore, if the aircraft is trimmed for the proper climb speed when the engine quits, retrimming for glide is minimized.

Many pilots habitually retard the throttle almost immediately after liftoff. This should be avoided. If the engine is running properly at maximum power, don't disturb a thing. Leave the engine alone and use it to achieve maximum climb performance. Do not reduce power until safely above the minimum turnaround altitude. Don't worry about damaging or overheating the engine; this procedure has no adverse effect on the modern engine.

Statistically, the most likely time for an engine failure (for mechanical reasons) is during the first power reduction after takeoff—another excellent reason not to touch the throttle until reaching a safe altitude.

Once airborne, get into the habit of looking for a place to land. It may be difficult to think about a forced landing during the early moments of flight, but this simple procedure can pay off handsomely. If a spot has been selected, the shock of an engine failure at low altitude isn't quite so traumatic. Suitable landing sites are not always ahead or behind; they may be off to the side. The point is that the pilot should look for one while he has the opportunity. It's like insurance; hopefully he'll never use it.

No one can be so presumptuous as to tell a pilot exactly what to do when his engine fails after takeoff. It is for each pilot to decide what course of action is best for him. The foregoing provides valuable techniques and data resulting from a rather lengthy and exhaustive investigation of the available options. Hopefully this will be of use to those who acknowledge the risk we assume during every takeoff.

Fortunately, the modern engine can tolerate considerable abuse and mismanagement before failing its master. But—like cancer and obesity—engine failures do occur. The thought of an engine failure after takeoff may be frightening; however, ignoring the possibility can be fatal.

MULTI-ENGINE IFR

*What to do when your twin
becomes a single in the soup*

There is a dangerous deficiency in the Federal Aviation Regulations.

Consider this. The average IFR pilot earns his instrument rating in a single-engine airplane. Generally, when he upgrades to a multi-engine rating he does so during a series of VFR flights. This pilot is then legally qualified to operate a light twin during actual instrument conditions.

This, according to numerous FAA inspectors and accident investigators, is blatantly dangerous because many (and perhaps most) nonprofessional, instrumented rated, multi-engine pilots have never been required to demonstrate engine-out proficiency during simulated IFR conditions. (Briefly, during 1973 and 1974, such a demonstration was required of applicants for the multi-engine class rating who had instrument ratings, but for some unknown reason this requirement was deleted.)

Those who are honest with themselves concede that the average "multi" pilot has difficulty managing an actual engine failure occuring shortly after takeoff during VFR conditions. Proof of this is the fatal accident rate caused by engine failures. *The rate for twins is double that of single-engine aircraft.*

But should a power failure occur after penetrating a low overcast, the effect can be traumatizing. The average pilot becomes bewildered by a spectacular array of deflected needles, spinning instruments and confusing data. The result is often fatal.

During a period of 12 months, I administered eight Biennial Flight Reviews to multi-engine, instrument rated pilots. Each was asked to don an IFR hood shortly after takeoff (about 300 feet agl). In each case, I simulated failure of the critical engine at between 700 and 900 feet agl. Instant disaster. Seven of the pilots lost control of the aircraft and admitted later that they had never before practiced the maneuver in other than CAVU conditions.

Curiosity compelled me to visit (and call) several FBOs where I inquired as to what maneuvers a pilot would be required to demonstrate prior to renting one of their light twins. Not one checkout was to include any simulated IFR flight. The industry-at-large (including the FAA) seems to assume that if a pilot has instrument and multi-engine ratings, he also has the ability to use them in combination. This illogical assumption has resulted in an unncessary loss of lives.

Many pilots are unable to prevent this type of disaster for one very simple reason: *they have never had to acquire or demonstrate the skills necessary to perform such a complex procedure.*

Since no one requires a non-professional to develop engine-out, IFR proficiency, the conscientious pilot must take it upon himself to obtain the necessary instruction. In the meantime, it might be worthwhile to consider what follows.

Numerous sources of information recommend the initial climb speed of a fully powered light twin be Vyse, the engine-out, best rate of climb airspeed (assuming all obstacles have been cleared and the gear and flaps have been retracted). The theory behind this is that the aircraft will be at the most efficient climb speed in case of an engine failure. Nice theory, but it doesn't work that way.

When an engine fails, it takes at least a few seconds for the pilot to react. In the meantime, airspeed erodes to less than Vyse (the blue radial marking on the airspeed gauge) and climb performance suffers.

Normally, it is wiser to climb at Vy, the best rate of climb airspeed when both engines are operating. Vy is better than Vyse for three reasons. First of all, when both engines are developing power, Vy results in the most rapid altitude gain—and altitude is one of a pilot's most precious commodities. With an ample supply, he has some room for error; without it, pilot performance must be flawless.

Secondly, Vy is usually faster than Vyse. Therefore, should an engine fail while climbing at Vy, some loss of airspeed cannot only be tolerated, it is desirable. This is because once the failure occurs, Vyse (a slower airspeed) becomes the new best rate of climb airspeed.

Thirdly, because Vy is faster than Vyse, it requires a slightly shallower pitch angle which represents a safer attitude in case of engine failure. The last thing a pilot wants concurrent with power loss is an unnecessarily high nose attitude. The larger the pitch angle, the more rapidly airspeed will decay.

When an engine fails during visual conditions, a pilot immediately recognizes the resultant yaw because of the eye-catching movement of the aircraft relative to the horizon. But when the natural horizon is obscured by cloud, the amount and direction of assymetrical yaw is not as easily determined (especially if the aircraft is in a turn when the failure occurs).

The pilot has only a pitifully few seconds to properly interpret the instruments and decide which engine has failed. This procedure is not as simple as it sounds, especially when the situation occurs unexpectedly during the initial phase of an IFR climb. Often, time is lost while simply trying to determine which instruments offer the most reliable, easiest-to-interpret information. Surprisingly, many pilots wastefully shift attention to the engine gauges to determine which engine has failed.

Instead, they should stick to basics—the gyro instruments.

The yaw created by assymetrical thrust is most accurately indicated by the directional gyro. Firmly apply rudder pressure to whichever pedal will prevent further heading change. Also, keep a sharp eye on the artificial horizon. If the bank angle increases, the odds are you're stomping on the wrong pedal.

Much more can be written to describe the interpretation of various instruments under these conditions, but nothing is as descriptive as actual experience. Dual instruction in this procedure is mandatory. A low altitude, IFR engine failure does not offer sufficient time for experimentation. A pilot must know precisely what to do without hesitation, or he and his craft may be scheduled for extermination. It's almost that simple.

Directional control cannot be maintained without sufficient airspeed, without a life-supporting flow of air rushing past the rudder. It would be ludicrous to suggest there are very many pilots who don't know about the need to maintain airspeed healthily above Vmc (minimum controllable airspeed). But if this is the case, why do so many accidents result from attempted single-engine flight at airspeeds slower than Vmc?

The loss of an engine often results in an unavoidable descent. This is especially true if the failed engine has yet to have its propeller feathered. Very few light twins can climb on one engine while the opposite propeller is windmilling. A pilot's instinctive reaction to an unwinding altimeter—especially when IFR—is to apply back pressure to the control wheel in a futile attempt to arrest sink rate. This often results in an airspeed bleed to less than Vmc whereupon control of the airplane is impossible without reducing power on the "good" engine.

The pilot must be willing to accept an altitude loss during the time it takes to feather the propeller and determine that the gear and flaps are retracted. If insufficient altitude is available, it is far wiser to impact the earth with control than to spin in. All of this emphasizes the need to climb at Vy when both engines are operative. A safe altitude must be attained as quickly as possible.

Until the airplane has been cleaned up, sink rate can be minimized by maintaining Vyse. Any airspeed, either faster or slower, results only in an increased rate of descent. If the airplane has sufficient power, of course, flight at this identical airspeed produces the maximum possible rate of climb. But such positive results are not likely to occur until the prop of the inoperative engine has been feathered.

It seems so simple a chore. Just keep the airspeed needle on the blue radial mark. So simple in principle; so difficult in reality. The survival instinct somehow overrides logic and rejects the acceptance of a low altitude, IFR sink rate, however temporary this condition may be. But cold logic must prevail and the pilot must concentrate almost totally on maintaining directional control and an optimum climb speed.

Once control of the airplane has been established, the prop of the malfunctioning engine must be feathered. This assumes, of course, that the problem cannot be remedied and that the ailing engine is not delivering sufficient power to overcome its own drag.

The feathering procedure must be executed as promptly as possible, but not so rapidly that a pilot risks shutting down the wrong engine. It happens.

The first step usually recommended is to retard the throttle of the inoperative engine (remember, "dead foot—dead engine"). This verifies that an excited pilot has the correct engine in mind. If throttle retardation results in sudden silence, advance the lever to its original, full forward position and shift attention to the other engine. Then, depending on advice found in the pilot's operating handbook, either retard the mixture to "idle cutoff" and feather, or vice-versa. (After the engine has been shut down, advance the throttle to eliminate distraction caused by the gear-warning horn.)

As the propeller feathers, the aircraft should accelerate to beyond Vyse (unless the nose is raised simultaneously) and this airspeed *carefully* maintained. Hopefully, the aircraft will climb, but don't count on it. Climb performance depends on density altitude and the pilot's ability to maintain the proper airspeed.

Unfortunately, Vyse is not a fixed airspeed as is implied by the blue radial marking on the indicator. The marking represents only the *maximum* Vyse and is valid only when the aircraft is at maximum allowable gross weight and at sea level. As altitude increases and gross weight decreases, Vyse decreases.

Take the case of a Cessna 310R. Maximum Vyse is 106 knots (blue radial marking), but Vyse is only 92 knots when the aircraft is lightly loaded at 5,000 feet msl. If this airplane, for example, is at 5,000 feet and the "blue line" airspeed (106 knots) is maintained, it will not climb nearly as well as when the slower airspeed is used. Often, flight at the "blue line" instead of at a more suitable, slower Vyse can mean the difference between climb and descent.

Most "multi" pilots don't have the various Vyse speeds committed to memory and yet these performance numbers can be critical to survival. It is strongly recommended that a small placard of Vyse speeds be prepared and placed on the instrument panel (near the airspeed indicator) for ready reference.

Now the airplane is aerodynamically clean and being flown at that Vyse which is appropriate to altitude and weight. Is this pilot out of the woods yet? No way. He's got other, perhaps more ominous difficulties ahead.

First of all, is the single-engine climb performance sufficient to climb to a safe maneuvering altitude from which an IFR approach can be executed? And, where will the pilot go to execute that approach?

The most immediate problem may be climb performance. Many light twins simply can't climb to a very high altitude especially when loaded to gross on a warm day.

For the purpose of this discussion, consider a Cessna 310C, a relatively good single-engine performer in anybody's book. At a density altitude of only 2,500 feet, the 310C has a single-engine climb rate of only 310 fpm. This doesn't sound too bad until you realize it equates to a 160 foot climb per mile of horizontal flight, which is a climb angle of only 1.7°. If the terrain ahead has an uphill slope of more than 1.7°, an involuntary landing is likely.

At 5,000 feet, the same airplane climbs at a rate of only 93 feet per mile (a 1° climb angle). Consider that this is a twin with better-than-average single-engine performance; most other non-turbocharged twins can't do as well.

All of this simply validates the maxim, "Twin-engine airplanes are equipped with two engines for the best of all possible reasons: they (usually) don't fly worth a damn on one."

Therefore, if the climb is being made toward rising terrain, the pilot is in deep trouble unless he has the presence of mind to reverse course and head toward lower terrain. And since he is IFR, it wouldn't be a bad idea for him to stay in touch with ATC.

Thus far nothing has been said about Vxse, that airspeed which provides the best angle of climb while operating on one engine. To overfly obstacles, Vxse is certainly more desirable than Vyse. But the use of this slower airspeed raises two cogent points. One, the already negligible single-engine climb angle usually is not increased significantly. At sea level, the increase in climb angle of a Cessna 310C is less than 15% and even this modest increase diminishes with altitude. But the pilot engulfed in cloud usually believes that the aircraft is climbing more steeply than it really is. A dangerous assumption.

Secondly, if the propeller has yet to be feathered, Vxse is not that much faster than Vmc. In the case of the Cessna 310C, Vxse is 83 knots and Vmc is 71 knots. This represents only a 12 knot margin of safety between the best climb angle and uncontrollability.

Once the propeller is feathered, however, Vmc reduces to a somewhat slower airspeed which increases the safety margin (and relieves that throbbing leg from having to apply almost full rudder).

Now let's assume that the departure airport is reporting less than landing minimums. The takeoff was legal, but a complete IFR approach may not be. At this point, however, perhaps legality isn't too important. After all, a pilot can exercise his emergency authority. But how safe would it be to shoot such an approach while maneuvering on one lung? Not very.

This, then, becomes a serious point to consider. When departing an airport with less than the needed minimums, a prudent pilot should have a nearby alternate airport in mind, one to which a complete engine-out IFR approach would be both legal *and* safe.

Once the pilot is enroute to a suitable approach fix, he must administer the necessary climb with the patience of Job. A climb from sea level to 5,000 feet in a 310R requires 19 minutes and 40 miles (an average altitude gain of only 125 feet per mile).

Consider that the 310R is relatively spunky on one engine. Several other non-turbocharged twins not only wouldn't do as well, but may be unable to climb to 5,000 feet at all. Here is where a pilot's knowledge of his aircraft's single-engine performance is mandatory. There's no point trying to climb to unreachable heights.

Generally, it is wise not to rely on being able to climb above the airplane's single-engine service ceiling (gross weight considered). This is the altitude above which a 50 fpm climb rate cannot be maintained (with one engine).

Once a safe altitude has been attained, the rest is all downhill, literally and figuratively.

But the engine-out, IFR approach also warrants special consideration. When on final approach, maintain an airspeed of at least Vyse until landing is assured. Should a missed approach become necessary (pray that it doesn't), it is convenient to already have the necessary airspeed. For the same reason, also delay gear and *total* flap extension until landing is assured.

On the other hand, avoid unnecessarily fast airspeeds that could result in an overshoot. Also, be aware that deceleration during the landing flare will be less than normal because the feathered propeller doesn't create nearly as much braking drag as when it is windmilling.

Also at this time, be alert for a yaw toward the "good" engine when its throttle is retarded. The severity of this yaw depends partially on how much contributory rudder trim had been applied earlier *in that direction* to prevent a yaw (during the approach) toward the "dead" engine.

Coping with an engine failure in a light twin during the initial phase of an IFR climb is one of general aviation's most complex procedures. But only a small percentage of non-professional, instrument rated, multi-engine pilots have ever been exposed to the necessary, life-saving practice. And this is a deficiency that defies reason.

MULTI-ENGINE 'DRIFT DOWN'

*Engine-out service ceilings are
not as restrictive as you think*

Aviation progress generally is measured by improvements in power, payload, speed and range. But because of revised priorities, this trend has been somewhat altered; added emphasis is being placed on smaller, quieter, more efficient designs.

Airframe manufacturers, for example, already have produced a family of very light twins with 400 or less total horsepower to meet the fuel-conscious needs of the eighties. These include Cessna's Model 303, the Beechcraft Duchess, Gulfstream American's Cougar and Piper's Seminole. Although these newcomers are welcome relief to those without their own oil wells, others consider such aircraft a giant step *backwards*. This is because of the *apparent* lack of single-engine performance that is characteristic of these new generation aircraft. All have relatively low single-engine service ceilings, which vary from 4,100 feet (the Seminole) to 6,170 feet (the Duchess).

One conclusion drawn from these specifications is that an engine failure while cruising over mountainous terrain converts a perky twin into little more than a powered glider that is compelled to descend helplessly towards the high-rise granite. Such a conclusion, however, is fallacious. The situation is *not* that critical. By allowing a twin to "drift down" gradually, a pilot is afforded considerably more time and distance than he might imagine. In all but extreme cases, such a crippled twin *can* hobble to an airport and perform a safe landing even when that airport is above the aircraft's single-engine ceiling.

To begin with, the failure of an engine does not necessitate descending to the single-engine service ceiling. At this altitude, after all, the aircraft is capable of *climbing* 50 fpm. The aircraft will descend, however, to its single-engine *absolute* ceiling, which is substantially above the service ceiling. For example, an engine-out Beech Duchess has a service ceiling of only 6,170 feet, but an absolute ceiling of 8,000 feet.

Secondly, these altitude limits apply only when the aircraft is at maximum allowable gross weight, an improbable condition considering fuel burnoff during climb and cruise. An aircraft weighing less enjoys dramatically higher service and absolute ceilings.

Consider, for example, a heavily loaded Beech Duchess cruising at 16,000 feet over the 14,000 foot peaks of Colorado. The aircraft will not "fall out of the sky" following an engine failure. At 16,000 feet, the Duchess can be held to a sink rate as low as 228 fpm. When the aircraft reaches 14,000 feet, sink rate is only 180 fpm. This provides ample time to head for lower terrain.

At 10,000 feet, the rate of descent is a mere 60 fpm because of increased power available from the operative engine. Considerably more than an hour after engine failure, the aircraft finally settles at and maintains its absolute ceiling of 8,000 feet. Surely, however, the Duchess will have burned off considerable fuel and weigh much less than its maximum allowable weight, giving an absolute ceiling of 9,000 feet or higher.

The drift-down range and the distance that a Duchess can be flown during an engine-out descent (at gross weight) can be illustrated by the following data. While descending from 14,600 to 10,200 feet, for example, the aircraft has a still-air range of 50 nm. From 14,000 to 9,000 feet, engine-out range is 80 nm.

Although published single-engine service ceilings do reflect practical climb limits, they obviously are well below the altitudes to which "single-engine" twins can descend and maintain. In this respect, airframe manufacturers are conservative. Often, a twin powered by only one engine can maintain an altitude twice as high as its engine-out service ceiling.

Since the above example reflects *theoretical* drift-down data for the spunkiest of the very light twins, it is appropriate to examine the actual drift-down performance of the Piper Seminole because of its minimal single-engine altitude capability. Such a flight test was conducted by this writer and resulted in the revealing data shown in Table 5-A.

While cruising at 14,000 feet, the left engine was throttled and feathered. Rudder trim was applied and the aircraft stabilized in a descent. The first 1,000 feet of altitude loss consumed 3 minutes and 36 seconds, an average sink rate of 254 fpm. Almost six minutes elapsed while drifting down from 13,000 to 12,000 feet, an average sink rate of only 168 fpm—not bad for an aircraft that was only 260 pounds under gross at "engine failure."

It took fully an hour to drift down to 8,000 feet where the sink rate was only 44 fpm. Extrapolation shows that the Seminole eventually would have leveled at 7,600 feet, almost twice as high as the published single-engine service ceiling of 4,100 feet.

It also is interesting to note that the still-air range during this descent was 104 nm; average sink rate during the 5,000 foot loss was less than 100 fpm.

Using this data and aeronautical charts of the Rocky Mountain states, it can be shown that no matter where in the 48 contiguous states such an engine failure might occur, the Seminole would almost always be within drift-down range of a suitable airport.

Certainly this indicates that once any of these very light twins has climbed to some minimum safe altitude, an engine failure—even when above the published service ceiling—rarely dictates the need to make an off-airport, single-engine landing.

ALTITUDE LOSS	ELAPSED TIME PER 1,000 FEET	CUMULATIVE TIME	AVERAGE SINK RATE	DRIFT-DOWN RANGE PER 1,000 = FT LOSS	CUMULATIVE DISTANCE	DESCENT GRADIENT	EQUIVALENT "GLIDE RATO"	TRUE AIRSPEED
14,000 to 13,000	3:56	3:56	-254 fpm	7.2 nm	7.2 nm	1.3°	44:1	110 kt
13,000 to 12,000	5:58	9:54	-168 fpm	10.7 nm	17.9 nm	0.9°	65:1	108 kt
12,000 to 11,000	6:34	16:28	-152 fpm	11.7 nm	29.6 nm	0.8°	71:1	107 kt
11,000 to 10,000	8:32	25:00	-117 fpm	14.9 nm	44.5 nm	0.6°	91:1	105 kt
10,000 to 9,000	12:19	37:19	- 81 fpm	21.1 nm	65.6 nm	0.4°	128:1	103 kt
9,000 to 8,000	22:46	60:05	- 44 fpm	38.5 nm	104.1 nm	0.2°	234:1	102 kt

Drift-Down Flight Test Data, Piper Seminole—Conditions: one engine inoperative, max continuous power on operating engine; 85 knots; gear up—flaps up—cowl flaps open (operative engine); 260 lb under gross weight.

Table 5-A

Unfortunately, manufacturers of very light twins have not developed specific recommendations for drifting down to a single-engine absolute ceiling following the failure of one engine. Thankfully, however, the procedure is relatively simple and applies to *any* multi-engine airplane being flown above its engine-out ceiling.

When the ailing engine rolls over and dies, the prescribed shutdown checklist should be completed. But don't be in too much of a hurry lest ye shall join the elite ranks of those who have feathered the wrong engine. Simultaneously, maintain altitude while the airspeed bleeds to that normally used for the best single-engine rate of climb. Vyse (the blue radial mark on the airspeed indicator). Then allow the aircraft to descend while maintaining this airspeed with the operative engine developing maximum power. It is important to recognize that Vyse results in the minimum sink rate (when above the absolute ceiling) or the maximum climb rate (when below the absolute ceiling). Under no circumstances, therefore, should the airspeed be allowed to vary either above or below Vyse. Otherwise drift-down performance suffers due to an increased rate of descent.

In other words, if maintaining Vyse doesn't result in a climb or the ability to maintain altitude, accept the sink rate (which will diminish steadily) and drift down to an altitude that can be maintained (the single-engine absolute ceiling).

It is very tempting when above the absolute ceiling to attempt maintaining altitude by raising the nose excessively and permitting airspeed to decay. Not only is this futile, it is extremely hazardous because of two significant factors.

First of all, the wings of a twin have different stall speeds when a propeller is feathered. Because of the absence of propwash, the wing supporting the "caged" engine stalls several knots faster than the wing with the good engine.

Secondly, because the naturally aspirated, operative engine develops considerably less than 100% power when at altitude, the minimum controllable airspeed (Vmc) is much lower than when the aircraft is at sea level. As a result, not as much rudder force is required to prevent yaw. But more significant is that Vmc may be considerably lower than the stall speed of the wing supporting the inoperative engine.

Therefore, if airspeed is allowed to drop much below Vyse, the "unpowered" wing probably will stall before directional control is lost. Such a stall conspires with the asymmetrical power condition to produce a most wicked spin. The maneuver is definitely counterproductive. Recovery necessitates throttling back the operative engine and involves a considerable altitude loss.

Although maintaining Vyse results in the minimum sink rate during drift-down, it does not necessarily maximize range. To fly the maximum horizontal distance during each thousand feet of altitude loss, it is necessary to maintain the "max-range" airspeed. Unfortunately, such a speed rarely is provided by general aviation airframe manufacturers. But in the case of very light twins, this speed is so close to Vyse that the difference in range is almost negligible. In the case of the Duchess, for example, max-range speed is 87 knots (CAS) while Vyse is 85 knots (CAS).

Once drift-down begins, use visual observations, sectional charts and an ATC radar facility (if available) to determine the safest direction in which to lose altitude. Usually it is best to head for down-slope valleys that lead to lower terrain and, hopefully, a suitable airport.

But don't be in a hurry to turn. Steep bank angles produce increased sink rates. A 15° bank angle should be considered a maximum. Although such a shallow bank angle may seem insufficient, the turn rate this produces when flying at reduced airspeed (Vyse) is usually more than adequate.

And if a pilot is having difficulty maintaining his sanity during an engine-out drift-down, he might consider advancing the throttle of the dead engine to silence the gear warning horn.

Also during the descent, try to hold a steady pitch attitude to maintain the desired airspeed; chasing the airspeed needle is inefficient and increases average sink rates. If an autopilot is available, by all means, use it to decrease cockpit workload (but only after the rudder has been trimmed properly). While descending at so slow an airspeed, be sure to maintain a watchful eye on the cylinder head temperature of the operative engine (which is developing maximum possible power). As altitude is lost, ambient temperature usually increases, as does the power output of the engine. This usually results in warmer cylinder head temperatures, but these probably will not become excessive at intermediate altitudes. If the CHT needle does creep toward the red line, however, reduce rpm slightly. This reduces internal engine friction without significantly affecting power and sink rate.

Since drifting down to the airplane's single-engine absolute ceiling can take well over an hour, consider the possible need to crossfeed. Yes, accidents have been caused because the only operative engine suffered a fatal case of fuel starvation while the opposite tank remained untapped.

Once the absolute ceiling is reached and a specific altitude can be maintained, the airplane continues to become lighter. Unless power is reduced, this results in a slight airspeed increase which can be used to "drift up" (at Vyse) to gain additional altitude.

There comes a time during such an emergency when a pilot's thoughts turn to landing . . . as soon as possible. In most cases, this requires little more than a single-engine approach to a low-lying airport. But if man and machine are over (or between!) the Rocky Mountains, for example, the nearest suitable airport may be near or *above* the airplane's single-engine ceiling. Such a problem requires considerable planning and cool heads-upmanship.

First of all, if an airport can be seen in the distance, it most likely is within range even if an initial appraisal indicates otherwise. Consider the data extracted during the Seminole flight test, for example (Table 5-A). Notice that the descent from 12,000 to 11,000 feet resulted in an effective "glide ratio" of 71 to 1, which is considerably better than could be expected from the world's most efficient sailplane. The descent from 10,000 to 9,000 feet resulted in a "glide ratio" of 128 to 1, which is equivalent to a descent gradient of only four-tenths of 1°.

Properly interpreted, this means that, yes, if an airport can be seen, it probably is possible to get there safely and execute a landing no matter how far away it appears to be. But to be certain, watch the airport carefully from afar. If the landing area moves up with respect to a point on the windshield, you may not make it. Consider, however, that during drift-down, the descent angle becomes much shallower (and eventually becomes horizontal), which might confirm the ability to reach an airport previously rejected. If and when the landing area moves down with respect to a point on the windshield, you've got it made.

The approach to such a high elevation airport must be executed carefully. Very carefully. Since a missed approach is virtually impossible because of the inability to climb (or even maintain altitude), the pilot is afforded only one opportunity. Fortunately, the maneuver doesn't require any fancy footwork.

To begin with, establish a long final approach. The aircraft should be lined up with the runway when at least three miles out. Use a normal, 3° approach slot. Although at least one airframe manufacturer recommends a higher-than-normal approach, this is not a particularly good idea because of the potential for an overshoot, which is at least as hazardous as an undershoot. If everything appears through the windshield as it normally does during a conventional approach, this helps to make the pilot feel more comfortable and enables him to more easily detect minor excursions from the visual "glide slope." And since the engine-out twin has such an outstanding "glide ratio" on one engine, there's no real problem if the aircraft dips somewhat below the slot. Simply maintain Vyse and sufficient power to recapture the "glide slope." A normal slot, after all, descends at 3° while a single-engine twin can be made to descend at only a fraction of a degree.

A slight excess of airspeed (about ten knots), however, is recommended until on short final approach.

Finally, when the landing is assured, extend the landing gear and flaps. During the flare and while reducing power, anticipate the need to apply rudder *toward* the dead engine to compensate for opposite rudder trim that had been applied earlier, as well as the drag created by the now-windmilling propeller of the good engine.

Occasionally a departure is made from an airport with a density altitude that is well above the single-engine ceiling of a light twin. An engine failure after takeoff, therefore, would result in a compulsory drift down to earth.

One way to avoid this is to load lightly because of the substantial effect this has on raising the single-engine ceiling. Instead of topping off the tanks before departure, for example, consider an enroute landing for fuel at an airport with a lower elevation. Otherwise be mentally prepared to descend should an engine failure spoil the climbout. If the aircraft has reached at least 1,000 feet agl, a turnaround to the airport may be possible because of the minimal sink rate that can be maintained when below 10,000 feet msl. If a turnaround is not practical, accept the notion of an off-airport landing. By maintaining Vyse and maximum available power from the operative engine, the outstanding "glide ratio" should offer a considerable choice of landing sites even when at a relatively low altitude.

Statistics indicate, however, that a multi-engine pilot is psychologically unable to accept the reality of an off-airport landing as long as one engine is developing power. This stems from the erroneous belief that having two engines is an insurance policy against a forced landing due to the failure of one engine. He attempts to climb or maintain altitude even when conditions dictate that such performance is impossible. More often than not, the result is an asymmetrically powered spin that punctuates the flight quickly and with finality.

If maintaining Vyse results in a descent and lower terrain is not within range, accept a forced landing while maintaining control of the aircraft. This is much preferable to a spin and increases the probability of survival dramatically.

The new generation of light, twin-engine aircraft are relatively economical and safe, but only when flown properly by a pilot who appreciates their and his limitations. By understanding their performance potential and planning conservatively, an engine failure at altitude won't seem quite so traumatic.

The author wishes to thank Mr. Ken Krueger of Krueger Aviation whose probing and curiosity lead to this investigation of the engine-out performance of very light twins.

FLIGHT CONTROL FAILURE

What to do if something sticks—or snaps

It happened during the student pilot's fifth lesson. The instructor was demonstrating an accelerated stall when the control wheel suddenly fell limp in his hand. As the nose plunged earthward, the instructor desperately pulled the wheel full aft. But there was no response. It was impossible to raise the elevator.

Or was it? During those agonizing moments of panic, the instructor caught a mental flash of a technique often discussed but rarely practiced. He reached for the pitch-trim wheel and rotated it rearward. The crippled aircraft reacted sluggishly; total nose-up control had not been lost.

For the next half hour, the crippled Cessna 150 was nursed toward a nearby airport. But during the landing approach a burst of power was applied to prevent an undershoot. The resulting pitch-up could not be countered sufficiently with trim. The beleaguered aircraft stalled 50 feet in the air and impacted the earth nose first. Both occupants were injured critically.

A portion of every pilot's training is devoted to the most common emergencies, especially engine failure. Unfortunately, there are other potential crises that are given little or no attention. One of these is the partial or total failure of a primary flight control.

Such an emergency occurs infrequently, but not so rarely that it can be ignored. NTSB records annually reflect numerous accidents attributable to flight control difficulties.

The most serious such problem, of course, is the loss of elevator control. Yes, the trim tab can be used to control pitch within limits, but few pilots appreciate how difficult it can be to *land* without a fully functioning elevator. Anyone who makes light of such a problem probably has never done it. This was demonstrated dramatically during a series of test flights with experienced pilots in the left seat. One of them was Cal Pitts.

Pitts is a Project Officer at NASA's Ames Research Center; he's also a veteran pilot and a highly seasoned instructor. After we had discussed a recent accident involving a failed elevator cable, Pitts expressed confidence in *his* ability to take off and land an airplane without touching the control wheel. A five dollar wager flew out of my hip pocket and landed neatly on the coffee table between us. It was met with an equal amount and we headed for the airport and a rented Cessna 150.

With his right hand, Pitts opened the throttle; his left hand, itching to grasp the control wheel, remained in his lap. At 50 knots, he cranked in a bit of nose-up trim. The 150 lifted off nicely. But at 20 feet agl, the Cessna pitched up unexpectedly. Rapid nose-down trim was applied and a stall averted, but now the Cessna was heading downhill. Nose-up trim was added—frantically. After more porpoising and trimming, the aircraft was stabilized in a normal climb. Pitts smiled smugly, not realizing that the most difficult challenge had yet to be met.

He skidded the 150 around the pattern with light rudder pressures and positioned us on the downwind leg. With one hand on the trim wheel, Pitts retarded the throttle with the other. The nose pitched down. Pitts decided it would be easier to raise the nose by reapplying power rather than bothering with excessive use of the trim wheel. Good thinking.

We were both surprised at the large amount of pitch change resulting from so little as a 100 rpm power change. In practice, aircraft attitude can be controlled, within limits, solely by judicious use of the throttle. Add power to raise the nose; reduce power to lower it.

While on base, Pitts made a major error—he extended the flaps. As soon as the spring-loaded switch was depressed, the nose pitched skyward—insistently. Considerable trim was required to return the nose to the horizon. But it didn't stop there. It kept going down. Nose-up trim was applied. Again, the nose returned to the horizon and failed to stop at the desired attitude. Several oscillations later, Pitts finally brought the Cessna under control. A lesson was learned: flap deflection can create pitch changes much larger than can be controlled by trim alone. Flaps, if they are used during "stick-free" flight, must be used gingerly, extending or retracting them only 1° or 2° at a time.

After stabilizing the aircraft on final approach at a modest sink rate, Pitts felt confidence return. As the wheels neared the concrete, he gradually applied nose-up trim. But at 10 feet agl and without warning, the plane began nosing toward the concrete. Pitts countered with rapid nose-up trim but it was too little and too late. He admitted reluctantly that had I not grabbed the wheel, the aircraft would have landed nose-wheel first. Damage, we concluded, would have been likely.

After cleaning up the aircraft (both inside and out), we taxied back to Runway 21 for another try. Six attempts later, Pitts made his first hands-off landing to a full stop. And his progress was better than other pilots tested.

Preparing for this type of emergency is difficult. Handling characteristics vary considerably from one airplane to another. Simply because a pilot can make a stick-free landing in one aircraft doesn't necessarily mean that he can do it in another. But some practice in any airplane helps to understand the complexities and variables. Stick-free landings, however, must never be attempted without a capable pilot with sharp reflexes in the right seat. Unfortunately, a stick-free landing cannot be simulated at altitude for reasons explained later. Also, be extremely careful during a "hands-off" missed approach. A gross and uncontrollable pitch-up may occur when full power is applied rapidly.

Five variables affect pitch: flaps, power, center of gravity, trim and ground effect. Each must be understood if a pilot is to successfully land an aircraft without a fully functioning elevator.

Consider a wing with flaps retracted. The center of gravity is forward of the center of lift. Visualize what would happen without a horizontal stabilizer. The lift would pull up on the center of the wing while the weight of the aircraft, acting through the center of gravity, would pull down on the leading edge. The result would be a nose-down pitching moment. To prevent this, the horizontal stabilizer is designed to produce a downward force (negative lift) that maintains equilibrium.

Now imagine what happens when flaps are extended. The airflow from the trailing edge of the wing (downwash) is deflected more sharply downward. The increased downwash strikes the upper surface of the horizontal stabilizer. This increases the tail-down force which causes the nose to rise and explains why flap extension causes a pitch-up and retracting them causes a pitch-down, a characteristic of most light aircraft. Some aircraft, however, behave oppositely (i.e., flap extension causes nose-down pitching) because of an aft shift in the center of lift. This is most typical of aircraft configured with cruciform or T-tails.

The probability of a successful stick-free landing, however, is increased when flaps are not used at all. With the flaps retracted, it is easier to maintain a nose-high landing attitude. Approaching the runway with flaps extended usually results in a nose-down attitude, requires larger pitch changes during the flare and increases the likelihood of landing nosewheel first.

The ability of the horizontal stabilizer to produce a downward aerodynamic force depends on wing downwash, the free airstream and propeller slipstream. It stands to reason, therefore, that when propwash weakens during a power reduction, the horizontal stabilizer loses some effectiveness. This is why power reduction causes a pitch-down; the horizontal surfaces cannot provide as much negative lift as when the propeller slipstream is stronger. Conversely, power application results in a greater downward force on the tail which causes the nose to rise.

With practice, a competent pilot should be able to counter the effects of flap extension or retraction by the timely reduction or addition of power, in such a way as to maintain a relatively constant attitude. This is an interesting exercise to try at a safe altitude.

The downwash from a wing that helps to produce a download on the horizontal stabilizer (on low- *and* high-wing aircraft) is altered when the airplane enters or leaves ground effect (about 20 feet above the ground for most lightplanes). When entering ground effect, the downwash is reduced, which causes a nose-down pitching moment. It was this unexpected attitude change that caught Pitts off guard during his first attempt at a hands-off landing.

Conversely, when climbing out of ground effect, wing downwash increases to produce a nose-up pitching moment.

These pitching forces created by changes in downwash occur during every takeoff and landing, but the pilot is rarely aware of them. Necessary corrections are made subconsciously with subtle pressures on the control wheel. But when making a hands-off landing, this effect must be anticipated. It can be countered only by a perfectly timed application of nose-up trim and/or a few timely jabs of power. Considerable practice is required to master this technique.

Another variable is the center of gravity. Landing without up-elevator capability can be simplified by shifting the adjustable cabin load aft. By moving heavy items to the rear, for example, it is easier to make a hands-off approach in a nose-high attitude, a particularly important consideration when flying tail-draggers.

Finally, there is the elevator trim tab. Little can be added to what a pilot already knows about this supplemental control except that the effect of a trim tab varies considerably from one aircraft to the next. It might prove interesting to determine just how well the trim tab can control pitch attitude in the plane you fly regularly. A practice exercise involves stabilizing the airplane in a full power climb. Then retard the throttle and see how rapidly the aircraft can be stabilized in a normal glide attitude (using trim only). Then reverse the procedure and re-establish the climb. Most pilots tend to overreact to this problem. Several roller-coaster-type oscillations usually are induced before an aircraft is brought under positive control.

A *single* broken or disconnected elevator cable usually doesn't result in a *complete* loss of pitch control. In most airplanes, a failed cable represents only a partial loss. For example, it is usually possible to apply "up" elevator even though "down" elevator capability has been lost, or vice versa.

Assume that the up-elevator cable has failed. The wheel moves aft easily, but produces no response. Forward wheel movement beyond the "neutral" position produces a nose-down attitude. In such a case, the pilot should apply considerable nose-up trim, enough to produce a moderately nose-high attitude. From then on, *any desired attitude* can be obtained by either relaxing forward pressure on the control wheel (for nose up) or increasing forward pressure (for nose-down). This technique essentially restores total pitch control to the control wheel. Conversely, if only nose-up elevator is available, pitch control can be maintained by applying considerable nose-down trim (refer to Figure 5-1).

Belonging to the same class of emergency is the more serious *jammed* elevator. Although various combinations of power and flap extension offer limited pitch control, the prospects of a successful landing are poor.

One incident serves as an example of this problem. A student was on his second solo cross-country flight. All sorts of paraphernalia were strewn on the cockpit floor: a plotter, a computer, a clipboard, a bag of sandwiches—you name it, he had it on board. During a period of

Landing With A Failed Elevator Cable

Loss of Up-Elevator Control	Loss of Down-Elevator Control
1. Apply *excessive* nose-up trim.	1. Apply *excessive* nose-down trim.
2. Push control wheel forward to maintain desired attitude.	2. Pull control wheel aft to maintain desired attitude.
3. Push harder to lower nose.	3. Release back pressure to lower nose.
4. Release forward pressure to raise nose or flare for landing.	4. Increase back pressure to raise nose or flare for landing.

Caution: Do not remove *excessive* trim prior to landing because two-way elevator control may be needed during a subsequent missed approach or go-around.

Figure 5-1

moderate turbulence, the E6-B computer was lifted off the floor and came to rest in a crevice behind the instrument panel in such a way as to prevent the application of down elevator. The frightened pilot used all of his strength in a frantic attempt to move the control wheel forward and lower the nose. Fortunately, the plastic computer gave under the strain and crumbled to the floor in pieces. Similar, sadder stories can be read in the NTSB accident files.

There is a theory, circulating among hangar flyers, stating that "reverse trim" can be used to control pitch in the event of a jammed elevator. If the elevator is jammed, so the hypothesis goes, the application of nose-down trim, for example, would cause the tab to rise and, in effect, act as a mini-elevator causing limited nose-up pitching.

This theory was tested and debunked in a Cessna 172. The effect of trim application alone (the control column was held firmly in place) caused no detectable attitude change. This effect, or lack of it, is attributable to slop in the elevator control system. Nose-down trim, for example, causes a very slight movement of the elevator in the opposite direction as the slack is taken up in the cable. This minute elevator deflection cancelled any effect the "reverse trim" technique might have.

This procedure might work, however, in aircraft with larger tabs, adjustable horizontal stabilizers, or the more rigid push-rod control systems.

The closest I ever came to a jammed control was on a flight to Las Vegas, Nev., in a Luscombe 8E. Joe Stanley, a long-time companion, sat in the right seat. He spent most of the trip maintaining a navigation log to break the monotony of a slow flight across the bleak Mojave Desert.

East of Clark Mountain, we encountered strong thermal activity. The left wing dipped and I countered by moving the stick to the right. Klunk! It stopped dead center. I tried again, but further attempts to move the stick to the right failed. Klunk! Klunk! Still no luck. The

Luscombe was now in a steep left turn. Stanley looked to me for an answer but I had none. Fifteen seconds and 180° later, I was attracted to a reflection on Stanley's lap. I reached over to his right knee and slapped away the aluminum clipboard positioned between his stick (the dual control) and the right sidewall. For one brief moment, we had felt that hollow sickness that creeps into the stomach when aircraft controllability seems lost. It's a feeling neither of us is likely to forget.

Although a loss of aileron or rudder control is not normally as serious as an elevator problem, it can be. Case in point: a charter pilot was departing Oakland after the Twin Beech had been in the shop for major maintenance. After liftoff, the control wheel was moved to the right to counter a small gust that had lowered the left wing. The airplane rolled farther left. The pilot turned the wheel farther right but the big twin had a will of its own. The left wingtip scraped the runway surface as the pilot suddenly realized what was wrong.

Reacting brilliantly, he turned the wheel *toward* the lowered left wing. The ship righted itself and the pilot nursed the aircraft around the pattern, substituting right aileron pressure when left was needed, and vice versa. Investigation revealed that a mechanic had rigged the ailerons in reverse. The whole problem could have been avoided by a more careful preflight.

Loss of total or partial aileron control because of mechanical failure can be combated by making shallow, skidding turns using rudder only. Another interesting technique can be used in airplanes with two cockpit doors. By opening both doors and allowing them to float freely, directional control can be maintained by pushing on one door or the other. Pushing open the left door of a Cessna 150, for example, results in a surprisingly coordinated right turn, and vice versa. But, watch your airspeed.

A combination of doors and ailerons can be used in case of rudder failure, but avoid crosswind landings.

Irrespective of the type of control difficulty, attempt to land only at an airport with ultra-long runways and crash rescue facilities. But most importantly, reduce the possibility of such an emergency by increasing the diligence of your preflight inspections.

PITOT-STATIC PITFALLS

*It's time for some straight talk when
even the pros get fooled by basics*

An accident investigator from the National Transportation Safety Board
claims that *many* more fatalities are caused by pitot-static icing than is
possible to determine.

With resigned frustration, he adds, "We often accuse a pilot of
disorientation and loss of control when we know instinctively that the
accident was really caused by erroneous flight data resulting from
blocked pitot-static lines. But the ice usually melts before an investigator
arrives at the crash site and the proof is gone forever."

A spectacular example of such an accident occurred in 1974 when
a Northwest Airlines Boeing 727 was being ferried from New York's
JFK International to Buffalo, N.Y. Although the aircraft was cleared
to FL 310 (31,000 feet), the ill-fated jetliner never reached its assigned
altitude. At 24,800 feet, the trijet entered a spin and crashed only 83
seconds later (the average rate of descent was more than 17,000 fpm).

Were it not for the voice and flight data recorders salvaged from the
strewn wreckage, it might have been inconceivable to conclude that
such a disaster was caused by a simple, yet lethal overdose of pitot
icing. But that's exactly what happened. And if a professional airline
crew flying an elaborately equipped aircraft can fall victim to such a
terminal fate, then so can the lone, general aviation pilot flying a less
sophisticated machine.

The 727 pilots were deceived by erroneous airspeed indications.
Because of ice-clogged pitot probes, both airspeed indicators behaved
like altimeters and responded only to changes in altitude (for reasons
explained later). During the climb, the IAS increased steadily and
persistently. This urged the pilots to raise the nose farther in an attempt
to arrest what appeared to be a dangerously fast airspeed. The action
resulted in an increased climb rate which compounded the problem.
As altitude increased, so did indicated airspeed. The pilots continued
to raise the nose until they had unwittingly forced the aircraft to stall.

There are three lessons to be learned from this accident:

• Always adhere diligently to appropriate checklists. (The 727 crew failed to turn on the pitot heat even though this item was on their taxi checklist.)

• When various instruments disagree, initially believe the one that indicates the most adverse condition. (Apparently, both artificial horizons in the 727 indicated properly at all times and reflected the dangerous 30° pitch angle prior to stall.)

• Distrust instruments that indicate performance beyond the capability of the aircraft. (Near the top of the 727's abbreviated climb, the pitot-static instruments indicated a continuous 5,000 fpm climb at an indicated airspeed (IAS) of 340 knots, a generally impossible feat unless the airplane is caught in the violent updraft of a thunderstorm "chimney.")

We should not, however, be too quick to criticize the 727 crew for not recognizing their problem. Contradictory instrument readings can be totally bewildering.

During subsequent experiments in a simulator, several professional pilots were subjected to similar flight conditions and instrument indications. More than half of them fixated on the erroneous airspeed indicator while ignoring the properly functioning artificial horizon.

Surprised? You shouldn't be. When a pilot takes his first flying lesson, he begins to develop the deep-seated habit of observing and reacting to airspeed indications. The IAS gauge becomes his primary key to survival. Later, he is introduced to the artificial horizon, a relatively complex device that is more subject to mechanical failure than the simpler, more reliable airspeed indicator. It is little wonder that—in a pinch—many pilots revert to airspeed.

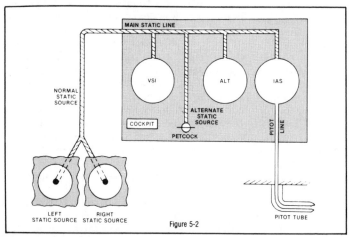

Figure 5-2

Figure 5-2 is a diagram of the pitot-static system typical of most general aviation aircraft. Its purpose is to provide static (ambient) air pressure to the altimeter, vertical speed indicator (VSI), and airspeed indicator as well as to provide pitot (ram air) pressure to only the airspeed indicator.

Many pilots are of the impression that two static ports (one on each side of the fuselage) are provided for system redundancy. Not so. Otherwise, considerate airframe manufacturers also would provide a backup pitot tube because this item is most prone to icing, for example. Dual static sources are *necessary* and equalize (balance) pressure variations that occur on both sides of the fuselage when the aircraft yaws (such as during turbulence).

To determine the effect of having available only one static source, for example, I enlisted the aid of noted aviation attorney Robert Cleaves. In addition to owning a Cessna 185 that would be ideal for simulating various types of pitot/static difficulties, Cleaves has been an experimental test pilot.

Prior to our first flight, we placed masking tape over the right-hand static source. During the subsequent climb, all instruments functioned normally, using air pressure from the left-hand static source.

After leveling at 4,000 feet. Cleaves alternately stabbed at the left and right pedals at which times the three pitot-static instruments behaved erratically. Why they did so is not mysterious.

During a yaw to the right, the only operational static source (on the left) was turned partially into the relative wind. This allowed the airstream to blow into that static port which increased the pressure in the static line and was interpreted by the altimeter in this instance as a loss of 400 feet. Also, the VSI indicated a substantial sink rate and the indicated airspeed dropped 13 knots. (The behavior of the IAS is explained later.)

Conversely, during a yaw to the left, the open static source was on the "downwind" side of the fuselage and sensed a decrease in pressure. As a result, the altimeter rose, the VSI indicated a climb and the IAS increased.

In turbulence, the three instruments were extremely sensitive and fluctuated wildly between high and low indications.

Should all three of these gauges act similarly during a normal flight, the odds strongly favor that one static port is clogged. By yawing the aircraft and observing the readings, a pilot can determine which of the two static sources is plugged.

Prior to a second flight, *both* static sources were covered with tape to simulate heavily iced static ports. During the takeoff roll, everything seemed normal. But during the climb from sea level to approximately 5,000 feet, the VSI remained at zero and the altimeter insisted we were still on the ground. The IAS gradually decreased from 78 knots at sea level to about 52 knots at 5,000 feet even though attitude and power settings remained constant.

Since the static sources were sealed at sea level, sea level pressure was trapped in the static lines and prevented the VSI and altimeter from sensing an altitude change.

Totally blocked static sources are extremely hazardous. Without an altimeter, how can a pilot execute an IFR approach or maintain an assigned altitude or remain clear of obstacles?

At such a time, a pilot has two choices. The most obvious one is to use the alternate static source. This is simply an extension of the main static line that is routed into the cockpit to where it is within reach of the pilot. This tube is sealed with a petcock so that cockpit air cannot normally enter the static system. However, when the normal static source is blocked, the petcock can be opened to introduce cockpit air to the static instruments. Since the air pressure in an unpressurized cabin is nearly the same as the ambient pressure outside the aircraft, this restores reasonable accuracy to the pitot-static instruments.

These instruments, however, will not be quite as accurate as when the normal static source is used because ambient pressure in the cockpit varies slightly with airspeed, attitude and the positioning of ventilation controls.

When the vents are open, for example, air rushing into the cockpit tends to pressurize the cabin. This increased pressure is sensed by the altimeter as a lower altitude. Closed vents, on the other hand, often result in cabin air having slightly less pressure than the air outside and results in a higher than true altitude indication.

When using the alternate static source during an IFR approach, open the vents fully, no matter how cold it is outside. In this way, the altimeter probably will read lower than true, a safeside error.

Unfortunately, many lightplanes used for IFR are not equipped with alternate static sources. This is ludicrous. When pilots can spend thousands of dollars on electronic redundancy, it is totally illogical for them not to invest 40 bucks to install an alternate static source and provide a backup supply of static air for the *single most important IFR device:* the altimeter.

Lacking an alternate static source, a pilot with an ailing static system has an emergency alternative: break the glass on the face of the VSI. Doing so allows cabin air to flow into the instrument and then through the normal static system plumbing to the altimeter and airspeed indicator. But when breaking the glass, try to do so without damaging the needle.

Cleaves' 185 has an alternate source. So, with the normal static ports still sealed at 5,000 feet, the petcock was opened and all three instruments sprang to life. After the needles stabilized, we closed the alternate source which "froze" the static system at 5,000 feet. As the flight continued, there was no way to detect gradual altitude changes. A subsequent steep, intentional descent was detected only by a significant increase in airspeed and noise level. As we levelled off a few hundred feet above the Pacific, the altimeter and VSI were still at 5,000 feet.

Many pilots contend that if icing conditions are so severe as to clog up the normally ice-free static sources, then unusually heavy structural icing would have created an earlier emergency. This is not always true because static sources are subject to other, more insidious forms of icing.

Take, for example, a pilot who flies after a recent rain or after his aircraft has been washed. Water droplets and/or condensation in the static lines may freeze after climbing to a sufficiently cold altitude—in VFR or IFR conditions. Bugs, dirt, wax and blowing sand are other culprits that attack the credibility of the static system.

These latter items can *partially* clog a static system, a particularly hazardous condition because the symptoms are difficult to detect and vary according to the degree of blockage.

To simulate this condition, we retaped the static ports and poked very small holes in the tape to allow only a restricted flow of static air pressure to the instruments.

During the climb, we noted that the altimeter and airspeed indicators were lagging and indicated less than true values; also, the VSI indicated less than the actual rate of climb. This was because the static pressure outside the aircraft changed faster than could be sensed through the pin-pricks in the masking tape used to cover the larger static ports.

After levelling off, the instruments slowly caught up and indicated correctly.

The danger of partially blocked static lines was accented during descent: the IAS was higher than actual, the lagging altimeter indicated higher than actual and the VSI indicated less than the true rate of descent. We were deceived into believing that we were safer than we really were.

One way to combat this problem is to temporarily open the alternate static source at least once during every IFR descent. If the needles move significantly when this is done, a static pressure problem exists and the alternate source should be used during the remainder of flight.

Figure 5-3 is a simplified diagram of the airspeed system and is useful in analyzing IAS errors resulting from partially/fully blocked pitot/static air sources.

When ram air enters the pitot tube, it flows into a sealed diaphragm within the airspeed indicator housing that expands with increasing pitot

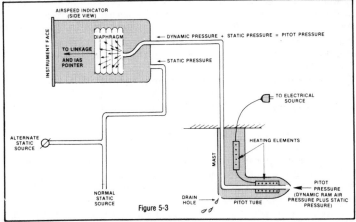

Figure 5-3

pressure. It is the expansion and contraction of this diaphragm which causes the airspeed needle to move. The ram air entering the pitot tube actually consists of two types of pressure: the static or ambient atmospheric pressure of the air surrounding the airplane and the *dynamic* pressure of the air caused by forward motion.

To prove this, consider an airplane at rest. Static air pressure enters the pitot tube and the diaphragm. Since the diaphragm is filled by static air pressure, why doesn't it expand? Because static pressure—from the static ports—enters the case of the instrument and surrounds the diaphragm. Since the pressure inside the diaphragm is then equal to the surrounding pressure, the diaphragm is "relaxed" and indicates zero airspeed. (For the airspeed indicator to work properly, static air pressure must be allowed to enter the case of the instrument to counteract the static—not the dynamic—pressure that enters the diaphragm through the pitot tube in flight.)

Assume that an airplane is in a steady climb during which the entire pitot tube freezes over with ice. The air in the diaphragm is trapped. But, as the climb continues, the static air pressure surrounding the diaphragm decreases. This reduction in surrounding pressure allows the diaphragm to expand and causes the IAS to increase even though the actual airspeed remains constant.

Conversely, during a descent without pitot pressure, the static pressure in the instrument case increases and compresses the diaphragm resulting in a decreased IAS.

In this manner, the airspeed indicator behaves like an altimeter and is the problem encountered by the 727 crew mentioned earlier.

Many pitot tubes are provided with a drain hole (see Figure 5-3) to allow water to leave the system. Assume that the main pitot entrance is clogged but the drain hole remains clear. What then? Static pressure then only will enter the diaphragm through the drain hole, pressure exactly equal to the static pressure surrounding the diaphragm. As a result, the diaphragm "relaxes" and the IAS drops to zero.

To prevent icing, pitot heat should be used *at all times* when flying in visible moisture. Also, turn it on before takeoff if there's a chance that taxiing through a puddle might have splashed the probe.

Frequently check the operation of the pitot heat on the ground by feeling the pitot probe. But don't grab it. A properly operating heater heats the tube sufficiently to burn the unwary. Also check the tube—before every flight—for foreign matter that might clog the works.

Unless the static source of an airplane is located on the pitot probe, an iced-over pitot does not affect altimeter and VSI indications. A static system that is not free and clear, however, does affect IAS even when the pitot is clear.

Assume the static ports are blocked during a climb. As a result, static pressure surrounding the diaphragm does not decrease as it should. The diaphragm, therefore, cannot expand as much as it should and the IAS indicates a lower reading than it should.

Conversely, during a descent the static air pressure surrounding the diaphragm does not increase as it should. Resultantly, the diaphragm expands more than it should and the IAS indicates a higher reading than it should.

When a pitot or static source becomes impaired, the instruments can present a bewildering display of flight data. The best preparation for such an emergency is to understand the system and know how to interpret its messages.

PRECAUTIONARY LANDINGS

*Are you mentally prepared to put
your airplane into a farmer's field
before your engine quits?*

Every pilot has an ace up his or her sleeve: the precautionary landing. Simply stated, this is a premeditated landing, on or *off* an airport, when continued flight is possible but inadvisable.

Consider, for example, the VFR low-flying pilot who becomes engulfed in deteriorating weather while relatively far from an airport. He has a choice: continue into potentially worsening conditions (ahead or behind), or make an off-airport landing.

The second choice often is the safest. Yet the records show that a non-instrument rated pilot caught in such a situation rarely exercises this option. Instead, he plunges onward, passing up one farmer's field after another until visual contact with the ground may be irretrievably lost. Eventually, he may collide with an immovable obstacle or lose control of the aircraft.

The National Transportation Safety Board (NTSB), which has the task of investigating and tabulating general aviation's fatalities, concludes: "Any pilot who becomes trapped in weather and does not give serious thought to the feasibility of a precautionary landing (on or *off* an airport), frequently accepts the most dangerous alternative: continued flight."

Consider also the pilot running low on fuel. He thinks he has enough remaining to reach the nearest airport, but isn't absolutely certain. Yet he often is willing to bet his life (and those of his passengers) on the unknown quantity of avgas sloshing in the tanks. This individual also has a choice: make a premeditated, off-airport landing *with power* or continue until a forced landing *without power* may eliminate the option.

Such a pilot is a natural candidate for exercising discretion by opting for a precautionary landing. But will he? The statistics say no and indicate that a pilot is much more likely to risk fuel exhaustion than to make an off-airport landing while the engine is still developing power.

The records also show many pilots go so far as to overfly enroute airports until the last drop of fuel is consumed, an often fatal syndrome known as "destinationitis". (One reason why airline pilots so rarely run out of fuel is that they have no personal involvement with the destination and aren't compulsively motivated to continue when common sense dictates otherwise.)

All of this leads to a logical question. "Why do so few pilots take advantage of the precautionary landing?" Countless lives could be saved by the timely employment of such a technique.

Part of the answer is that a precautionary landing is not a technique at all. Rather, it is a state of mind. It is the willingness to consider and possibly accept an interrupted flight plan and the damage that could result from landing on unimproved surfaces. But the rational mind must be prepared to at least weigh this alternative against the potentially lethal consequences of flying into increasingly adverse conditions.

Off-airport, precautionary landings are rare because pilots are not mentally prepared to consider this alternative; the subject seldom is discussed seriously. Pilots do learn about forced landing procedures during their pre-solo instruction, but not about precautionary, off-airport landings with power. We are programmed to consider landing only at airports ... unless the engine fails. It's one extreme or the other.

Many situations which might justify an intentional, off-airport landing often develop into the drama of a forced landing under more difficult circumstances simply because pilots are reluctant to correctly evaluate their difficulties. Some are afflicted with either the "I-can-make-it" or the "it-won't-happen-to-me" syndrome, which is known also as the inability to face reality.

There is no doubt about how extremely difficult it is to land in a pea patch while the engine is still running. But there are occasions when the hazards of continued flight may be less desirable. This is when a heads-up pilot will weigh the variables and arrive at the safest conclusion before the passage of time, distance, and fuel eclipse the available option. In short, he must be the captain of his fate, not the victim.

The primary objective of this discussion is not to recommend a precautionary landing under any specific set of circumstances. Rather, it is an attempt only to bring attention to a lifesaving procedure that is not implemented as often as it could be. Being aware of the alternative at least helps to simplify the decision should it become necessary.

An objective discussion of this nature requires playing the devil's advocate. In other words, a precautionary landing may not be the best alternative. Perhaps there is enough fuel on board to hobble to the nearest airport. Perhaps the VFR pilot flying into worsening weather will find improving conditions on the other side of the pass. Perhaps continued flight would be the safest course of action.

Another reason not to land on the nearest highway is that we know from experience that a pilot usually is able to extricate himself from most difficulties. If every pilot who ever became nervous were to make a precautionary landing, there might be more planes than cars on some highways.

Also, a precautionary landing is not without hazard. Aircraft damage is not unlikely and injury to those on board is certainly possible. A pilot who intentionally lands in a wheat field, totals the aircraft, and later finds that he did have enough fuel remaining to reach an airport is going to be hard pressed for an explanation. But the action probably increased the *probability* of survival and that's what the precautionary landing is all about.

On the other hand, there might not have been sufficient fuel.

There are times, however, when a pilot should be willing to accept aircraft damage. It is far better to sacrifice the machine if this helps to protect the safety of those inside.

Some pilots feel that scratching or bending an airplane denigrates his or her piloting skills. But if life is preserved in the process, the converse may be true.

So when *is* a precautionary landing advisable? Unfortunately, there is no cut-and-dry answer. It boils down to weighing the variables and exercising judgment. If a pilot is beginning to fear the outcome of continued flight because the risks are expected to increase beyond acceptability, he should consider a precautionary landing before it is too late.

Adverse weather and inadequate fuel reserves are not the only reasons that might warrant a precautionary landing. Other possibilities include:

• A visible oil leak of some magnitude.

• An indication of low oil pressure, excessive and uncorrectable cylinder head or oil temperatures, or low fuel pressure. (An alarming indication by a single instrument usually is insufficient cause for emergency action unless an additional sign of abnormality confirms that something is amiss; the problem could be a faulty gauge.)

• Partial power loss.

• Any worsening engine difficulty (in single-engine airplanes).

• Serious airframe or powerplant vibrations.

• In-flight structural damage (bird strike, broken or cracked windshield, hail damage, strut failure, etc.).

• Impending nightfall when the pilot is untrained and the aircraft is inadequately equipped.

• Being hopelessly lost when help is unavailable and fuel reserves are low.

• A partially incapacitated pilot, especially when the condition is worsening.

• Any other situation likely to become more hazardous with continued flight.

Is it legal to make an off-airport, precautionary landing? Considering only the FARs (and not state, county, and municipal laws), no regulation prohibits landing on other than an airport. Additionally, a pilot-in-command has the emergency authority (and perhaps the obligation) to do whatever appears to be in the best interest of safety.

If a pilot opts to execute an off-airport, precautionary landing instead of risking an eventual forced landing (or worse), he shifts the odds of survival strongly in his favor. With the engine still running (or the visibility still reasonable), the pilot has time to gather his wits and select a suitable landing site—something that might not be possible later. He has time to drag the proposed landing area and reject it should it appear undesirable. With power, he can land more slowly and with the precision needed to avoid the likelihood of an under- or overshoot. And, with power, he can always reject the landings and try again.

But, once the fuel is exhausted or the ground becomes obscured, these advantages also disappear.

Although a planned, precautionary landing is almost always survivable, the same cannot be said about forced landing or untimely descents caused by other emergencies.

If a decision is made to land at other than an airport, a pilot should make the necessary preparations while time is still available.

The first step might be to attempt notifying someone of his intentions. This radio call should include aircraft identification and type, precise location of the landing site (if possible), and the number of souls on board (SOBs). If communications cannot be established with the ground (on 121.5 MHz), attempt to contact a nearby aircraft by making a call in the blind on a frequency you would expect to be monitored in that area.

Also, turn on the ELT while airborne (if possible) and set the transponder to the emergency code of 7700 (if available).

Next, prepare both aircraft and passengers. Securing the cockpit is the easy part: turn off unnecessary systems, reduce the electrical load as much as practicable, stow loose objects, and make sure a flashlight is kept handy (at night).

Calming the passengers and gaining their confidence may not be so easy. If time allows, explain the situation in unruffled tones. Don't give them cause for unnecessary alarm. If possible, keep them preoccupied during the descent with such perfunctory chores as calling off altitudes every 500 feet or watching for traffic (even though the nearest aircraft may be 100 miles distant).

Passengers also should be told how to protect their faces with pillows (or coats, blankets, etc.) during the touchdown and landing roll. Also brief them on the operation of normal and emergency exits, if any.

If aircraft damage is considered possible, entertain the notion of opening a door or two prior to landing, but only if such action is known not to have an adverse, aerodynamic effect on tail surfaces. Otherwise, a twisted fuselage may make it impossible to open the door(s) on the ground. This is a particularly important consideration if the landing is to be in water. A jammed door can prevent evacuation during the short time it takes to drown. Conversely, an open door reduces aircraft buoyancy.

Also consider having passengers remove dentures and eyeglasses.

However, if the landing is to be made on a paved, straight, miles-long highway clear of traffic, much of this is unnecessary.

Ideally, the landing should be made on a level, smooth surface and into the wind. But try to select a site from which a subsequent takeoff can be made safely (with permission from the constable, of course). Consider also that landing uphill considerably reduces landing roll distance, a rather convenient arrangement especially if conditions later will allow a downhill departure.

Unfortunately, there's not usually a wind sock available to determine wind direction, so use some savvy and look for tell-tale signs such as drifting smoke and dirt, or trees leaning with the wind. Or, look for a herd of cattle. The vast majority of these bovine beasts usually stand with their backsides into the breeze. This is an instinctive habit that allows them to see enemies approaching from ahead and smell those who approach from behind.

Once the landing site has been chosen and time permits, drag the field at least once to confirm that you've chosen wisely. Fly parallel to the runway at approach speed with the flaps partially extended. This allows for a relatively nose-low attitude and provides better visibility to search for potholes, ditches, wires, and other hazards that may not have been visible from a higher altitude.

When on a heading parallel to the direction of intended landing, set the directional gyro to 360°. This is especially important if the approach is to be made during curtailed visibility because it helps to standardize the "traffic" pattern and find the "runway" should the pilot become temporarily disoriented.

A book could be written to describe the techniques recommended to land on various types of terrain. Consequently, space permits only a few generalizations to be included here.

• When landing on a broad field of snow or in water, depth perception may be poor. Use a power-on descent to the point of touchdown.

• When ditching in a river, land *downstream* unless strong winds dictate otherwise. This reduces the relative touchdown speed between aircraft and water thereby reducing damage potential.

• When landing on highways or roads, land with the traffic and be on the alert for wires and other man-made obstacles.

• If a tree landing must be made, attempt to allow both wings and the fuselage to contact the tree crowns simultaneously (and pray that the trees aren't tall and widely spaced).

• In mountainous terrain (good luck), try to select an uphill slope. Avoid a situation where an excessively long landing roll would bring the aircraft to either a sharp dropoff or an area of severe lateral twist that might force the aircraft to perform a wingover into a canyon. When about to land on a steep upslope, maintain enough airspeed to convert the descent profile angle into a steep climb angle that closely matches that of the upslope gradient.

• In most cases, damage and injury are minimized by touching down as slowly and with as reduced a sink rate as is possible and practical.

Most of the time, however, pilots are not confronted with these extremes. Usually, it's a simple matter of finding a long field and landing parallel to the furrows. Or it may be as mundane as squatting on a dirt road in the desert.

But, if the aircraft is damaged during the landing, be sure the fuel selector valve, master switch, and magnetos are turned off. (It is recommended that these items not be turned off prior to touchdown because this would eliminate the option of executing a last minute go-around.) Then, with premeditated calm, evacuate the machine and lead the passengers safely away. Don't return until the probability of fire or an explosion is nil.

In the final analysis, there can be no precise determination as to the causes and circumstances that dictate executing a precautionary landing. In each case, a pilot must evaluate all factors on a balancing scale. If one side tips in favor of a precautionary landing, then, objectively and philosophically, he should exercise the option to land as soon as possible—airport or no.

WIND SHEAR: THE MYSTERY OF THE VANISHING AIRSPEED

How to fight a hard-to-detect enemy

On June 24, 1975, an Eastern Airlines Boeing 727 crashed on short final approach to New York's JFK International Airport. More than 100 passengers perished, making this one of the worst air disasters in U.S. history.

According to the NTSB, this tragedy resulted from an encounter with a strong wind shear.

Because of this accident's spectacular nature, considerable attention is suddenly being focused on wind shear. It is almost shameful that a disaster of this magnitude was required to attract industry-wide attention to a phenomenon with which pilots have always had to cope.

Air carrier aircraft, of course, are not the exclusive victims of this invisible hazard. General aviation aircraft also fall prey to this misunderstood, underestimated menace. Hundreds, if not thousands, of accidents presumably caused by pilot error may have direct or indirect results of wind shear encounters. It is imperative, therefore, that pilots be familiar with the potentially lethal effects of wind shear and the various conditions during which these effects are most likely to occur.

Simply stated, wind shear is a variation in wind velocity (speed and/or direction) that occurs over a relatively short distance. *Airspeed is affected* when an airplane is flown from one wind condition—through a wind shear—into another wind condition in less time than *groundspeed* can adjust to the new environment. The consequences can range from annoying power and attitude corrections to complete loss of control.

Wind shear is a unique hazard not only because it is frequently undetectable, but because many pilots do not acknowledge the threat. They consider it incredible that a change in wind velocity can alter airspeed; it is contrary to their earliest lessons of flight.

"Airspeed," they were taught, "is determined solely by variations in aircraft attitude, configuration and power setting; wind affects only track and groundspeed."

Unfortunately, this simplistic axiom is but the tip of another iceberg and applies only when the wind is constant or changes gradually. Unless a pilot examines what lies beneath the surface, he is liable to fly unwittingly into the jaws of what has come to be regarded as one of aviation's most insidious killers.

To understand wind shear is to recognize an airplane has inertia and as a result resists a change in groundspeed. This is best stated by paraphrasing Sir Isaac Newton, the brilliant English physicist who developed the inescapable laws of motion: An aircraft in flight at a given groundspeed tends to remain at the same groundspeed unless acted upon by an exterior force.

For example, a temperature inversion overlies a coastal city from the ground to 2,000 feet. Within the inversion, the wind is westerly at five knots. Immediately above, the wind is easterly at 20 knots (not an unusual situation). The narrow band separating the two "air masses" is called a "shear line."

An aircraft descending toward the shear has an airspeed of 120 knots; its groundspeed is obviously 100 knots. This groundspeed represents aircraft momentum with respect to the earth and, according to Newton's First Law of Physics, is the quantity resisting change.

As the aircraft penetrates the shear line and enters the inversion, groundspeed does increase, but not instantly. Because of aircraft inertia, groundspeed after crossing the narrow shear line is very nearly what it was earlier, 100 knots.

But since the aircraft is now under the influence of a five knot tailwind, something has to give. That something, unfortunately, is airspeed, which reduces from 120 knots (above the shear line) to 95 knots (below the shear line), a net and rapid airspeed loss of 25 knots. Notice that the theoretical airspeed loss (25 knots) is equal to the difference between the headwind and tailwind components above and below the shear line.

The reduced airspeed, of course, results in reduced drag. Assuming neither attitude nor power is changed, the aircraft accelerates to its original trimmed airspeed (120 knots), at which thrust and drag are again in balance. But because of inertia, this acceleration takes time; lost airspeed cannot be recaptured instantly.

Just how long it takes to recover lost airspeed was dramatized in a USAF report by Major C. L. Hazeltine. He demonstrated that if a given aircraft, maintaining a constant altitude and power setting, encounters an abrupt 20 knot loss (due to wind shear), recovery of only 10 knots would require 78 seconds; recovery of 16 knots would require 176 seconds. Adding power and/or sacrificing altitude reduces recovery time significantly and points out the alarming need for pilots to be particularly alert for a low level wind shear when on final approach or when climbing out at marginal airspeeds. The problem of airspeed recovery is critical if the airspeed loss results in the drag rise associated with flight behind the power curve, when required power and altitude may not be available.

(In reality, the airspeed loss is not quite as large as shown in this example because some acceleration occurs while the aircraft crosses the shear line, depending on the line's width.)

Would the pilot have any warning about the impending airspeed loss? In this case, yes. When two opposing air currents rub shoulders, there is bound to be some frictional turbulence. The degree of turbulence increases in proportion to the change in wind velocity and decreases in proportion to the width of the shear line. For similar reasons, the air surrounding a jet stream is often turbulent, even though a smooth ride can be found within the core.

The aircraft encountered a rapidly decreasing headwind, which has the same effect as an increasing tailwind: an airspeed loss. If the direction of the aircraft is reversed, so that it flies into an increasing headwind (or decreasing tailwind), airspeed will *increase* when the shear line is crossed. The theoretical gain is 25 knots.

The effect of wind shear is similar to what happens to a hobo who jumps from a bridge to the top of an express train passing below. As the man leaves the bridge, his groundspeed (forward motion) is nil. The train, however, is clipping along at 60 mph. When the hitchhiker first touches down, it should be obvious that he cannot remain on the roof at the point of initial contact. His inertia prevents him from being accelerated so rapidly, from 0 mph to 60 mph. Instead, the hapless hobo will fall and roll backwards with respect to the train. Eventually, the friction of the train acting on his body will accelerate him to 60 mph. Whether he survives to realize this is questionable.

If the unfortunate chap were to misjudge and jump immediately in front of the train, the locomotive would force his body to adapt quite rapidly to the speed of the train. But the acceleration would exert such overwhelming and crushing G-loads that the hobo would instantly regret not having purchased a ticket and boarded the train under more comfortable circumstances.

For those who cannot correlate the hobo and the train with an aircraft in flight, consider this extreme, but illustrative, example. A Cessna 150 is cruising at an airspeed of 100 knots, directly into the teeth of a 100 knot headwind. The 150's groundspeed is obviously nil. Assume, also, the headwind disappears, suddenly and without warning.

The pilot—just as suddenly—finds himself high and dry without any airspeed whatsoever. The beleaguered 150 pitches down rapidly and loses considerable altitude before the combined effects of diving and power can accelerate the aircraft from a standstill to an airspeed/groundspeed of 100 knots in the calm air.

Conversely, had the 100 knot airplane been flying with a 100 knot tailwind, the groundspeed would have been 200 knots. The sudden disappearance of this wind would cause an immediate pitch-up, a healthy increase in airspeed (theoretically to 200 knots), and a substantial gain in altitude.

In the foregoing examples, the pitching is a result of longitudinal stability, the designed-in characteristic of an airplane by which it automatically seeks its original trimmed airspeed.

All pilots have encountered some form of wind shear without realizing it. Perhaps, after a period of smooth flight, a pilot runs into a patch of light chop, followed by more smooth air. A comparison of groundspeed/drift before and after the turbulence might reveal a wind velocity change. Airspeed fluctuations under these conditions are rarely perceptible, however. The shear line is usually wide, allowing ample time for groundspeed to adjust to the new wind condition.

Whenever an approach to landing is made on a gusty day, the pilot is actually encountering numerous wind shears. Every gust of air causes extremely localized shearing. Carefully monitor the indicated airspeed during such an approach and notice how the needle shifts rapidly above and below target airspeed. Some of this erratic needle movement is caused by gusts punching the pitot tube at oblique angles, but, for the most part, actual airspeed varies every time a gust is encountered or left behind.

Curiously, an approach or departure in gusty air is not normally as dangerous as flying through a strong, smooth shear. This is because gusts provide a seat-of-the-pants warning of possible hazards. A pilot is more alert to needed power and attitude corrections. Also, most pilots use slightly higher approach speeds in gusty air to maintain controllability. This also provides a hedge against higher, G-load induced stall speeds and possible airspeed losses due to wind shear.

An excellent rule-of-thumb suggests at least half the gust factor be added to normal approach speeds. For example, if the surface wind is reported at 22 knots, gusting to 38, the gust factor is 16 knots. At least eight knots (half the gust factor) should be added to the normal approach speed.

This rule provides ample protection except when the turbulence is caused by thunderstorm activity. The only protection against this type of severity is to avoid any well-developed cell by at least 10 miles, especially when taking off or landing. A healthy gust in advance of an approaching thunderstorm can quickly steal 20 to 30 knots of airspeed (or more).

Pilots should also be on the alert for local obstacles, on or near the airport, which can disrupt the flow of a reportedly smooth, strong breeze. Consider an aircraft about to touch down into a strong, quartering headwind. As the aircraft begins to flare downwind of the large hangar, the headwind component all but disappears, leaving the pilot insufficient airspeed to avoid the impending plop. Numerous hard landings (or worse) can be traced to similar circumstances.

Two small hills are situated farther down the same runway and form a venturi-like constriction. This can change normal wind flow into a jet of high speed air streaming across the runway from between the hills. Entering such a localized condition could lead a departing pilot to believe he has sufficient airspeed to fly. But not for long. When this "river of air" has been crossed, the resultant shear causes an airspeed loss that could be sufficient to force the aircraft back to the runway.

When the wind is strong, local velocities are easily affected by topographical features. It is not unusual for windsocks at opposite ends of a runway to point in opposite directions and indicate different wind speeds. A wind shear lies somewhere in between.

The type of wind shear that seems to catch most pilots off guard is the wind gradient, a condition where wind-velocity changes are somewhat more gradual. Although airspeed changes are not as abrupt as in the case of a narrow shear line, the final results have spectacular potential. Gradients are particularly hazardous because flight conditions can be deceivingly smooth; pilots are lulled into a sense of complacency and frequently are *unable* to determine that something is amiss until it is too late.

Imagine a wind pattern overlying relatively flat terrain. Near the surface, the wind is light, flowing directly from high to low pressure. But as altitude is gained, the frictional effects of the ground are reduced and the influence of the earth's rotation (Coriolis force) increases. This causes wind speed to increase and wind direction to shift clockwise (in the Northern Hemisphere) so that above the ground the winds are considerably stronger than at the surface and flow approximately parallel to the isobars.

Another example illustrates the problems encountered when approaching the ILS runway from, say, either the east or the west. Assume that in each case an approach speed of 100 knots is used, and wind velocity over each outer marker (at glideslope-intercept altitude) is from the east at 40 knots.

When the aircraft is approaching from the east, groundspeed over the OM is 140 knots. Over the runway threshold, where the wind is essentially calm, groundspeed should be only 100 knots if the target airspeed has been maintained during the approach. During the approach, therefore, groundspeed must be reduced from 140 to 100 knots, a deceleration rate of 23 knots per minute.

But if the pilot is unaware of the strong tailwind over the OM he won't anticipate the need to decelerate. This is the crux of the problem. When a tailwind decreases faster than groundspeed is reduced, airspeed is forced to rise. The excess airspeed results in a tendency to rise above the glideslope (either visual or electronic) and, to compound the confusion, a possible pitch-up. Unless judicious control and power adjustments are made during the descent, the aircraft will wind up over the approach lights with excessive altitude and airspeed. The diminishing tailwind (or increasing headwind) approach has been responsible for innumerable overshoot incidents.

If the pilot executing this approach doesn't know why he is experiencing excessive airspeed and why he keeps "floating" above the glideslope, there is yet another clue (in this case) to warn him of the presence of a wind shear. As the descent continues, the counterclockwise shifting of the wind necessitates a constantly changing crab angle if the aircraft is to remain on the localizer.

This example utilizes a wind gradient of 40 knots per 1,100 feet, or 3.6 knots per 100 feet. During wind shear studies in Florida and Texas, this has been found to be an *average* gradient. Low level wind shears ten times this magnitude (35 knots per 100 feet) have been observed. A gradient of 10–15 knots per 100 feet is not considered unusual.

Curiously, this situation (descending into an increasing headwind) also can result in an undershoot. As the shear is encountered and the aircraft begins to rise above the glideslope, a pilot usually reduces power to keep the ILS needles centered. But once stabilized at the new, slower groundspeed, considerably more power is required to remain on the glideslope. And unless sufficient power is added in timely fashion, the aircraft could wind up sinking into the approach lights.

When the pilot is approaching the runway from the west, conditions are reversed. Groundspeed during the approach must be increased from 60 to 100 knots. If this is not done, airspeed will decay in proportion to the headwind loss that occurs during the descent.

To avoid sinking below the glideslope, losing critical airspeed, and encountering a possible pitch-down, considerable and seemingly excessive power must be applied during the descent. This poses another threat, since less reserve power is available for a pullup and missed approach. Such a loss of headwind requires considerable pilot attention and action to avoid the potential undershoot. During such conditions, aircraft have developed high sink rates and contacted the approach lights with all engines developing full power. Similarly, aircraft *departing* into an area of either an increasing tailwind or a decreasing headwind have settled into the ground with engines developing full power.

When a pilot finds himself nearing the ground while having difficulty maintaining a safe airspeed/sink rate combination, he must execute a missed approach and either try again, wait for the wind shear to subside, or divert to another airport.

Anyone who is under the mistaken notion that wind gradients cannot affect him in this manner should be interested in what happened at JFK one day in April 1971. Aircraft approaching the airport encountered a decrease in tailwind of 20 knots per 1,000 feet, and during a two hour period nine professional pilots executed missed approaches (some diverted to other airports) even though the surface wind was light and the ceiling was 700 feet with adequate visibility below.

The effect of penetrating a squall line, front, or sharp pressure trough during a left turn deserves particular emphasis. This is uniquely dangerous because an aircraft could simultaneously encounter a rapid airspeed loss because of an increasing tailwind component, a sudden increase in bank angle caused by the side component of the tailwind acting on wing dihedral, a severe downdraft localized at the leading edge of the shear, and turbulence of moderate or greater intensity. Several fatal approach and departure accidents have been traced to these causes.

When you turn away from a squall line (or any severe weather condition), do so with a right turn, not a left one (in the Northern Hemisphere).

With respect to fronts, low level wind shear can be expected during frontal penetration when the system has a speed of 30 knots (or more) or when the temperature difference across the front is 10°F (or more).

Presently, the pilot's only weapons against wind shear are caution, conservatism, wit, and attention to the elements. But the future may offer some help of a more scientific nature.

In the meantime the general aviation pilot is left to his own devices. He must learn to recognize the existence of wind shear, understand how it can affect his very survival, and, above all, obey one of aviation's most golden rules: "Maintain thy airspeed lest the earth shall arise and smite thee—mightily."

THE HOW AND WHY OF TURBOCHARGING

Understanding what makes a turbo tick

Like man, the naturally aspirated (free breathing) engine is designed to develop maximum power at sea level. At altitude, it runs short of breath, and this has a frustrating, eroding effect on aircraft performance.

Consider the Piper Lance as but one example of this inescapable fact of life. This muscular retractable can take off at gross in less than a thousand feet, cruise at 165 knots and climb 1,000 fpm while hauling up to 1,644 pounds of useful load.

The trouble is, it can only achieve these feats at sea level; as altitude increases, performance wanes.

The only way to combat this common problem is to retrofit the aircraft with a turbocharger system developed by Rajay Industries. (The only other manufacturer of aircraft turbochargers, Garrett AiResearch, no longer offers retrofit systems.)

The result is a shot of high altitude adrenalin. Service ceiling is more than doubled, from 14,500 to 30,000 feet and the time required to climb from sea level to 12,000 feet is slashed from 22 to 12 minutes. Maximum cruise speed increases steadily from 165 knots at sea level to 191 knots at 22,000 feet and takeoff performance at high elevation airports is similarly impressive.

Although Rajay has developed turbocharger systems for numerous other aircraft, the Lance system is unique. This was the first retrofit installation of an automatically-controlled wastegate. Other Rajay "kits" incorporated manually controlled wastegates.

But before describing the specifics of how turbocharging benefits a specific aircraft such as the Lance, it would be appropriate to explore the world of turbocharging in general with emphasis on various systems and how they differ.

Figure 6-1 is a simplified view of a typical turbocharger installation. A turbine wheel is placed in the path of escaping exhaust which causes it to rotate like a rapid windmill at up to 100,000 rpm.

The turbine wheel is connected to a compressor impeller by a short, rigid shaft. Therefore, when the turbine is powered by exhaust, the impeller rotates at the same rpm and compresses the induction air prior to its being ingested by the engine. In short, induction air density and manifold pressure are increased, which allows the engine to develop much more power than it could without a turbocharger.

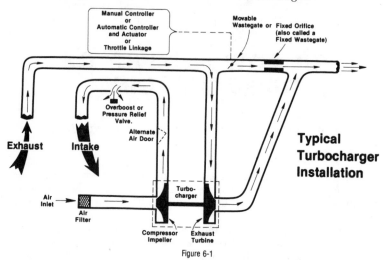

Figure 6-1

Some find it difficult to comprehend this principle. They feel as though they're getting something for nothing. Not really. The hot, high velocity exhaust gases that exit the naturally aspirated engine represent a tremendous waste of energy. The turbocharger simply extracts some of this energy to drive a compressor. Measurements show that after the exhaust leaves the turbine, its velocity *and* temperature are reduced considerably.

The first such units were superchargers, mechanically driven devices used to increase the power of diesel engines before Wilbur and Orville had ever heard of Kitty Hawk. The earliest aviation application occurred in 1918 when General Electric attached an exhaust driven turbocharger to a Liberty engine which produced more horsepower at the top of Pike's Peak than at sea level and resulted in a 1920 altitude record of 33,000 feet. The first production airplane to be equipped with "blowers" was the Boeing B-17 in 1939.

When a turbocharger is used to maintain up to (but not more than) 29.5 inches of manifold pressure at altitude, the engine is said to be *normalized*. In other words, the engine never develops more than the *normal*, naturally aspirated, maximum allowable sea level power. Almost all retrofit turbocharger installations normalize the engine.

The highest altitude at which a turbocharger can maintain maximum rated manifold pressure is called the "critical altitude," which, in the case of the Lance, is 22,000 feet.

Although a *sea level power setting* (29.5 in mp and redline rpm) can be maintained up to the critical altitude, *this does not mean that the engine is developing sea-level power.*

Whenever air is compressed, its temperature must increase. As a result, turbocharged induction air is also heated. Such a temperature rise decreases induction air *density* causing a power loss. Generally, each 6 to 10°F increase in induction air temperature decreases horsepower by 1%. So remember, engine power is determined by manifold pressure, rpm *and* induction air temperature, not manifold pressure and rpm alone.

At the critical altitude of the Lance (22,000 feet), for example, the air temperature at the compressor outlet is hot, about 220°F. Because of this, it is estimated that at 22,000 feet the Lance produces only 81% power *even though sea level* manifold pressure is indicated. Without a turbocharger, however, only 44% power is available at this altitude.

If an intercooler (or heat exchanger) is placed downstream of the compressor, induction air can be cooled to prevent some loss of power caused by heat, but such a luxury is seldom seen on light aircraft installations.

Most retrofit turbocharger systems incorporate a manually controlled wastegate. After the throttle is opened fully, the pilot detects the normal decrease in manifold pressure accompanying an altitude gain. To recapture this lost power, he begins to close a wastegate (either electrically or manually) which diverts exhaust to the turbine. As altitude continues to increase, he must gradually close the wastegate farther to divert more and more exhaust to the turbocharger in order to maintain a constant manifold pressure.

Finally, at the critical altitude, the wastegate is closed fully and all exhaust passes through the turbine. This is the altitude at which an aircraft with a normalized engine achieves its maximum cruise speed (22,000 feet and 191 knots for the Lance). Above this altitude, manifold pressure and cruise airspeed decrease.

With a manual system, caution must be taken not to close the wastegate too much at too low an altitude. Otherwise, excessive manifold pressure and engine damage will occur. Some installations are equipped with an overboost valve to vent excessive manifold pressure and protect the engine.

The Lance was the first aircraft to be retrofitted with an automatically controlled wastegate.

When taking off in a normally aspirated Lance, the throttle is advanced fully, which results in about 28½ inches of manifold pressure.

A full 29.92 inches cannot be attained because of induction losses common to all piston engines.

But when a turbocharger is equipped with an automatically controlled wastegate, takeoff manifold pressure is 29½ inches. This is because of the "pressure controller," a device that senses manifold pressure. When the throttle is wide open, the controller is dissatisfied with anything less than 29½ inches. It sends a signal to an actuator which closes the wastegate slightly. This, of course, increases manifold pressure.

Throughout the climb, the pressure controller and actuator position the wastegate to maintain precisely that manifold pressure selected with the throttle. As a result, whenever the throttle is fully open, the engine produces 29½ inches of manifold pressure (but only up to 22,000 feet).

Such an automatic system is similar to those developed for the Aerostar 601P, the Bellanca Turbo Viking, and others.

One question of concern to those considering a retrofit turbocharger system: Does the addition and use of a turbocharger have any adverse effect on engine life and reliability? Probably not. After all, when an engine is normalized with a turbocharger none of the engine manufacturer's original specifications or limitations are exceeded. As a result, turbo or no turbo, engine TBO (recommended time between overhaul) remains the same.

There is an important consideration however. Since the turbocharger increases induction air temperature, cylinder head and exhaust gas temperatures also increase. As a result, the margin between cylinder head temperature and the point at which detonation can occur is decreased. Therefore, leaning is more critical, and extra care is required to maintain normal engine operating temperatures.

Other automatic systems are designed to "ground boost" an engine. In other words, these systems are designed to produce more than 29.5 inches of manifold pressure. One purpose of this is to create the additional manifold pressure needed to compensate for the loss of horsepower caused by hot induction air temperatures. Example aircraft are the Cessna 421 and the Beech Duke.

When flying an engine with such an installation, a pressure controller automatically positions the wastegate (through an actuator) to maintain a preselected manifold pressure. But as altitude increases and the induction air temperature increases, the pilot will have to occasionally nudge the throttle forward to obtain the additional manifold pressure needed to *maintain constant horsepower.*

The ultimate turbocharger system utilizes a density controller instead of a pressure controller. Instead of maintaining a constant manifold pressure, this device controls the wastegate so as to maintain constant air density to the engine, which results in a near-constant maintenance of a pre-selected horsepower setting.

Assume that a pilot initiates an 80% power climb at 5,000 feet (32 in mp and 2,500 rpm, for example). As altitude increases, the density controller senses a decrease in air density (horsepower) caused by warmer compressor outlet temperatures. It gradually closes the wastegate to increase the manifold pressure to that required to maintain constant air density to the engine. At 10,000 feet, this could be 33 inches, for example. Density controllers are the most expensive and are found on the Piper Aztec, Navajo and Chieftain.

There are two interesting points to be made about ground boosted engines. First, the TBOs of these engines are usually less than those of their naturally aspirated counterparts. Secondly, the additional manifold pressure (more than 29.5 inches) makes one wonder how these engines can take so much boost. After all, we are constantly warned to avoid overboosting a free breathing engine by reducing manifold pressure before reducing rpm after takeoff.

The explanation is simple. Ground boosted engines have reduced compression ratios to provide wider detonation margins. Such a reduction in compression ratio requires additional manifold pressure to compensate for the loss of power this creates. But, overboost the naturally aspirated engine that has a high compression ratio and you may have problems.

Two other turbocharger systems are worth mentioning because of their increasing popularity.

The first incorporates a "slaved (or coupled) wastegate" (developed by Lycoming for the Rockwell 112TC and the Enstrom Helicopter). The wastegate is mechanically linked to the throttle in such a way that, as the throttle is advanced, the wastegate begins to close. During the takeoff roll, the pilot must advance the throttle only as far as necessary to obtain maximum allowable, ground boosted, takeoff power. Full throttle application would completely close the wastegate. However, a pressure relief is provided to prevent damaging overboost. But this protective valve could fail; never rely on it.

The simplest system (developed by Continental) is found on the Seneca II and the Turbo Arrow III and is unique because it does not incorporate an adjustable wastegate. Instead, the exhaust manifold is fitted with a fixed orifice (also called a fixed wastegate). Exhaust gas takes the path of least resistance which leads to the turbocharger. This, however, allows some exhaust to escape through the fixed orifice.

This system is operated similarly to that with a slaved wastegate. As soon as the throttle is opened, even slightly, the turbocharger begins to do its stuff. Takeoff power is achieved with less than a wide open throttle. During a climb with either the slaved wastegate or fixed wastegate system, the pilot must incrementally advance the throttle to maintain a given manifold pressure. However, since the fixed orifice system always allows some exhaust to bypass the turbo, it has a relatively low critical altitude, on the order of 12–15,000 feet.

It is interesting to note that in the case of the Turbo Arrow III, for example, 40 inches of manifold pressure is required to obtain the same 200 hp that a similar engine without turbocharging obtains with only 30 inches of manifold pressure. The additional ten inches is needed to compensate for warmer induction temperatures, reduced compression ratio, exhaust back pressure and induction interference losses (which includes a partially closed, "blocking" throttle valve).

With respect to the turbochargers only (and not the wastegates), those manufactured by Rajay and Garrett are essentially the same. Rajay, however, manufactures only one size (weighing 12 pounds) and is used on engines with up to 360 cubic inches of displacement. Larger engines (including the Lance's Lycoming IO-540-K1) require a pair of turbochargers acting in unison. Garrett "blowers" come in four sizes (weighing from 15 to 43 pounds each) so that only one is required for any given engine. An exception is Riley's conversion of the Cessna 414 which uses two Garrett turbos per engine.

Referring specifically to how a retrofit turbocharger affects the Lance, takeoff performance at sea level is essentially unchanged. The first noticeable difference occurs early in the climb. Manifold pressure remains constant and the decline of climb performance is barely noticeable. A particularly nice feature of the climb is that turbocharged, best rate of climb airspeed, 92 knots, varies only slightly with altitude. As a result, trim and body angle remain essentially constant.

During my flight in a turbocharged Lance, the time to reach 16,000 feet from the start of takeoff roll was only 16:14, an average of about 1,000 fpm. The aircraft was loaded to 150 pounds less than its maximum allowable gross weight of 3,600 pounds. How long would this take in a conventional Lance? Hard to say; the time-to-climb chart in the handbook stops at 13,000 feet.

At 16,500, FL185 and FL220, maximum cruise speeds are 183, 184 and 191 knots, respectively.

Another significant advantage of turbocharging is increased fuel mileage. At 8,000 feet, for example, the non-turboed Lance cruises 133 knots at 55% power while burning 14 gph. This results in a fuel efficiency of 10.9 mpg.

But at 16,500 feet, the turbocharged Lance can cruise at 151 knots while consuming only 12 gph which yields 14.5 mpg. This is a 33% increase in fuel efficiency while flying 18 knots *faster*. This doesn't consider, however, the additional fuel required to climb to 16,500 feet and the need to consume supplementary oxygen.

Some pilots are under the impression that since (almost) sea level horsepower is available at high elevation airports, takeoff distance is essentially the same as at sea level, a dangerous assumption.

Remember, at high elevations, the aircraft must be accelerated to a faster groundspeed even though liftoff indicated airspeed (IAS) remains unchanged. This, of course, requires additional runway length even with a turbocharged engine.

At this writing, high altitude takeoff tests in the turbocharged Lance had not been conducted. Estimates, however, indicate that it gets off the ground at an elevation of 4,000 feet in 12½% less distance than a conventional Lance. Takeoff distances at 6,000 and 8,000 feet probably are reduced by 25% and 35%, respectively.

The cost of adding a turbocharger system to a single-engine airplane varies from $5–8,000, installed. Much of this, however, is ultimately recovered because the aircraft's resale value is increased. Rajay and AiResearch agree that turbochargers would be considerably more expensive were it not that both companies sell the vast majority of their units to diesel manufacturers and other industrial users. This is not to imply, however, that AiResearch and Rajay don't take their aviation business seriously. They do.

Turbocharger system maintenance rarely requires more than an occasional adjustment. The turbocharger itself is virtually maintenance-free. Although the TBO of a turbocharger usually exceeds that of the engine, Rajay and AiResearch recommend replacing turbos when an engine is overhauled. The cost for a remanufactured Rajay unit is $400, exchange.

Turbocharger failure is rare, but should such an improbability occur (usually due to improper lubrication), most systems automatically revert to a naturally aspirated condition.

ARE YOU READY FOR PRESSURIZATION?

Some tips—and cautions—on operating the new breed of high-flying general aviation aircraft

There are probably more absurd misconceptions about aircraft pressurization than about any other aspect of flight.

Consider, for example, the popular belief that a bullet shot through a pressurized fuselage will cause explosive decompression and an uncertain fate for those inside.

And how about the myth perpetuated by the motion picture *Airport '77*? After the Boeing 747 came to rest at the bottom of the Caribbean, the intrepid captain (Jack Lemmon) allayed his passengers' fear of drowning by proclaiming authoritatively, "Don't worry, folks; this airplane is pressurized!" Apparently pacified, the naive passengers headed for the piano bar to sip martinis until rescued.

Someone should have nominated this movie for the "Best Comedy of the Year" award.

Unfortunately, many general aviation pilots also are unrealistic about pressurization. Modern technology enables them to cruise nonchalantly at 25,000 feet (or higher) in living-room comfort without fully appreciating that only inches away is an alien, hostile environment that can challenge their very survival. Man cannot tolerate such extremely frigid temperatures and oxygen deprivation for very long without suffering partial or total incapacitation.

Pressurization failure is unusual, but considering the proliferation of these systems in the general aviation fleet, it is appropriate to consider the potential hazards. But first, let's review some basic principles.

Pressurizing an aircraft cabin (the pressure vessel) is similar to pumping air into a tire that has a controllable leak. In the case of piston-powered aircraft, pressurizing air is provided by engine turbochargers. The "leak" consists of one or more outflow valves at the rear of the cabin. These valves allow air to escape continuously. This prevents excessive pressure from causing structural damage and provides an exit for venting stale air overboard. Pressurization is maintained by pumping in as much air as is allowed to escape.

Many believe that cabin pressure is determined by varying the amount of air pumped into the aircraft. Not so. The flow of incoming air is approximately constant. Cabin pressure is determined by the outflow valves, which modulate automatically to vary the amount of air flowing overboard and maintain the selected degree of pressurization.

In effect, the cabin is always "open." The addition of a bullet hole, therefore, would have no effect on cabin pressure. The outflow valve would compensate by closing slightly and automatically to maintain a constant flow of air through the cabin. Larger holes in the structure, however, may result in decompression.

In the case of jetliners, the outflow valves are so large that the loss of an entire cabin window may not affect cabin pressure significantly. (It would be unfortunate, however, to be seated near such a window.)

Should an outflow valve stick closed, an emergency relief valve opens automatically to prevent excessive cabin pressure and possible structural damage.

Maintaining cabin pressure obviously relies on a continuous source of air from the turbochargers. At least one engine, therefore, must always be developing a moderate amount of power. Retard the throttle(s) excessively and cabin pressure will be lost. (One can only wonder how the Boeing 747 in *Airport '77* was able to provide sufficient engine power while underwater to maintain cabin pressure and prevent sea water from flooding the aircraft.) Engine power, therefore, should always be maintained until the cabin has been depressurized conventionally.

This raises an interesting point regarding pressurized singles such as the Cessna P210N. An engine failure at altitude would result in rapid decompression. Although the outflow valve would close automatically in a vain attempt to preserve cabin pressure, other leaks in the aircraft would allow cabin pressure to escape. There is no such animal as a completely airtight cabin. Allowing one fuel tank to run dry before switching to another, therefore, is not recommended when operating a pressurized single.

Since air used for pressurization is compressed by the turbochargers before being pumped into the cabin, it is much warmer than ambient air outside the aircraft. As a result, pressurized air often must be cooled before entering the cabin, especially when flying at the lower altitudes on a warm day. This is done by ducting the high pressure air through a heat exchanger (or radiator) where it is cooled by ram air.

When ambient temperatures are well below freezing, the pressurized air may not be warm enough to maintain a cozy cabin. At such times, a conventional cabin heater is used.

Although a turbocharged, pressurized airplane allows flight above *much* of the weather, it certainly can't get above *all* of it. Anything that flies can expect to encounter some form of weather, no matter how high the altitude. In his book, *Operation Overflight,* Francis Gary Powers related how he gazed upward at the nearly 100,000-foot top of a Middle Eastern thunderstorm while cruising near the operational ceiling of his Lockheed U-2. And what pilot can ever forget the quip transmitted by one of America's pioneer astronauts after being established in earth orbit: "Another thousand feet and we'll be on top."

It can be said, however, that as one flies higher, he will experience increasingly less weather, but he must be careful not to become complacent. Weather at the middle altitudes can be damnably inhospitable.

During the winter of 1978, for example, a 160 knot jet stream was found as low as 18,000 feet msl over the United States and the associated clear air turbulence (CAT) varied from light to severe.

Although similar turbulence can be found in the lower layers, it can be more hazardous at altitude. Consider, for example, the 145 knot maneuvering speed of a Cessna 414A Chancellor. When cruising at 25,000 feet (FL 250) on a standard day, true airspeed is 200 knots. But at this altitude, indicated airspeed is only 134 knots, nine knots below the maneuvering speed. During a turbulence encounter, the aircraft would not have the stall protection it has at the lower altitudes. Above 25,000 feet, indicated airspeed and the available stall margin become significantly less. The obvious solution to such a problem is to descend.

One advantage of flying in the frigid climate of the middle altitudes is that structural icing is rarely encountered because the indicated outside air temperature usually is less than −15°C. Such air is simply too cold for water to exist in the liquid state. Most clouds consist only of harmless ice crystals, which do not cling to an airplane. (Exceptions to this rule can be found within the chimney of a thunderstorm.)

Although the lack of moisture eliminates icing worries, the arid air can be physiologically concerning. This is because long flights at altitude result in some dehydration.

Anyone who has ever flown commercially is aware of how flight attendants brief passengers on the use of emergency oxygen. This is because pressurization systems can fail. And if supplemental oxygen isn't *immediately available*—especially to the pilot—the airplane and everyone on board may be in jeopardy.

Unfortunately, many general aviation pilots apparently consider oxygen to be immediately available as long as the tank is full and the masks are *somewhere* on board. But if rapid decompression occurs, sufficient time may not be available to find the masks, connect the hoses and turn on the system. Cockpit masks should be connected and *tested* prior to every high altitude flight.

At 25,000 feet, a man deprived of an oxygen mask has only three to five minutes of useful consciousness; if oxygen deprivation is caused by rapid decompression, the time available is reduced by 50%; if the pilot is a smoker, he may have less than a minute of useful consciousness. At 30,000 feet, these times are cut in half.

With an oxygen mask at hand, decompression usually is not a serious problem (unless caused by airframe failure); without a *handy* supply of oxygen, it can be disastrous.

Rapid decompression—inaccurately called explosive decompression—is not as dangerous physiologically as it sounds unless the victim is suffering from blocked ears or sinuses. The feeling is that of a sudden expansion of air in your lungs followed by an outrush through your nose and mouth. It's sort of like having the wind knocked out of you without being hit. Your cheeks and lips may flap somewhat as the wind goes out, but that's about it. No one is incapacitated or knocked out. (And you get to find out if anyone on board is wearing an inflatable brassiere.)

One of a pilot's first considerations is to determine whether an emergency descent to a lower altitude would be appropriate. Moderate or heavy icing reported in the clouds below, for example, might make it more prudent to remain aloft and suffer the indignities of an oxygen mask until conditions below improve. In such a case, be certain to determine that all passengers are properly masked.

An untimely descent also could affect range adversely because of increased fuel consumption and loss of tailwind, an unfortunate set of circumstances when over large bodies of water.

If decompression is caused catastrophically by a blown-out window or other structural failure, it's possible for someone on board to have been injured from flying debris; an emergency descent could be dictated by medical reasons.

Also, be aware that a large hole in the fuselage can decrease cabin pressure to *less* than that outside the aircraft because of Venturi effect.

If the decision is to remain aloft for awhile, be extremely careful about opening a thermos of hot coffee. When at altitude, the boiling point of water can be so low that opening the thermos could result in an explosion of steam that can have serious consequences to those nearby.

Decompression isn't always involuntary. There may be times when it's desirable. One way to fight a cockpit or cabin fire, for example, is to starve the fire of oxygen. A controlled decompression does this nicely. It's also a handy way to remove smoke caused by an electrical or air conditioning malfunction. With the outflow valves open, the cabin can be cleared almost immediately.

If a rapid decompression dictates an emergency descent, be careful about simply lowering the nose and accelerating to redline airspeed (Vne) as is usually recommended. Consider the possibility (and sometimes the probability) that turbulence may be encountered when penetrating the lower altitudes. Such an encounter while diving at Vne may be difficult for the airframe to sustain.

When at high altitude (20,000 feet or above), indicated airspeed is so much below the redline that a large, negative body angle may be required for timely acceleration. But don't be in too much of a hurry to dump the nose lest the negative G-load toss objects (and unbuckled passengers?) against the ceiling. One technique to help avoid this is to roll into a moderately steep bank during the pitch-down. In this way, the positive G's of the turn help to offset the negative G's created when pushing forward on the yoke. When the desired pitch attitude has been established, the turn can be stopped.

Time permitting, notify ATC about the predicament and squawk code 7700 on the transponder. A midair collision with IFR traffic would be even more disturbing than a sudden loss of cabin pressure.

Fortunately, pressurization malfunctions are rare. But a professional attitude toward flying demands system familiarization and emergency preparedness.

FADS AND FALLACIES

Debunking some old wives' tales about flying

It is said that truth is stranger than fiction and a thousand times more fascinating. The aeronautical corollary to this states that fiction often seems more logical than truth, a paradox that produces many widely accepted misconceptions.

This article deals with some of these delusions and endeavors to displace fallacy with fact. But attacking someone's entrenched beliefs is like assaulting his spouse, religion or political persuasion. Nevertheless, truth must prevail.

During a landing roll, for example, a pilot needs to hold the nosewheel off the ground as long as possible. Should he use nose-up trim for assistance?

It would be logical to answer this in the affirmative, but would be incorrect if the plane is configured with a conventional elevator trim tab (as opposed to an adjustable stabilizer).

Although the use of nose-up trim makes it *easier* to maintain a nose-high attitude, positioning the tab in this manner actually reduces elevator effectiveness.

Assume, for example, that a pilot is about to land with a flat nosewheel tire or a retractable nosewheel that fails to extend. Since he needs to prevent the nosewheel from touching the ground until the last possible second, he applies as much nose-up trim after touchdown as is tolerable. Unwittingly, this pilot has defeated his purpose.

Figure 6-2a is an exaggerated sideview of a raised elevator with the trim tab deflected downward (nose-up trim). Notice that this positions the tab almost parallel to the relative wind, which reduces the "effective area" of the elevator and its ability to maintain a nose-high attitude at progressively slower speeds.

The most effective way to hold off the nosewheel requires precisely the opposite. After touchdown and with the nosewheel still off the ground, apply nose-*down* trim while holding the wheel aft. Pitch pressure does increase, but this is manageable at such a reduced airspeed.

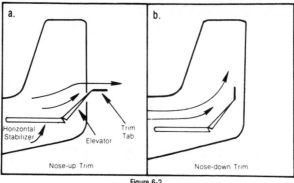

Figure 6-2

Figure 6-2b shows that when nose-down trim is applied, the tab is deflected more vertically which increases the effective area and power of the elevator. This keeps the nosewheel off the ground at slower-than-usual airspeeds.

* _____ *

Every once in a while, pilots are presented with an operational procedure which seems logical in theory, but fails miserably in practice. One of my favorite such pieces of advice falls neatly into this category. It is the commonly suggested method of escaping structural icing when flying in the vicinity of a warm front.

As every pilot knows—or should know—a warm front separates a cold air mass from an overriding, warmer air mass. In theory, therefore, icing conditions can be evaded by climbing from the cold air, through the frontal surface and into the *relatively* warm air above. This procedure is presented in numerous flight training manuals, but I doubt if the authors have ever put such a technique to the test in light, general aviation airplanes. Otherwise, they would have been compelled to withdraw their advice.

Advocating that a pilot climb through a warm front to escape structural icing is like throwing a concrete life jacket to someone who's drowning.

Of prime concern, is the 0°C isotherm, a line that defines the lower limits of freezing temperatures and icing conditions across the frontal system. In other words, structural icing can be expected when flying in clouds above the isotherm, but can be avoided by flying below it.

Of particular significance is that freezing temperatures and structural icing typically can be found in the "warm" air mass above the frontal surface.

Consider an aircraft, for example, which has just flown through the "freezing" isotherm into icing conditions while in the cold air mass below the frontal surface. Should this pilot climb toward the warm air mass? No, because this would not be an escape route from subfreezing temperatures; he'd still be above the 0°C isotherm. In all probability, the climb simply would parallel the sloping frontal surface and keep the airplane in the thickest cloud layers.

Now consider another aircraft, which is heading toward the frontal system from the opposite direction when it begins to accumulate ice. Would a climb result in warmer temperatures and ice evasion? Nope.

In each of these cases (and in most others), the most prudent procedure is to employ one of aviation's most valuable and proven safety tools, the 180° turn (unless a safe and timely descent can be executed to warmer temperatures or visual conditions).

There may be isolated instances, when a climb through a warm front can result in the shedding of accumulated ice, but only when a pilot is intimately familiar with the dynamics of a given frontal system. But this data rarely is available.

* _____ *

Whenever a pilot executes a stall, he is exploring the slow end of the airplane's performance envelope. When he nudges the airspeed needle toward the red line (in smooth air, of course), he approaches the other extreme of the envelope.

But one "outer limit" seldom investigated by most pilots is the absolute ceiling, the altitude at which further climb is no longer possible. Reaching such a performance pinnacle has no significant practical value; it simply is an engineering expression which helps to evaluate an airplane's overall climb capability.

But what is life at the top really like? Since so few have been there, misconceptions abound. The most popular states that when at its absolute ceiling, the airplane hangs on the verge of a stall and that no airspeed loss can be tolerated. Wrong. Another notion claims that control reactions are sluggish and it may be difficult to maintain a safe attitude. Wrong again.

In reality, life at the top is quite nice, thank you. Although control responses are not crisp, they are certainly adequate. And, believe it or not, there is a healthy margin of airspeed; a stall is not imminent.

This may seem incongruous because so much additional airspeed above stall should enable the airplane to continue climbing, but not so. The answer to this apparent contradiction can be found with the help of some climb data for a typical lightplane.

At sea level, the airplane has a stall speed (Vs) of 70 knots, a best angle of climb airspeed (Vx) of 80 knots and a best rate of climb airspeed (Vy) of 100 knots. As altitude increases, the stall speed remains constant, but Vx and Vy do not. It is typical for most light airplanes that Vx increases slightly with altitude and that Vy decreases slightly so that at the absolute ceiling, Vx and Vy become one and the same, which in this case is 85 knots.

A climb to absolute altitude requires the patience of Job, a certain finesse with the flight and mixture controls, and the ability to maintain airspeed with exacting deliberation. Such a height can be reached only by maintaining the appropriate values of Vy. (But once there, prepare to head for the barn because most of the onboard fuel may have been spent.)

Upon reaching the top, airspeed will equal Vy, otherwise the airplane would not have gotten there in the first place. In the case of our fictitious airplane, this means that airspeed will be 85 knots, no more, no less. And notice that this is fully 15 knots above stall.

If a turn is initiated or if airspeed is allowed to either increase or decrease even slightly, altitude will be lost. When at the top, only Vy and a wing's level attitude will keep you there. But note that a slight speed bleed does not result in stalling. And while maintaining Vy (85 knots in this case), control response will be no, different than when flying at the same airspeed at sea level.

Exploring the upper limit is an educational experience and provides a challenge to those who think it easy to get there.

* ——————— *

Comrade Kochinko, a pilot in the Soviet Air Force, was given a most unusual flight assignment. He was told to fly to any point of his choosing in the Northern Hemisphere and, once there, perform the following navigational exercise:

"Fly a true course of 360° for 500 nm, turn right and maintain a true course of 090° for another 500 nm, and then turn so as to track along a true course of 180° for an additional 500 nm."

This didn't sound particularly difficult until Kochinko read the final requirement of his flight orders: "After flying each of the three 500-nm-long legs, the aircraft must arrive at the same point from which the first leg started."

Initially, Kochinko was much concerned about this seemingly impossible assignment because he knew that failure to comply would result in a Siberian vacation. Eventually, however, the Soviet pilot realized that, yes, he could perform such a mission.

If *you* were Comrade Kochinko, how would you resolve this dilemma? Remember, the entire flight occurs within the Northern Hemisphere and the equally long legs must be flown in the designated sequence: north, east and then south. So that you are not tempted to peek, the solution has been placed at the end of this article.

* ——————— *

Murphy's Law claims that whenever something can possibly go wrong, it will. There are, of course, numerous corollaries to this adage, but one of concern to pilots states that headwinds occur more frequently than tailwinds.

In a way, the statement is accurate, especially with respect to round-robin flights. Given any specific wind direction and speed, a round trip takes longer than when the wind is calm.

For example, assume that a pilot is flying due east from A to B, a distance of 300 nm. With a calm wind and true airspeed of 150 knots, the round trip (600 nm) would require exactly four hours (excluding time lost during climb, departure and arrival maneuvering).

But now introduce a 50 knot westerly wind. The 300 nm outbound flight would be flown with a 200 knot groundspeed and require only one hour and thirty minutes. The groundspeed for the return leg, however, would be only 100 knots and require three hours enroute.

Total time for the round trip would be four hours and thirty minutes, half an hour longer than had there been no wind at all.

The reason for the additional flying time is that the aircraft spends more time under the influence of a headwind than it does benefiting from the tailwind. Consequently, the average groundspeed is less than had the wind been calm.

With respect to round-robin flights, therefore, it can be said that *any* wind is an "effective headwind" because flight time is prolonged.

But what about one-way flights? Does Murphy's Law affect these, too? Do headwinds really prevail over tailwinds? Logic suggests that for any given flight, the odds in favor of a headwind are equal to those in favor of a tailwind. Right? Wrong! Sad to say, Murphy is once again correct. Headwinds do prevail, but not simply because the contrite, Irish gentleman has a vendetta against pilots. The reason is a bit more obscure.

Imagine a compass rose about an airplane, a diagram used commonly in textbooks to describe the effects of various wind directions. For example, winds blowing toward the airplane from the directions encompassed by the upper two quadrants are headwinds while those blowing from the lower two quadrants define tailwinds. Do you agree? Well, you shouldn't. This popular presentation is inaccurate.

The textbook diagrams imply that a crosswind from either 090° or 270° has no effect on groundspeed. In other words, these crosswinds would be neither headwinds nor tailwinds. Not so.

In order to correct for a crosswind and maintain the desired true course, it is necessary to establish a wind correction angle, or crab. But the act of crabbing necessitates turning *into* the wind. The result? A loss of groundspeed. The stronger the crosswind, the greater the loss. In other words, a direct crosswind also is a headwind.

For example, if a 160 knot airplane is required to crab 20° into a crosswind to maintain course, the groundspeed loss is 10 knots.

Very strong winds that blow from even slightly behind the aircraft may appear to be beneficial, but by the time the wind correction angle is applied more groundspeed may be lost (by crabbing) than would be gained from the tailwind component.

Consider a pilot who wants to fly a true course of 360° in a 150 knot airplane. The prevailing wind is 260° at 60 knots. Certainly this appears to provide a slight tailwind. But if the problem is resolved on a computer, groundspeed along the desired course is only 148 knots. Although this wind provides a 10 knot tailwind component, 12 knots are lost by having to crab 23° into the wind.

So, to the glee of Mr. Murphy, headwinds do prevail.

* _____ *

Several years ago, an airline ground instructor posed a brain teaser to a large group of pilots to test their knowledge of basic meteorology. Unhappily, only a few could solve the problem. Feel like putting your expertise to the same test?

Consider two pressure systems; one is a high while the other is a low. Two airports, one in each of the systems, are at sea level and observers at each report identical weather conditions: clear skies, light winds and standard atmospheric conditions (59° F, dry air and an altimeter setting of 29.92 inches of mercury).

Each of two pilots flying identical light airplanes departs simultaneously from each of the airports. Everything else being equal, above which of the two airports will one pilot encounter better climb performance than the other?

Most pilots recall early lessons that teach how air circulates clockwise about a high pressure system and counterclockwise about a low (in the Northern Hemisphere. But most seem to forget that a high pressure system consists also of subsiding (descending) air. Conversely, air rises from within a low.

This helps to explain why there generally is so much more weather in a low pressure system as compared to a high. Rising air condenses to form vertically developed cloudiness and precipitation.

Being aware of this basic information provides the solution to our problem. The pilot climbing within the low experiences the best performance because his plane is assisted by rising air—a spritely climb because of a "vertical tailwind." This does not refer to local vertical movements such as thermals. Rather, this refers to a huge mass of slowly rising air.

Conversely, the pilot flying in the high pressure system must climb against subsiding air, which is much like fighting a vertical headwind. This condition has been known to evoke a comment such as: "This thing doesn't seem to be climbing very well today; we must be flying through *dead* air."

Most pilots solve the stated brain teaser incorrectly because they conclude that an airplane performs better in high pressure than in low. Quite true. But recall that the problem stated the atmospheric pressure at each airport was identical (29.92"). The only difference is the pressure *surrounding* the two airports; one is *in* a high while the other is *in* a low.

* _____ *

Solution to navigation problem:

As one proceeds north from the equator toward the pole, the circles (parallels) of latitude become progressively smaller. If you proceed far enough, you eventually reach a circle of latitude that has a circumference of exactly 500 nm. (At 89° north latitude, for example, the circumference of that parallel is only 377 nm.)

Comrade Kochinko simply began his flight assignment at a point 500 nm south of the circle of latitude which has a circumference of 500 nm. He then flew due north for 500 miles, turned eastward and flew around the pole in a 500 nm circle. At the end of his circumpolar leg, Kochinko turned south and flew for another 500 nm until arriving over the starting point.

(For the technically oriented, a circumpolar track of 500 nm occurs at 88° 40.4' N. Kochinko began his flight assignment 500 nm south of this parallel, or at 80° 20.4' N.)

AVIATION
MINUTIAE AND MEMORABILIA

*Brain Teasers to chew on while
waiting for the fog to burn off*

Aviation has a colorful, glamorous heritage, but much of it is hidden within the yellowing pages of long-forgotten volumes. Some of the glorious past, however, is kept alive by numerous expressions that, although currently used, originated in another era and for obscure reasons. We know, for example, the meaning of "Mayday," but how did such a joyous-sounding word come to be an expression of dire plight? Dust covered books of the past hold the answer to this and innumerable other questions frequently asked by modern pilots.

During World War II—when almost everyone had more than a casual interest in aviation—Milton Figen wrote a delightful pocketbook about flying that was designed to enlighten pilots and nonpilots about the little known yet fascinating facts of flight.

With the aid of Figen's treasury of aviation lore and memorabilia, a most entertaining and informative quiz has been constructed. So, if you're a nostalgia nut and have a thirst for trivia, abandon the electronic airways and join us on a fun flight into the past. Take an aerial I.Q. test designed for pilots of another era. (Answers follow).

1. What is wrong with this statement: After his engine died, the pilot glided to a landing on the frozen lake and taxied his plane to shore?

2. What does a pilot mean when he is "counting insulators?"

3. What are "cloud landings?"

4. For what purpose did World War I pilots use stove lids.

5. Virtually every type of aircraft has played a role in modern warfare. Have kites ever been used?

6. Why did some conventional bombs "scream" after being dropped?

7. Why did some Allied bombers carry pigeons while conducting raids over Europe?

8. What kind of gun was used on the first Allied fighter planes of World War I?

9. Why was it dangerous to pick up an English "calling card?"

10. Why were the discarded belly tanks of Japanese fighter aircraft sought after by Americans in the Pacific during World War II?

11. What is the difference between a cowling and a nacelle?

12. Were balloon fenders found on airplanes or balloons?

13. Which aircraft engine manufacturer used to name its engines after insects?

14. True or false: Most of the noise from the average piston-powered airplane is produced by the engine.

15. What is the Lufbery Circle?

16. When a pilot has a fatal accident, it is said that he has "bought the farm." What is the origin of this expression?

17. If you "buzz-sawed" an enemy airplane, what would you be doing?

18. Why would wearing a parachute be imperative if you were going to sickle-thrust an enemy aircraft?

19. Why were there more "black eyes" in Midland, Tex., during World War II than in any other place in the United States?

20. Why are life jackets called "Mae Wests?"

21. True or false: Some World War II carrier-based fighter aircraft were equipped with flotation gear to prevent the aircraft from sinking after ditching in the ocean.

22. Is it true that parachutes were used long before airplanes and balloons were invented?

23. Which Hollywood film star was an aerial gunner during World War II: Charlie Chaplin, Joe E. Brown, Victor Mature, Clark Gable, or Jackie Cooper?

24. Is it true that a woman soloed a powered aircraft five months before the Wright Brothers first flew?

25. What famous one-time child movie star was a glider pilot in the Army Air Corps during World War II?

26. True or false: The first nonstop flight across the United States occurred before the first nonstop flight across the Atlantic?

27. What is the origin of the word "Mayday?"

28. How was the smoke bomb used as a navaid?

29. Why is it dangerous to leave airplanes unguarded in a cow pasture?

30. On April 3, 1844, a prestigious newspaper, the New York *Sun*, carried the astounding news that the Atlantic Ocean had been crossed by air in three days. This story, called "the greatest air hoax ever known," was perpetrated by what famous American author?

31. What is a subcloud car?

32. If you ordered a "three-point landing" from an informed waitress at an airport restaurant, what would you get to eat?

33. If a fighter pilot were "playing pussy," what would he be doing?

34. If a *bombardier* releases bombs, what does a *bomphleteer* release?

35. Students who have not soloed are often likened to an extinct pigeon called a _____.

36. What do Filbert, George and Iron Mike have in common?

37. What is the universal definition of a good landing?

38. When a pilot speaks of a "dead-stick" landing, is he referring to the engine or the control stick?

39. What product important to aerial warfare was derived from spiders?

40. The initials used in the designations of World War II Army planes denoted the purposes for which the planes were designed. For example, a B-19 was a bomber. But what was the purpose of each of these aircraft: O-39, TG-3, A-31, AT-9, L-4, UC-78, Z-4, CG-3, R-4?

41. What were all Japanese aircraft designed in the 2600th year of the Nipponese dynasty called?

42. Which American fighter of World War II was frequently described as "paying off through the nose?"

43. When aviators were downed at

sea, their emergency equipment usually included a portable transmitter powered by turning a hand crank. Why was this device called a "Gibson Girl?"

44. Why were some World War II pilots given extensive training in crash-landing techniques and given very little instruction in conventional landing techniques?

Answers:

1. How can a pilot taxi an airplane with a dead engine?
2. Early barnstormers used to fly so slow and low over highways and railroads that they were able to count the insulators on telegraph poles.
3. The tops of flat clouds were used as imaginary runways when teaching students to make conventional landings.
4. They sat on them for protection against enemy ground fire. Stove lids were the first armor used in airplanes.
5. Yes. Russia used them to drop propaganda leaflets during World War II. Also, they were sent up from Allied naval convoys as a defense against dive bombers.
6. They were equipped with whistles to terrify the enemy.
7. The pigeons were sent back carrying reports that could not or should not be transmitted by radio.
8. None. The first weapons were rocks, which passing pilots hurled at one another. They later took to fighting with pistols, shotguns, rifles, hand grenades and, eventually, machine guns.
9. These were pieces of cardboard about the size of playing cards that were treated with yellow phosphorus. They were scattered moist from aircraft, but belied their innocent appearance by bursting into flames upon drying.
10. The belly tanks, when cut in half and cleaned, made admirable bathtubs in an area where sanitary facilities were few and far between.

11. Each encloses an engine, but a nacelle houses an engine located away from the fuselage. For example, a Bonanza has a cowling while a Cessna 310 has two nacelles.
12. Airplanes. Balloon fenders were special guard rods extending from the wingtips to the nose of an airplane to protect the ship from entanglement in the cables of barrage balloons.
13. Pratt & Whitney. The two best-known "insect" engines are the Wasp and the Hornet.
14. False. About half the noise (or more) is produced by the propeller.
15. An aerial defense maneuver invented by Raoul Lufbery, American ace of World War I. In this classic maneuver, a group of planes on the defensive form a tight circle similar to the formation used by covered-wagon trains when attacked by Indians. The circle of planes, however, is mobile and can spiral toward home base without breaking rank.
16. Early pilots frequently made forced landings on neighboring farms and usually were required to pay for crops and other property damaged in the process. In other words, each of these pilots "bought" a part of the farm. From this, pilots who failed to survive were said to have bought the "whole" farm.
17. Slicing off part of his tail with your propeller.
18. Because you would be making a ramming stab at him with your wing or other part of your plane—in which case you should be ready to bail out!

19. The Army's largest bombardier school was in Midland. The soft rubber eyepieces of the bomb sights left sooty marks, "black eyes," on the bombardiers.

20. When the jackets were inflated, they reminded early pilots of the buxom Hollywood actress.

21. True. Large rubber bags were packed in the wings. After ditching, these bags were inflated with carbon dioxide from highly charged flasks.

22. Yes. One of the earliest known users of the parachute was an Italian, Fauste Veranzio. In the 16th century, he leaped from the Leaning Tower of Pisa. His parachute was a square, textile-covered frame.

23. Clark Gable.

24. Yes. She was Aida de Acosta, a Cuban. While in Paris in 1903, she became acquainted with Santos-Dumont, pioneer balloonist. On June 29 of that year, after several days of instruction, she flew Santos-Dumont's powered balloon, the *Runabout,* from its hangar to a nearby polo field.

25. Jackie Coogan.

26. False. The first nonstop aerial crossing of the Atlantic was in 1919 by Alcock and Brown. The first nonstop crossing of the United States was made four years later by Army Lieutenants Kelly and Macready.

27. Mayday comes from the French *m'aidez,* which means, "Help me."

28. While enroute, a pilot would drop a smoke bomb and circle the area until it hit the ground. He then observed the smoke released by the bomb to determine wind direction and drift.

29. Because cows are attracted by the smell of dope, the chemical finish used on fabric covered surfaces, and will chew on these parts.

30. Edgar Allan Poe. Arriving in New York nearly penniless and with a sick wife, he concocted the story and sold it to the *Sun* to raise needed funds.

31. The subcloud car was a small observation compartment attached to the belly of some dirigibles. It was lowered by cable during flight through clouds so that the observer sitting in it could make weather and terrain observations in clear air while the mother ship hid from the enemy.

32. Ham and eggs.

33. Hiding in the clouds either to evade or stalk enemy aircraft.

34. Propaganda pamphlets. The word was coined by British pilots making pamphlet raids over Europe.

35. Dodo. This bird had rudimentary, almost functionless wings.

36. These were names used by pilots when referring to an autopilot.

37. A good landing is any landing from which you can walk away.

38. Neither. He is referring to the propeller which, when failing to produce thrust, has the utility of a stick.

39. Spider-web filaments were used as cross-hairs on most bomb sights.

40. O = Observation, TG = Training Glider; A = Attack; AT = Advanced Trainer; L = Liaison; UC = Utility Cargo; Z = Obsolete Aircraft; CG = Cargo Glider; R = Rotorcraft.

41. Zeroes, or to be more accurate, Zero Zeros, which represent the last two digits of the year (also known as 1940) in which they were designed.

42. The P-39 Airacobra. The description arose from the fact that the plane mounted a 37 mm machine gun that fired through a hollow propeller shaft in its nose. The engine was located behind the cockpit.

43. The transmitter was housed in a rectangular container with a narrow waist that reminded some pilots of the idealized American girl of the 1890's as represented by the illustrations of Charles Dana Gibson.

44. These glider pilots were trained to make only one flight which consisted of crash landing their load of commandos behind enemy lines at night and without the help of landing lights.